How To Use
Solar Energy in Your Home and Business

by Ted Lucas

Ward Ritchie Press
Pasadena, California

For Bill Chleboun and Ann Harris

Copyright © 1977 by Ted Lucas

Second printing

Library of Congress Catalog Card Number:
77-891-85

ISBN: 0378-06380-4

Printed in the United States of America

Contents

FOREWORD
by William B. Edmondson

Editor, *Solar Energy Digest*

When I first started reading the galleys of HOW TO USE SOLAR ENERGY, my first thought was that the explanations about solar energy and solar hardware were needlessly detailed and the language used much too simple.

But then I thought back to the day in 1944 when the wife and I stopped at a motel on our way to Orlando, Florida, where I was scheduled to attend a school on how to teach Marine aviators how to survive if they were forced down on land or sea.

The first thing that caught my eye was a huge black box about 8 or 10 inches deep on the motel roof. So, curiosity getting the better of me, I asked the desk clerk what it was. His reply almost floored me.

"It's a solar water heater we use to supply hot water for all our units."

Mouth agape, I hurried the wife off to our unit and immediately put the shower to the test. The water was so hot I almost scalded myself!

From that day to this, my one consuming passion has been solar energy in all its forms, but the difficulty learning about solar energy from scratch in those days was enormous, particularly starting with absolutely no knowledge or previous interest in the field.

And I remembered how such terms and concepts as selective surface, insolation, Carnot cycle, Rankine cycle, photovoltaics, and hundreds of others were so difficult to find out about and I thought,

"What a godsend such as book as this would have been to me in those days. It would have saved me months—or even years—of research and effort."

So, if you are a beginner in the solar energy field—and most of us still are these days—or even if you have attained some degree of sophistication—this is a book which "brings it all together" in a chatty, informal, yet detailed and informative manner.

1
How to Cut Your Utility Bills

The true question about solar energy is not "Are we going to use it?" Instead, some millions of Americans are asking, "How soon can I have a solar installation in my house and cut down on my utility bills?"

The answer is simple. Right now you can plan to save at least 50% and perhaps as much as 90% of your utility bill for domestic hot water by installing a solar water heater. This is the first and easiest step. You can put in a solar device for hot water in almost any kind of building, from a single suburban home to a condominium or apartment house.

Using solar heating for all the water consumed by an average family for showers, baths, and washing clothes and dishes results in significant dollar savings immediately. You can figure on saving up to $30 per month as against your utility costs for water heated by conventional fuels. And that's at price levels of February 1977. Based on utility company estimates, their costs—and your bills—are climbing at a rate of about 7% each year. That says you'll be saving up to $40 or more each month in three years because you've installed a solar water heater.

There are all kinds of systems for heating your domestic water with the sun's energy. Although most people may prefer to have the work done by a professional, it's quite possible for anyone adept with hand tools to build his or her own solar water heater. Literally millions of people have installed such systems. In using sunlight for this simple practical application, we Americans are somewhat backward. Fuel-scarce nations like Japan, with more than 3 million solar water heaters, and Israel, with more than 100,000 solar water heaters, are far ahead of us in this application.

But we're beginning to catch up. In 1976 more than 10,000 solar water heaters were installed in the United States—more than in the previous three decades. Because heating domestic water consumes about 5% of our national energy bill, the accelerating move toward solar hot water systems is a healthy sign indeed.

It will be increasingly healthy for your pocketbook, as well as for our nonrenewable supplies of fossil fuels and uranium, when you install your solar heater. Average cost of a solar water heating system connected to your present hot water heater and taking over most of the load will range from $700 to

$1000, including installation and warranty. If you do the entire job yourself, including building solar collector panels as described in the next chapter, your cost for materials will range from $300 to $600, depending on the kind of system you choose and the area where you live.

If your solar water heater saves you $35 a month, it's going to pay for itself in about two years. From then on you can put that $35 in the bank every month and be proud that you're saving scarce fuel.

Greater Savings with Solar Space Heating

Although a solar installation for heating your house is more complex than a water heater, again there is a wide variety of hardware and techniques available to help almost everyone who wants to use the sun's energy. And it is even more important to consider a system that will keep your home comfortably warm, while also heating your water.

About 18% of our national energy consumption goes up the flue for space heating. This is an appalling amount of our dwindling fuel supplies to waste in warming buildings when we can let the sun do most of the job. It is even more shocking when you realize that much of our present space heating is electrical, and a typical electric power plant is less than 30% efficient in burning fuels to generate electricity.

Described in detail in later chapters are systems and hardware you can use to supply solar heat to almost any building—old or new, single dwelling, condominium or apartment complex, commercial or industrial building. Many careful studies have been made on the economics of solar-heated buildings. Based on costs in early 1977, your solar heating system will pay for itself in from 5 to 10 years. The reasons for this spread in payoff time might be summarized as follows:

- In your existing building, the type of construction may limit your choice of solar system.

- It is most efficient, except in unusual cases, to design your solar system as a major supplement to your existing heating system. This will also limit your choices, as you will understand when you read later chapters.

- The climate of your home, especially the average number of hours of insolation (solar radiation), determines the area of solar collector panels you need for adequate space heating.

- The initial cost of your solar heating system depends on both the equipment you decide to use, including choice of a liquid- or air-type or hybrid (both liquid and air) technique for capturing and storing the sun's heat energy, and the amount of time you can devote to the project in planning and/or do-it-yourself labor.

- If you're building a new home, apartment building, or commercial structure, be sure to include a solar heating system. By including it in your original plans, you will reduce your installation cost and you'll have a more efficient system. Recouping your initial investment in such a system is quite possible in three years or less. Typical costs for a house with 1,800 to 2,000 square feet of living area range from $2,500 to $3,500, depending upon the area you live in and the other factors just cited. This investment provides solar space heating and domestic hot water.

It is quite possible that your solar heating system may cost you no more initially than a conventional setup. In several houses built recently in the Mexico City area, the cost of installing a solar hydronic system for furnishing 100% of both space heating and hot water was no greater than a propane installation. Owners of solar homes incorporating a system designed by Piper Hydro, Inc., described in detail in Chapter 4, are putting from $50 to $70 a month in the bank because of their savings in fuel costs.

Because of the severe 1977 winter and the natural gas shortages, even those who scoffed at the energy crisis are aware that "something must be done." The most intelligent something is to apply solar energy right now. Several progressive utility companies, including gas utilities in Texas, New Mexico, Idaho, and other states, are offering to install solar heating and hot water systems just like any other appliance. Then you pay for your solar equipment on the monthly bill, partly from savings in fuel. These savings will increase as fuel costs— and your utility bill—go up.

Another approach, where a maker of solar water heaters in Florida is installing these units at no cost to the home owner, is described later in this chapter. The householder gets a free solar water heater and a lower electric bill, pocketing part of the savings achieved by solar energy.

Insulation for Energy Conservation

Before you plan a solar heating or cooling system for your home or any other building, be sure your structure is well insulated. This advice has been given frequently by utility companies. Recently, the National Bureau of Standards pointed out that if you live in a region of relatively mild winters and have no ceiling insulation, an investment in 6 inches of attic floor insulation will be returned in fuel savings within one year.

It makes no sense at all to plan an efficient solar heating system if your home is not well insulated. Before you "solarate," insulate. The savings you achieve will depend on how much insulation you have to begin with, the attic area of your home compared with the wall area, the number and size of your windows and doors, and how adequate your weather stripping is.

Look at your house critically. Most houses, built during recent decades when fossil fuel energy was plentiful and cheap, don't have enough insulation. You can almost invariably add insulation to your home, save money, and do all or most of the work yourself.

SELECTING INSULATION

Your building supply dealer will be glad to show you the variety of modern insulating materials he has available to apply to your existing home. These materials include mineral wool, cellulose fiber, vermiculite, and perlite; various plastic foams including polyurethane, polystyrene, and urea formaldehyde; reflective aluminum foil; sealants and plastic tapes.

Mineral wool of either the fiberglass or rock wool types is the most widely used insulating material. It is available in several forms:

- Blankets or rolls of wool insulation, with or without vapor barriers.
- Batts, which are similar to blankets but cut in 4-foot or 8-foot lengths.
- Pouring wool, which is loose insulation you can pour into your attic floor between the joists.
- Blowing wool, another form of loose insulation generally applied by contractors, who use pneumatic equipment to blow the insulation into place.

You can buy blankets, batts, and pouring wool from a building supply dealer, hardware store, or supermarket home center. Blowing wool is furnished by the insulation contractor who installs it.

The efficiency of insulating materials is measured in R-numbers. This "R" signifies resistance to winter heat loss or summer heat gain. When you buy insulation, check the R-number because it will tell you more about the material's resistance to heat flow than if you merely measured its thickness. Here are typical examples:

R-22 mineral wool batts are about 7 inches thick.

R-19 batts are 5 inches thick.

R-13 blankets are 3-1/2 inches to 3-5/8 inches thick.

R-11 blankets are about 3 inches thick.

When you buy insulation, you'll find R-numbers plainly marked on packages and vapor barriers.

WHERE TO INSULATE

You should insulate all ceilings having cold spaces above them. Also insulate attic living space between collar beams and between sloping rafters. Be sure to leave an air space for ventilation between the insulation and the underside of the roof, selecting the thickness of your insulation by measuring available space. In the attic area insulate between the studs of knee walls, as well as dormer walls and ceilings.

All exterior walls should be insulated. If you own a split-level house, don't neglect the short walls. Also insulate walls between your living space and an unheated garage or storage area.

It is important to insulate all floors above cold spaces. This includes vented crawl spaces in basement areas; floors above unheated garages or open porches; and any portion of a floor that is cantilevered beyond the exterior wall or walls below it.

For attic floors or top-floor ceilings, if you have less than 6 inches of old insulation, you can use more. With 3 inches or more of insulation, add at least R-11 blankets to give you an additional 3 inches. If you have less than 3 inches of old insulation, play it safe and add R-19. These amounts are consistent with current FHA standards for new homes.

Insulation thickness greater than R-19 is often justified, particularly if you live in a cold climate—or have very hot summers. Good attic and floor insulation helps to compensate for poorly insulated walls.

Where your walls are accessible and it is feasible to insulate, use R-11 or R-13 material and cover it with an interior finish. If you must insulate finished walls, have mineral wool pneumatically installed by an insulation contractor.

HOW TO INSULATE YOUR HOME YOURSELF

If you are insulating an attic floor where there is no insulation, lay batts between the joists. You do not need to staple the batts. The vapor barrier must face down. (The vapor barrier is either a plastic or aluminum foil cover for one side of the insulating material to keep water vapor from going through it.)

If you have some existing insulation, add a layer of batts or blankets of mineral wool on top of the old material. Your new insulation should *not* have an effective vapor barrier. Try to purchase unfaced insulation. If it is not available, use faced insulation but remove the vapor barrier or slash it repeatedly with a knife and install the insulation with the slashed surface down.

You can also use pouring wool effectively to insulate an attic floor. Pour this insulation out of its bag and level it with a rake or piece of board.

When you are insulating a wall, fit the end of a mineral-wool blanket snugly against the top framing. Working from the top, staple the blanket edges to the studs on either side. If you are using blankets faced with aluminum foil, be sure to staple each blanket to the sides of the studs (rather than the stud face) so as to create an air space. This is necessary to take advantage of the foil as a heat reflector. This foil vapor barrier must face the inside of your wall.

When installing a mineral wool blanket on a wall, space staples about 8 inches apart on the studs. Cut the blanket to fit tightly against the framing at the bottom. If you use more than one piece of blanket in the same space between two studs, butt the blanket ends tightly together and apply tape over the seam.

To insulate stud spaces which are narrower than normal, cut your insulation about 1 inch wider than the space to be filled. Staple the leftover flange, then pull the vapor barrier on the other side to its stud and staple through the barrier.

As an alternative to using faced insulation on your walls, you can apply unfaced blankets and a separate vapor barrier. This barrier is typically a 2-mil-thick polyethylene sheet or foil-backed gypsum board. If you use polyethylene sheeting, keep it taut and staple it in place.

Install insulation behind, as well as around, pipes and ducts to keep them warm. Also insulate behind electrical boxes. Any spaces such as those behind pipes, ducts, or equipment may easily be packed by stuffing them with loose wool. Just pull material for this purpose from a blanket of insulating wool.

Cracks and narrow spaces like those around window frames should be stuffed by hand with loose wool. Then cover them with a vapor barrier such as gummed polyethylene tape.

When you're insulating masonry or basement walls, first fasten wood furring strips in place vertically. The furring may be 1 x 2, 2 x 2, or 2 x 4 inches. Place these furring strips either 16 inches or 24 inches center-to-center, depending on the width of your insulation blanket.

With 1 inch x 2 inch furring, use special masonry wall blanket insulation. This is unfaced, with an R-3 rating. It should be covered with polyethylene sheeting or foil-backed gypsum board to provide a vapor barrier.

If your walls require more insulating thickness, use 2 inch x 2 inch or 2 inch x 4 inch furring and install R-7 to R-11 blanket insulation with suitable facing. You'll find that mineral-wool blankets and batts are available to fit 16-, 20-, and 24-inch spacing between studs, joists, or furring.

To insulate floors above cold spaces, push the batts or blankets between the floor joists from below. Keep the vapor barrier on top. To support this insulation, lace wire back and forth between nails spaced about 2 feet apart in the bottoms of the joists. Along the sill at the ends of the floor area, you should stuff in pieces of blanket cut to size, with vapor barrier in.

Be sure to insulate under attic walkways, pulling or pushing the insulation into place. If most of the walkway area is covered with flooring, you will have to remove some boards in order to apply the insulation. When working in any attic space, watch out for nails that might be sticking through the roof sheathing above your head.

Work from the outer edge of the attic space toward the center. It's much easier to cut and fit insulation in the center of your attic than near the eaves, where headroom is limited. Stuff openings around interior chimneys.

Be careful to avoid covering eaves vents with insulation. If you're using batts or blankets, cut them where necessary to allow space for vents. When you use pouring wool, either make a baffle around each vent with boards, or lay pieces of thick batts (R-19 to R-22) next to the vents.

Be sure not to place insulation on top of recessed lighting fixtures, motors, and other heat-producing equipment protruding through the attic floor. To meet requirements of the National Electrical Code, you must keep your insulation 3 inches away from the sides of heat-producing electrical equipment. You can easily make a sheet-metal shield using metal from empty tin cans if you want to be thrifty.

Put the vapor barrier side of insulation blankets and batts down when insulating your attic. As mentioned earlier, if you're adding new insulation on top of old, slash the vapor barrier to permit passage of moisture, and put the slashed side down.

When applying wall insulation, patch any tears in the vapor barrier. You can strip a piece of vapor barrier from a scrap piece of insulation, or else tape on a polyethylene sheeting patch. Don't allow vapor barriers to be exposed. Cover them with gypsum board or some other noncombustible covering. Be sure to take "breather paper" off your batts if you've purchased insulation with this kind of disposable covering. Breather paper is the covering on the side opposite the vapor barrier; on some batts, it is on the side without flanges. This paper is intended only to protect insulation during shipment and while you're installing it. After your batts are in place, strip the paper

Be sure to avoid gaps, or "fishmouths," at the vapor barrier edges when you are insulating walls. Keep the edges of your insulation tight against the studs. If you have a contractor install blowing wool in your interior walls, paint these walls immediately with two coats of a vapor-resistant paint.

VENTILATING ATTICS AND CRAWL SPACES

You must provide ventilation above the insulation you have installed in your attic. In winter, while insulation keeps heat inside your living space below the attic, open vents are necessary to permit moisture to escape. In summer, air moving through the vents reduces heat buildup.

Your attic should have at least two vents located so that air will flow in one and out the other. Generally you will need more than two vents. A combination of vents at the eaves and at the gable ends is better than gable vents alone. The best combination provides eaves vents and continuous venting along the roof ridge. Here are some guides as to the minimum amounts of attic vent areas your home should have, according to the informative booklet, "Solar Heating for Residential Use," prepared by E & K Service Company of Bothell, Washington, a leading manufacturer and installer of solar systems in the Pacific Northwest.

With a combination of eaves vents and gable vents without a vapor barrier, provide 1 square foot of inlet and 1 square foot of outlet for each 600 square feet of ceiling area. At least half of the vent area should be at the tops of the gables and the balance at the eaves.

When you provide only gable vents with a vapor barrier, again figure on 1 square foot of inlet and 1 square foot of outlet for each 600 square feet of ceiling area. If you have only gable vents without a vapor barrier, double the vent area: 1 square foot of inlet and 1 square foot of outlet for each 300 square feet of ceiling area.

In an unheated crawl space, you should provide at least 2 vents opposite each other. It's best if you provide a moisture seal by using such materials as 4-mil polyethylene sheeting or 55-pound asphalt roll roofing, lapped at least 3 inches. With such a moisture seal on the ground, furnish 1 square foot of vent for each 1,500 square feet of crawl space area—but be sure there are at least 2 vents to permit air flow in and out. The best design is to provide 4 vents, one on each side of your crawl space. If you do not have a moisture seal in this crawl area, you must have 10 times as much vent area—1 square foot of vent for each 150 square feet of crawl space.

It is usually desirable to protect your attic or crawl space vents with screening or rain louvers, which means that the basic sizes of vents specified in the preceding paragraphs should be increased by factors indicated in the following table.

TABLE 1-1. Sizes of Screened Vents for Attics and Crawl Spaces

Type of Covering	Size of Opening
1/4" hardware cloth	1 x net vent area*
1/4" hardware cloth and rain louvers	2 x net vent area
8 mesh screen	1.25 x net vent area
8 mesh screen and rain louvers	2.25 x net vent area
16 mesh screen	2 x net vent area
16 mesh screen and rain louvers	3 x vent area

*Net vent area is the area specified in previous paragraphs for attic and crawl space vents.

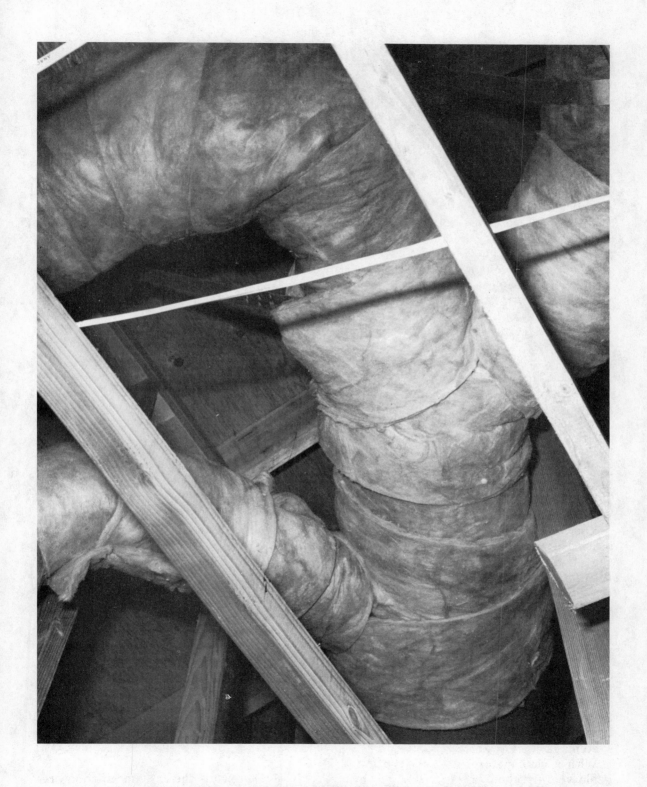

Hot Air Ducts Should Be Carefully Insulated

Thick Insulation Applied to Walls and Ceiling Will Save You Many Energy Dollars

Reduce Heat Loss at
Your Windows and Doors

Anyone who can use simple hand tools can install weather stripping. There are many different kinds available: felt strips, foam rubber, flexible vinyl, spring bronze, and others. Choose the kind of weather stripping you prefer to install after you've consulted with an experienced person at your local hardware or building supply store. Most good brands of weather stripping include an instruction sheet in the package. If not, get one from your dealer.

You should apply weather stripping to sides, tops, and bottoms of windows and doors. Don't neglect the meeting rail where the top and bottom sash of double-hung windows come together.

It is most important to weather-strip entrance doors as well as attic doors, and both inside and outside basement doors. A good rule is to weather-strip any door between a heated space and an unheated area.

If you live in an area with cold winters, be sure to install storm windows and doors. According to the National Bureau of Standards, if your area is similar to Washington, D.C., your investment in storm windows will pay for itself in 5 years or less at present utility costs for heating. And your utility bills are continuing to climb.

You can figure that, with a good installation, storm windows and storm doors will reduce your heat loss at those openings in your house by about 50%. Insulating glass, with two panes sealed together at the edges, will accomplish almost as much at your windows. In an extremely cold climate, you are wise to use triple glazing—insulating glass plus a storm window. To make it easier to install a storm door, get one that is prehung in a frame cut to the size you need.

If you're not a do-it-yourselfer and can't afford storm windows and storm doors right now, there is a simple and inexpensive alternative that works reasonably well. Get some polyethylene or other suitable plastic sheeting from your hardware or building supply store. Tape this plastic sheeting to the inside of your windows and to any glass areas in your outside doors. Also, there are several types of plastic storm windows that are easy to install.

Basic Facts About
Solar Heating Systems

Once you have done a good job of insulating your home, you are ready to slash your utility bills drastically by installing a solar heating system. The first thing to keep in mind is that there is no magic in using the sun's energy to heat and cool your house as well as to warm all the water you need, no matter how large your family.

The basic elements of a solar heating system are shown in Figure 1-1. This is a liquid-type system, where the sun's energy is used to heat a liquid. This liquid is water in most of the systems described in this book. However, some systems use a mixture of ethylene glycol and water, generally a 50-50 mix of antifreeze and water, in areas where freezing temperatures occur.

It is worth noting right away that even if you live in an extremely cold climate, you can have a solar heating system using plain tap water, without antifreeze. All that is involved is draining the water from your solar collector panels and associated piping when the heat supplied by the sun is not sufficient to prevent freezing. Your system will do this automatically if correctly designed. And there's another clever trick described in detail in Chapter 4—very small amounts of warm water are trickled through your solar collectors on cold nights.

The solar collector, marked (A) in Figure 1-1, consists of one or more panels made of glazing at the surface; a metal absorber plate including metal tubing, with inlet and outlet, the entire assembly painted black; and a layer of insulation under the absorber plate.

In Figure 1-2 you see how the tube that carries sun-heated water forms an integral part of the absorbing surface in one collector

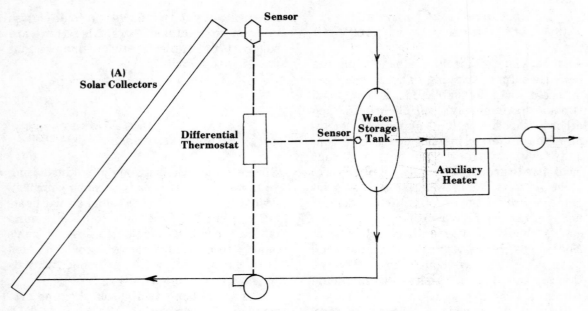

FIGURE 1-1.   Diagram of a Solar Water Heater

design manufactured by Reynolds Metals. A cross section of the complete Reynolds panel is shown in Figure 1-3. If you looked down on four of these collectors and were able to see the tubing carrying hot water, you would see a serpentine of tubing and finned absorber plates arranged as shown in Figure 1-4.

Consider the detailed cross section in Figure 1-3. There are two plastic sheets held in place by a glazing assembly. The top sheet is 4 mil thick (0.004 inch) Tedlar, and the lower sheet is 4 mil Teflon (Tedlar and Teflon are Du Pont trademarks). The purpose of these two plastic cover layers is to trap the sun's heat by means of the greenhouse effect. That is, the sunlight goes through the two plastic layers and heats the black absorber plate labeled "finned tube collector." Some of the solar heat would be lost by radiation from the absorber plate without this double glazing of plastic sheeting.

After years of experimenting, solar engineers have found that several plastic materials as well as glass will do a good job of trapping sunlight and its heat energy—just as do the roof and walls of a greenhouse. Sunlight goes through the plastic or glass sheets, heats the absorber panel and tubing because they are painted a heat-absorbing

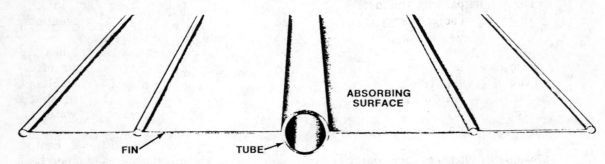

FIGURE 1-2.   Cross Section of the Reynolds Solar Collector

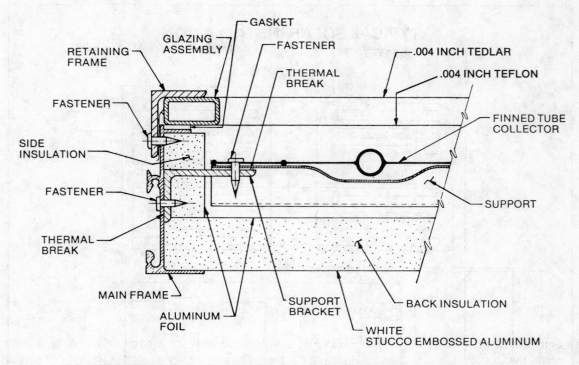

FIGURE 1-3. Cross Section Through Frame of Reynolds Solar Collector

black, and the major part of the solar energy reflected by the absorber is trapped by the glazing and helps to heat the absorber still further.

Note in Figure 1-3 that there is heavy insulation at the sides of the absorber panel and under it. Also there is aluminum foil attached to the upper side of the back insulation, since this foil reflects heat back to the absorber and helps, with the insulation, to minimize escape of solar energy from the absorber plate and its tubing. Most well-designed liquid-type solar collector panels include these essential elements: absorber plate and tubing painted black, with an air space above it and one or two layers of glazing, backed up by insulation—at the sides, too—and contained in a suitable frame.

In subsequent chapters are described many different kinds of liquid-type solar col-

lectors and others using air as the heat exchange medium. You'll also find information on how to build your own solar collector, as well as instructions on assembling solar heating and hot water systems.

Looking again at Figure 1-1, which illustrates a simple system using the sun to heat domestic hot water, the water from the solar collector panels is fed into a hot water storage tank. Water from this tank is pumped by pump to your conventional water heater. In some climates you can expect to furnish 90% or more of the heat for your domestic water, and cut your utility bill accordingly. In New England or Minnesota, a good solar heating system should furnish 60% to 70% of your hot water requirements.

Water from your conventional heater, taken from its coldest zone, is pumped back through the solar panels to be reheated and

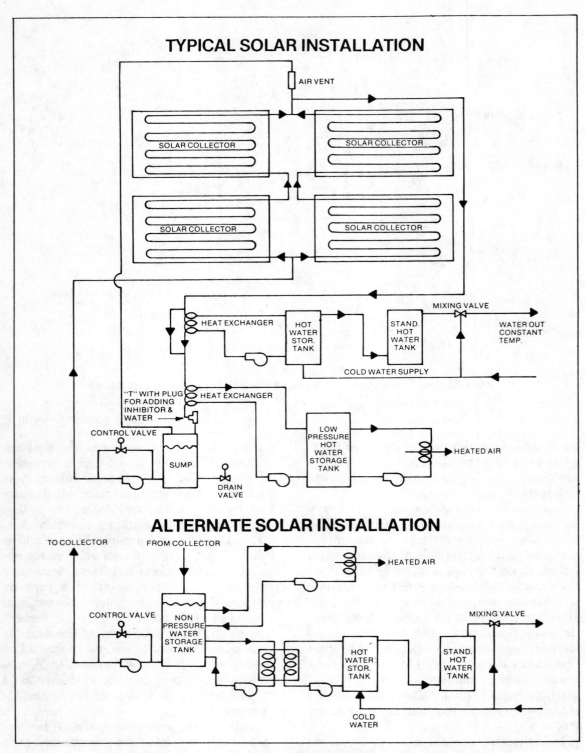

FIGURE 1-4.   Typical Solar Installation (drawings by Reynolds Metals)

12

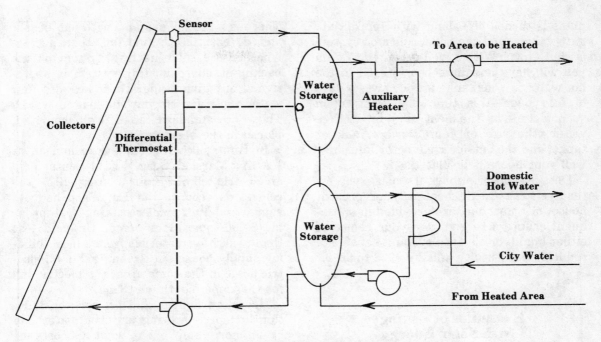

FIGURE 1-5.   Liquid-Type Solar Water Heating System

returned to hot water storage. Temperature sensors are provided at the outlet port
of the solar collectors and in the hot water
storage tank. These two sensors are connected to a differential thermostat and
simple automatic control system described
in more detail in Chapter 9. A differential
thermostat is a device that compares two
important temperatures, T_{out} from the solar collector panels and T_{tank} of the stored
water, and then automatically starts the
pumps and valves operating efficiently. The
purpose of this control is to turn off the
main circulating pump when the temperature of the sun-heated water coming from
the collector panels drops below the temperature of the water in the storage tank.

When the solar collectors are no longer
furnishing heat, the differential thermostat
automatically turns off both the pump and
the electrically controlled bypass valve. As
a result there is circulation of water only
between the hot water storage tank and the
conventional water heater.

Elements of a Solar Space Heating and Hot Water System

Figure 1-5 is a diagram of a liquid-type solar
heating system that serves both for space
heating and for domestic hot water. Sun
heats the water in the collector panels, and
this warmed water flows into the water
storage tank. Hot water from this tank goes
into an auxiliary heater and then into a loop
through the house, with coils of pipe carrying hot water at each point where you need
space heating. Room thermostats turn on
blowers to circulate air past the heated coils
of water.

Additional sun-heated water flows into a
second storage tank and from it into your
conventional water heater. Again there is a
differential thermostat to compare the
temperature of the water coming out of the
solar collectors with the water temperature
sensed in the upper storage tank. When the
outlet temperature falls a preset number of
degrees below the storage temperature, the

pump is turned off, along with appropriate gate valves, and the solar collector system is shut down. With a well-designed system you will have adequate heat stored in the hot water in your tanks for one or two days of carryover—this time depending upon such factors as the heat of your storage water, the size of your storage tank or tanks, and the outside chill factor, plus how well your house is insulated.

Detailed descriptions of solar systems that you can use in heating your present house, or a new one, are provided in subsequent chapters to give you your choice of either liquid- or air-type systems capable of reducing your utility bills by 60% to 90%.

Examples of Savings with Solar Energy

There are about 70 million homes in the United States. In an active building year, only about 2 million new housing units are constructed. One of the most frequently asked questions is: "Can you put a solar heating system in an old house?" It's a very good question for most of us.

The answer is a resounding *yes*. A solar installation in your existing home may be slightly more costly than if you designed it into a new house, but thousands of them are being made in older houses. Remember, to get the most of your solar heating system, it is essential to insulate before you solarate.

In an old 3-story brick house in Philadelphia, a solar installation has saved more than 50% of the annual costs for heating and hot water. This example is a 12-room row house 70 years old. It is typical of turn-of-the-century housing in cities from Boston and Baltimore to Chicago.

This urban solar installation makes use of the old water heater, furnace, and hot air ducts and vents in the row house. It includes a support system for black-surfaced collector panels with 540 square feet of surface facing southward on the roof of the building.

There is a control system, with sun sensor and differential thermostat, that decides whether the solar heating system or the backup standard heating system is operative at any given time. There are also four water tanks for storing sun-heated water. These are standard tanks, well insulated, placed in the basement.

In Huntsville, Alabama, a technician at NASA's Marshall Space Flight Center paid an electric bill of $70 for January 1977, the coldest on record. Jim Harrelson had designed and built a solar heating system for his 3,000-square-foot home. He paid less than $1,000 for materials from a local building supply house. In a comparable all-electric home in the same area, the electric bill for the same month was $240.

Harrelson figures that his solar installation for space heating and hot water had saved more than 75% of what his costs for those services would have been—during the worst winter ever. He uses air-type solar collector panels with ribbed aluminum painted black as the absorber, and glazing of glass. Thermal energy from his collectors is stored in a bin 4 feet deep, insulated and filled with crushed limestone. Details of similar air-type solar heating systems are provided in Chapter 5.

This Solar Hot Water System Costs Home Owners Nothing

A completely different approach has been taken by the Wilcon Corporation of Ocala, Florida, who have already made it possible for more than 200 owners of all-electric homes to cut their electric bills by an average of 35%. This company installs solar water heaters as a supplement to existing electric units. Solar energy does such a good job that Wilcon provides its solar heaters at no cost to the home owner—and collects its money as a portion of the savings.

Shown in Figure 1-6 is a diagram of this solar water heater. The solar collector, instead of being a flat absorber plate with

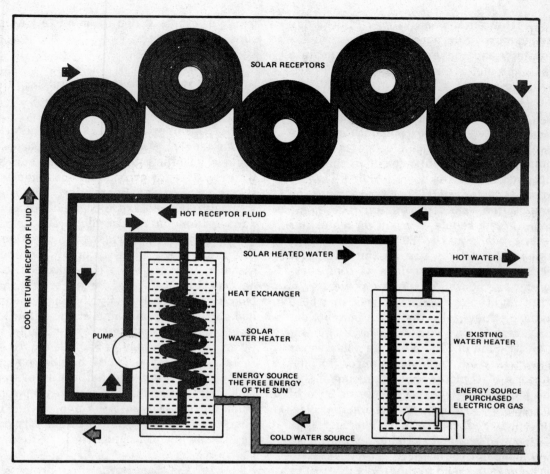

FIGURE 1-6.   Wilcon Corporation's Solar Water Heater

glazing and insulation, consists of coils of extruded vinyl tubing containing a green antifreeze solution. The vinyl tubing is formulated with an inhibitor to prevent deterioration from the sun's ultraviolet radiation. The coils are made of 1-inch OD (outside diameter) tubing, and the diameter of each coil is 48 inches, with 5 or 6 coils in series as the total collector. Coils can be placed on a roof or on the ground.

Sun-heated fluid from the coils is transferred through PVC (polyvinyl chloride) plastic pipe to a heavily insulated 120-gallon storage tank. The transfer fluid goes through a copper coil heat exchanger inside this tank and thus warms the water in the tank. The pump used to circulate the green

antifreeze transfer fluid through the coils is a Bell & Gossett 1/12-HP (horsepower) unit. It is activated by an electronic control system which detects the temperature difference between the sun-heated transfer fluid and the water in the storage tank and turns the pump on when the green fluid is hotter than the stored water.

Another interesting feature of the Wilcon system is its BTU (British Thermal Unit— see Glossary) meter. This assembly consists of a water flow meter, temperature sensors, and electronic controls. The BTU meter measures the temperature difference between cold supply water and warm water, sun-heated, leaving the 120-gallon storage tank; it also measures how many gallons of cold water enter the system. Multiplying temperature difference by gallonage electronically and converting this product into BTU, the meter displays a four-digit decimal figure.

In Ocala, where the city owns the electric utility, the meter reader notes this BTU meter in each home each month when he reads the conventional electric meter. A computer at the utility converts the solar energy savings into kilowatt-hours. The city is paid $1.00 for the BTU meter reading, the computation, and the billing. The home owner gets a rebate, a credit on his or her electric bill, equal to 20% of the savings achieved by solar water heating. The city receives 10% of the savings as compensation for the nonsale of electric power.

Putting typical dollar figures on these savings achieved by the solar installation, an average Ocala home owner pays a monthly electric bill of $75. With the solar water heater, this bill could be reduced to $50. Thus the BTU meter shows a saving of $25. The home owner gets a rebate of 20% of this savings, or $5, so that the actual electric bill is reduced to $70. The city gets $2.50 and Wilcon gets $16.50, amounting to the balance of the savings after credits to the home owner and to the city power utility plus the $1.00 for BTU meter reading, computation, and billing.

Added to the saving of $5 per month on the home owner's electric bill is an addition to his or her hot water supply of 120 gallons and a solar water heating system at no charge. At the end of 10 years, the owner can buy the solar water heater, which has been maintained at no charge by Wilcon, for the nominal sum of $1.00.

For the home owner who wants to buy his own solar water heater, Wilcon offers another alternative. He can finance his solar heater through a local bank. Monthly payments on a 36-month loan covering the solar heater come to about $25, or the equivalent of savings on the utility bill. At the end of this 3-year period the home owner has paid for his solar heater, and now it starts giving him a $25 profit each month. And he and his family continue to enjoy a big additional supply of hot water.

Cooperative Solar Systems in Low-Cost Homes

One of the finest examples of cooperation among federal, state, and local agencies to achieve an efficient solar heating and hot water system for existing low-cost homes is taking place in San Bernardino, California. Although these solar projects have received a modest amount of federal aid, it would be quite possible to undertake the same kind of program in any suburban area. You and a group of your neighbors could provide solar heating and hot water for all your homes from a central source. By sharing expenses and getting local financing, it should be possible for each of you to cut your utility bill by an annual average of $50 per month.

Assume that your share of this cooperative solar heating and hot water system, including interest over a 5-year period, amounts to $3,000. At the end of the five years, your solar system is completely paid for. Meanwhile, it has paid for itself in lower utility bills.

One of the San Bernardino projects is shown in Figure 1-7. This conceptual drawing shows how a Solar Energy Center can supply sun-heated water to 10 houses for space heating and domestic hot water. The Energy Center consists of a large number of solar collector panels mounted on racks and connected by pipes, pumps, valves, instruments, and wiring to a central control area. The solar collectors face south and are tilted at about 45° from the horizontal. This is ideal positioning in San Bernardino's 32° N. latitude to achieve maximum insolation during the winter months, when you need the greatest amount of solar energy for heating. Also, this southward direction and tilt of the solar collectors works quite efficiently during other seasons.

In this installation, where all the houses were carefully insulated prior to the system's construction, solar energy takes care

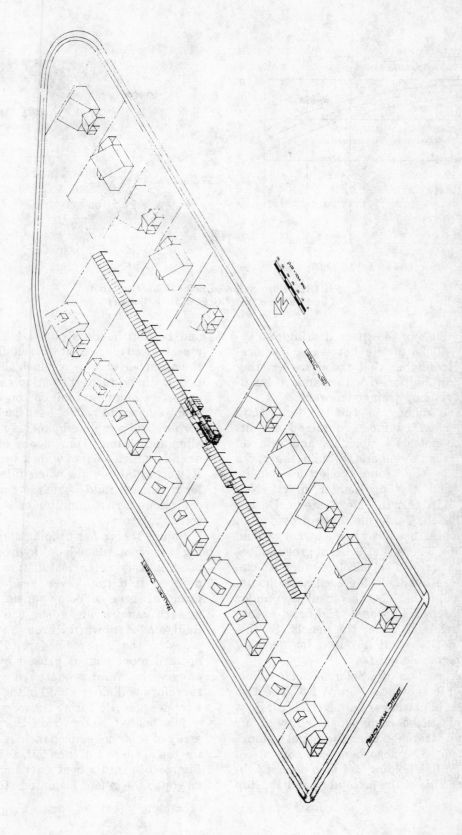

FIGURE 1-7. Cooperative Solar Heating and Hot Water System Serving 10 Homes in San Bernardino, California

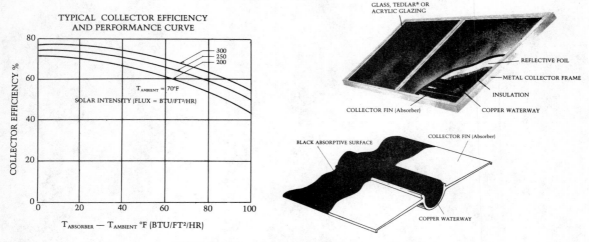

**FIGURE 1-8.   Solarcoa Solar Collector Panel
and Performance Curve of Its Efficiency**

of nearly 80% of the space heating and essentially 100% of the hot water requirements. Remember that these are existing houses, reconditioned with standard building materials by trainee laborers.

To save money in this project, Nate Rekosh, chief engineer, obtained surplus telephone poles for uprights and railroad ties for cross members to build the racks supporting the solar collector panels. Rekosh and the project architect, Neil Pinney, AIA, Earth/Life Systems Design of Seal Beach, California, have provided an additional feature most home owners would appreciate. There is a series of greenhouses under the array of solar collectors, with one greenhouse available for each solar home. Even though there is thick insulation under each Solarcoa solar panel used here, excess heat is available under the panels. So this heat is not wasted; it's used for growing family vegetable gardens.

A cross section of a Solarcoa solar collector panel is shown in Figure 1-8. The two top layers of glazing are 4-mil thick Du Pont Tedlar plastic sheeting separated by an air space and stretched over the panel's aluminum frame. The absorber plate consists of aluminum fins holding 3/4-inch copper tubing, with this entire assembly and the top

and bottom headers of 1-1/2 inch copper pipe painted black to absorb sunlight. Under the absorber plate is a 2-inch thick layer of polyurethane foam insulation covered with reflective aluminum foil on the upper insulating surface to reflect heat back to the absorber. The completed panel is housed in an aluminum frame. Dimensions of one panel are 8 feet high x 4 feet wide x 4 inches thick. It weighs 80 pounds when filled with the heat transfer fluid, which is usually water containing a rust inhibitor or a water-antifreeze mixture.

Figure 1-9 is a basic piping diagram showing the continuous-loop hydronic system used in this solar installation. Water is pumped into the lower headers of each group of three collector panels. The water in each panel is heated by the sun as the fluid moves upward through the copper pipes to the upper headers. Part of this upward movement is caused by *thermosiphoning*: as water is heated, it expands and therefore will move uphill in the confines of a copper pipe, defeating the force of gravity.

The heated water from the top of the array of solar collector panels is collected in the top headers and then fed, as indicated in Figure 1-9, into a heat exchanger inside a large (2,000-gallon) insulated storage tank.

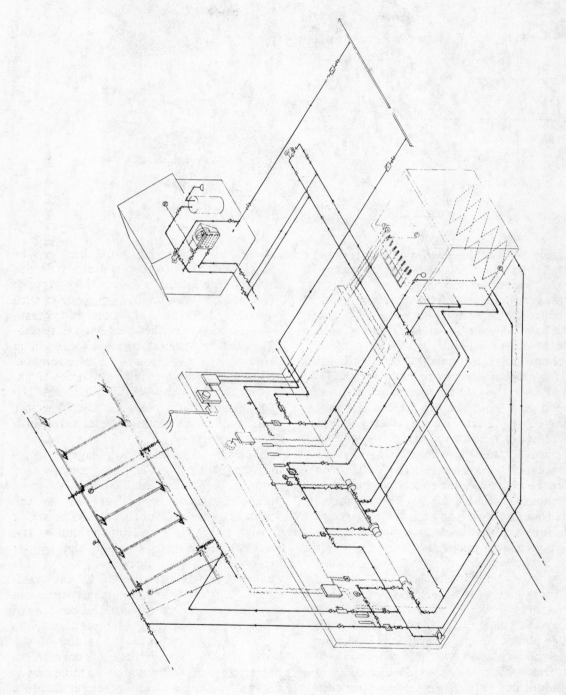

FIGURE 1-9.   Continuous-Loop Hydronic System

19

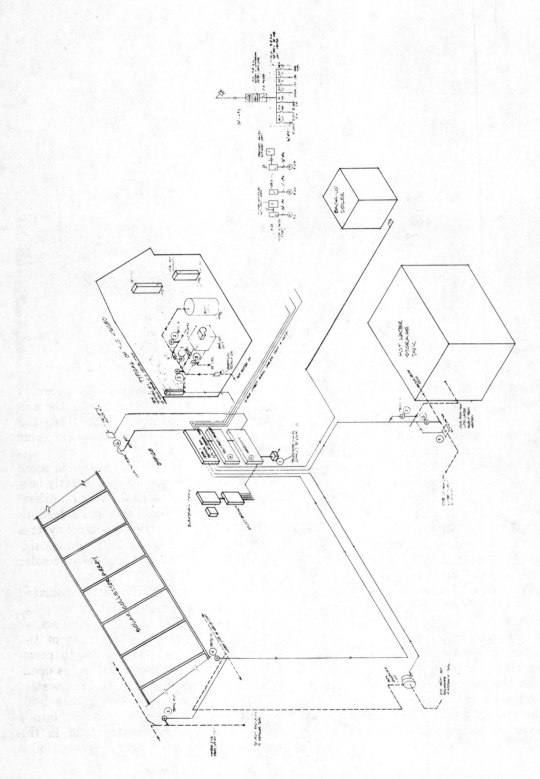

FIGURE 1-10. Typical House with Space and Water Heated by the Sun

20

**Solar Energy Center for Space Heating and Hot Water Supplied to 10 Homes
in San Bernardino, California**

The heat exchanger consists of a coil of copper tubing that transfers heat from the sun-warmed water in the exchanger coil to the surrounding water in the big storage tank. A return pipe from this large tank carries water back to the solar collector panels for further heating. All exterior and connecting piping is well insulated to avoid heat loss.

Temperature sensors in the upper (output) line from each group of collector panels continuously report to the control system in the Energy Center. This temperature of the sun-heated water is compared with the temperature of the water in the large thermal storage tank. So long as the sun-heated water is a few degrees hotter than the stored water, the control system keeps the pumps working to bring additional warmed water from the solar panels, through the heat exchanger, to raise the water temperature in the storage tank. Toward evening, or whenever the solar radiation stops heating the water in the collectors sufficiently,

the control system automatically operates valves and pumps so that water in the collector panels drains into a sump. Then the pumps are shut down until the next solar heating period.

This control process is described in more detail in Chapter 9 to show you exactly how it works and the reasons for using a differential thermostat. You'll also find a description of the new proportional control system developed by Rho Sigma, Inc., and considered the most efficient design yet for solar installations.

When the water in the large insulated storage tank has reached a useful temperature, typically 140°F, a temperature sensor in the tank enables another part of the Energy Center's control system to pump this sun-heated water into the houses needing space heating and domestic hot water. One typical house appears in Figure 1-10. The hot storage water is brought into a conventional insulated water tank in the home. The sun-heated storage water is also circulated through the coils of fan-coil heaters. In this type of heater, a fan flows air over a copper coil containing sun-heated water whenever a room thermostat demands heating and turns the fan on.

As a backup for the solar system, a gas boiler is provided in the Energy Center. During prolonged periods with little or no sunshine, this boiler heats the water in the large storage tank.

Useful Pointers on Solar Heating Systems

This community system in San Bernardino illustrates several useful points applicable to practically all solar heating systems.

From a dollars-and-sense standpoint, don't plan your solar heating system to provide all your building's space heating and hot water. Carrying 100% of the load means too large a system—too many solar collector panels and other equipment—and therefore too high an initial cost. Be satisfied with an installation that carries 70% to 80% of your heating and hot water load in favorable climates such as the South and Southwest, and perhaps only 50% in extremely cold climates with less annual insolation.

It is quite possible to build an effective solar heating system, such as the one described for 10 houses, with relatively unskilled labor if you provide skilled supervision and a well-engineered design.

In the San Bernardino installation the houses, which had been repossessed by the Veterans Administration, were first carefully insulated. The work was done by carpenter trainees under a CETA (comprehensive employment training) program, with federal and state funding. These young workers were also taught elementary plumbing and electrical wiring. They installed all the solar collector panels, built the Energy Center, and installed the neces-

sary additional equipment including the large thermal storage tank, supplementary boiler, insulated piping to each home, as well as its fan-coil space heater and hot water heater with connections to the central solar system.

Supervision was headed by a retired federal construction engineer, Nate Rekosh. He had years of distinguished service with the Navy Seabees and the Army Corps of Engineers. He was aided by engineers of Solarcoa, Inc., of Long Beach, California, makers of the solar equipment, as well as by Neil Pinney, the architect.

In the course of this program, assisted by a relatively modest grant from the U.S. Department of Housing and Urban Development (HUD) made available from funds of the Energy Research and Development Association (ERDA), several workers were sufficiently trained so that each could qualify as a foreman on a future solar installation project.

It is well worthwhile to undertake a cooperative program of this kind in almost any suburban area. The solar heating and hot water installations in San Bernardino are being extended to 35 low-cost homes for senior citizens. These homes are owned by the VA. Within the next year or so, several hundred modest houses will also get solar equipment from various Energy Centers in this progressive community. As a result the home owners will reduce their utility bills for space heating and domestic hot water by an average of 80%. Rekosh and his associates, headed by Valerie Pope, a dynamic general manager, are planning solar installations for schools, several federal buildings, and then, industrial and commercial structures.

Average cost of these solar utility systems for a typical 3-bedroom house—the 10 VA houses in Figure 1-7 and 35 senior citizens' homes—is less than $3,000, using trainee labor. Including insulation, the total bill for making *livable housing from existing rundown homes* was so low that these houses are being sold for less than $20,000 each. And that price includes a solar system that cuts the home owner's utility bill for space heating and hot water by an average of 80%.

This kind of program doesn't have to be limited to low-cost housing with federal grants. You can do it anywhere with the cooperation of a group of concerned neighbors. Just be sure to:

1. Learn as much as possible about various kinds of solar equipment.

2. Get some expert professional help in planning your installation and in supervising the first phases of the job if you and your neighbors are going to do much of the work. As you will see in later chapters, there is a considerable list of plumbing and electrical items, in addition to your solar collector panels, needed to do the job adequately.

3. Insulate your building before installing any solar system.

There is a list of solar equipment manufacturers in Appendix 1. Most of them will provide you with information if you write and enclose a self-addressed stamped envelope. You can also get the names of expert solar engineers and consultants in your area from the nearest chapter of the International Solar Energy Society, American Section. If you are building a new home or other building, your nearest office of the American Institute of Architects (AIA) can help you find an architect with solar experience.

Reducing Your Future Utility Bill

Beyond what you as a homeowner, landlord, or business executive can do immediately to use solar energy for heating, cooling, hot water—and in the next few years, electric power—in the structures you own, there is something else you can do to reduce your future utility bills.

The facts of the continuing energy crisis are common knowledge. Because our supplies of oil and natural gas are either depleted or distant, the costs of processing these fossil fuels continue to rise. If you are 40 or under and with a normal life expectancy, you can probably count on outliving United States petroleum and gas as natural resources. Supplies of uranium are limited, the cost of building nuclear power plants has risen enormously, and the disposing of nuclear wastes remains an unsolved problem. Coal is certainly a partial answer but costs of mining and converting it escalate, and the pollution problem it brings is acute.

Scientists and engineers interested in the earth's *renewable* resources—solar and geothermal energy, methane from garbage, as examples—have been pleading for years, "Let's do something big with these resources so that we can save our dwindling supplies of fossil fuels to make medicines, plastics, and other useful items." Now concerned nontechnical citizens are taking notice. Record cold in the 1977 winter in large areas of the United States turned the heat on solar energy.

Even though you're not a member of the board of directors of a utility company, as a taxpayer and a utility bill-payer you have an important voice. The work being done to build large-scale solar power plants, described in detail in a later chapter, should be expedited. Here are some interesting facts:

- It costs no more to build a big solar power plant than to build a comparable nuclear power plant.

- After the original investment in construction, everything favors the solar power plant. Its cost of operation is much lower than that of an electric power plant fueled by petroleum, natural gas, coal, or uranium. There is almost no pollution from a solar plant. You don't have mines, wells, refineries, pipelines and other means of transportation to produce and deliver the fuel used by a solar electric plant.

- In most cities and industrial areas, we can improve the amount and quality of our free solar energy by using more of it. By harnessing solar energy and thus reducing atmospheric pollution, we'll guarantee ourselves more sunshine—as well as healthier air to breathe.

- Building more solar electric plants will tend to bring the cost down as the technology advances and certain components are manufactured in quantity. These cost reductions, as well as the lower operating expenses of solar electric plants, should make it possible to reduce the bills for the electricity used in your home, office, and factory.

- If we don't do something big with solar energy, we can look forward unhappily to a succession of energy crises, each worse than the previous year's.

- Many of the OPEC nations, blessed with abundant sunshine and cash, are beginning to use American technology to develop their solar resources for large-scale electric power and salt water desalinization—as well as for heating and cooling their buildings and domestic hot water. It is one further irony. American geologists and petroleum engineers have made these countries rich. Our accelerating solar technology will make them more comfortable than many Americans in the very near future.

What can you do about it?

Look at what's been done to solve our national problems with water and air pollution, automobile safety, the quality of foods and pharmaceuticals. What is possible with the combined action of concerned citizens should surprise no one.

Become informed as to the potential of solar energy. There are many U.S. congressmen and congresswomen who are willing to promote solar projects. The new administration is far more sympathetic to developing solar energy than its predecessor.

But you can do your part, too. Every communication to a political or business leader, insisting that we push solar technology, is effective. Popular demand as well as dollars will convince General Electric and Westinghouse that some day soon they'll make more money from solar energy than from their nuclear equipment. Exxon, Mobil, and Shell have already invested an estimated total of $100 million in the development of solar cells, as described in Chapter 11. It's an investment with a bigger future payoff than any field of Texas towers.

In an Associated Press interview dated February 21, 1977, Jacques Cousteau said:

"Solar energy, well exploited, could easily represent four-fifths of the world's energy by the year 2000. . . .

The biggest danger is nuclear energy. Any other catastrophe can be repaired. A nuclear one cannot. Many scientists say there's no danger, but there is."

Cousteau said United Nations estimates showed that if $850 billion were spent for nuclear power by the year 2000, only 20% of the world's energy needs would be met. And $1 trillion spent in the same time on solar energy would provide energy for 80% of the planet.

"What we have to decide is if we're going to be enslaved to arbitrary decisions of kings in the Middle East or are we going to develop a reasonable national energy program to be out of reach of blackmail," concluded Cousteau.

In Chapter 10 you'll see what is being done to plan several kinds of major solar power plants, including ocean platforms and electric generators in space, in addition to big solar power plants already under development in desert areas. These are productive avenues of research. One or more will assure you of *having* an electric bill to pay in future decades.

2
Solar Water Heating:
New Techniques for Saving Money

One of the simplest ways to use solar energy is to heat water. A complete system, easily built with hand tools as described later in this chapter, requires no outside source of energy—no electricity, no gas, no fuel oil, no pumps, no thermostats or other instrumentation. This basic system takes advantage of the fact that heated water, confined in pipes, will rise and defeat gravity. Such a phenomenon, called thermosiphoning, makes it possible to place a storage tank for hot water above your solar collector panel, where the water is heated by the sun. Then gravity delivers the hot water to outlets at a lower level while feed water goes into the lower end of your collector (see Figure 2-1).

Several thousand systems like this were built and used in Florida, Georgia, Arizona, California, and Nevada in the period before natural gas or electricity became readily available and cheap. In countries like Israel, Japan, and others with fuel shortages, millions of solar water heaters provide hot water for practically every farm and many city homes.

For the very simplest method of heating water by sunlight, you don't even need a so-

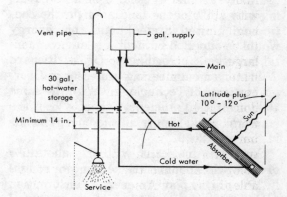

FIGURE 2-1. Layout of Solar Water Heater Installation

lar collector panel. See the description later in this chapter of a new low-cost Solar Preheater. Also as mentioned in the previous chapter, the Wilcon Corporation in Ocala, Florida, is putting in solar heaters consisting of coils of plastic tubing containing a green antifreeze solution that absorbs solar heat. Many home owners and ranchers in warm climates have used lengths of plastic garden hose painted black, the best color for absorbing sunlight. In one current California installation, the owner of a swimming pool has 300 feet of black plastic hose—six 50-foot garden hoses painted black—in a serpentine on his garage roof near the pool. His only other expense is for valves to permit including this solar heater in the water circulation loop of his swimming pool system, for either including solar-heated water or shutting it off. More sophisticated swimming pool solar systems are described in Chapter 8.

Sunlight: Enormous Source of Free Energy

Even though the United States is by far the world's biggest energy consumer, we could satisfy all our energy requirements by using only a tiny fraction of our total land area to collect solar energy. On the assumption that our collection of solar energy is only 10% efficient, "the total energy needs of the U.S. could be supplied by solar collectors covering only 1.5% of the land area [in the continental United States], and this energy would be supplied without any environmental pollution," according to Dr. J. Richard Williams, an engineering professor at Georgia Institute of Technology. "With the same 10% utilization efficiency, about 4% of the land area could supply all the energy needs in the year 2000."

Since we Americans, with only about 6% of the world's population, account for roughly 35% of this planet's energy consumption each year, and the rate is going up, we need to think seriously and act rapidly to replace energy from fossil fuels with solar energy. For many applications, including heating domestic hot water and space heating, we can achieve far more than 10% efficiency— as high as 60% under some conditions—in using solar energy. Thus, by devoting less than 2% of our total land area to collecting power from the sun, we should be able to eliminate many of the disastrous effects of prolonged cold waves like those that paralyzed much of the eastern half of the United States in the winter of 1967-77.

The sun's output of energy is enormous. You might think of the star around which we revolve as a giant nuclear fusion reactor. In its core hydrogen atoms are fused to form helium atoms in a transformation that consumes about 4 million tons of hydrogen each second. This process results in a temperature at the core of about 14 million°C (25.2 million°F) and a loss of mass. But astronomers reassure us: the sun's hydrogen supply is adequate for another 6 billion years.

Heat at the surface of the sun is about 5,700°C and this heat is radiated toward our planet, which is less than one-millionth the size of the sun, at the speed of light, or 300,000 kilometers per second (186,000 miles per second). Solar energy arrives at the surface of the United States at an average rate in June ranging from about 1,850 BTU to about 3,000 BTU on one square foot in one day.

Following the Glossary are listed many of the units of measurement used in solar work. However, it is helpful to note that one BTU is defined as the amount of energy required to raise the temperature of one pound of water by one degree F at 39.2°F. Another useful fact is that one kilowatt-hour (KWh) is equal to 3,414.43 BTU. Thus we can say that, on an average June day, each square foot in the United States receives more than 1/2 kWh of solar energy.

Another term widely used among solar engineers as a measure of energy density is the *langley*, which corresponds to one calorie per square centimeter, or about 3.7 BTU per square foot. *Insolation*, the amount of solar energy reaching the earth's surface, is usually expressed in langleys, as shown in the maps of the continental United States (excluding Alaska) in Appendix 4. You can see how insolation varies regionally from 80 langleys per day to more than 300 langleys per day in December, while in June the solar energy totals range daily from 450 langleys to more than 800.

SUN'S POSITION IMPORTANT

Several facts about the relative positions of the earth and the sun are important when you're designing a system to take advantage of solar energy. Changes in season occur because of two factors:

- The earth's axis of rotation is tilted 23.5° from the perpendicular to the plane of its orbit.
- The earth travels around the sun in an elliptical orbit requiring 365.24 days (one calendar year) to complete.

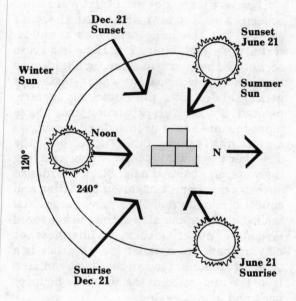

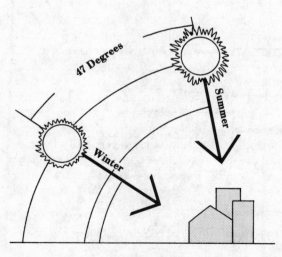

FIGURE 2-2. Typical Positions of the Sun for 40° North Latitude

The result of these two factors is shown in Figure 2-2.

Another useful point to consider is that the sun appears to travel in a curved path above the earth from dawn to dusk. The zenith, or maximum solar altitude, occurs at noon. The extent and altitude of the sun's path vary widely from midwinter to midsummer. For instance, at 40° north latitude (about the middle of the continental United States) the sun appears to travel through an arc of 120° on December 21, the winter solstice, while its path on June 21 describes an arc of 240° from east to west. Also, at its zenith, the sun is 47° lower in distance above the horizon in midwinter than its position almost directly overhead at noon in midsummer.

These factors greatly affect the amount of insolation you can collect when you're using solar energy for heating. It has been determined by solar engineers that if you want to place a solar collector at the best angle for heating during winter, you will tilt it at an angle equal to the geographic latitude plus 15° and aim it toward the south, or 10° west of south, in the Northern Hemisphere. If your objective is to obtain maximum solar energy in the summer—to operate a cooling system, for instance—your solar collector panels should be tilted at your latitude minus about 10°. For year-round collection, a compromise angle will work well, set somewhere between the +15° and -10° indicated, added to or subtracted from your area's latitude.

Actually, as you can judge from the maps in Appendix 4 showing variation in langleys per day between winter and summer, the length of time your solar collector receives sunlight is far more important than the collector's tilt.

THE GREENHOUSE EFFECT

Radiation from the sun is composed of numerous spectral frequencies, with wave lengths from less than 0.3 micron (one micron=one-millionth of a meter) in the invisible ultraviolet region, through the visible

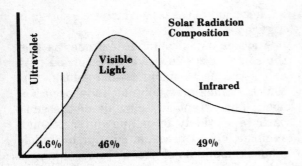

FIGURE 2-3. Composition of Solar Radiation

spectrum, to more than 14 microns in the invisible infrared region. This distribution of solar radiation by frequency, in terms of what we receive on the earth's surface, is shown in Figure 2-3. Note, about one-half the sun's energy is in the infrared region.

Visible sunlight penetrates all levels of the earth's atmosphere. The upper atmosphere contains ozone, which protects the lower levels from dangerously large amounts of ultraviolet radiation and X rays. The atmosphere also acts as a shield to absorb or reflect infrared as well as ultraviolet sunlight in varying amounts at different altitudes above the earth.

Architects as well as gardeners have long made use of the fact that glass and some plastic materials are transparent to sunlight but act to trap the infrared wave lengths

radiated or reflected back from any surface under this glazing. This is the greenhouse effect, which results in concentrated warmth from the sun inside a structure with a glass or plastic roof, enclosed on its sides often by glass.

This leads logically to the reason why the most efficient flat solar collectors provide a layer or two of glazing, transparent to sunlight but trapping the infrared heat energy absorbed by a black collector plate.

There are many designs of flat plate solar collectors used to heat water with the sun's energy, but the basic principles are illustrated simply in Figure 2-4. Here is a cross section of the solar collector. Sunlight goes through the transparent cover plates or glazing and strikes the absorbing surface, painted black. This absorber may have pipes mounted on it or include the piping as an integral feature. In any case, both the absorber plate and pipes or tubing carrying the water are painted a flat black in order to absorb a maximum amount of insolation and reflect a minimum of the sun's energy. Attached on the upper side of the thick layer of insulating material such as fiberglass or polyurethane foam under the absorber is a sheet of aluminum foil so that heat radiated from the underside of the absorber bounces back and is not wasted.

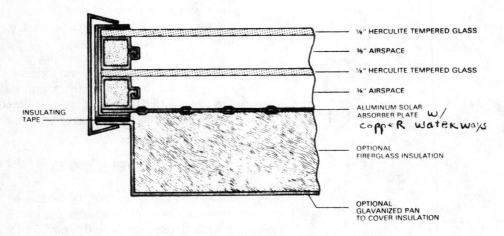

FIGURE 2-4. Cross Section of a Solar Collector

28

Making Your Own Solar Water Heater

Although most people will prefer to buy one of the numerous solar water heaters available commercially—and some types are de-

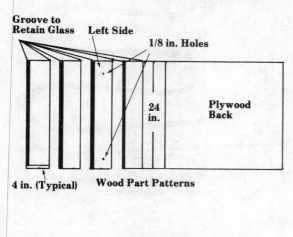

Groove to Retain Glass   Left Side

1/8 in. Holes

24 in.

Plywood Back

4 in. (Typical)   Wood Part Patterns

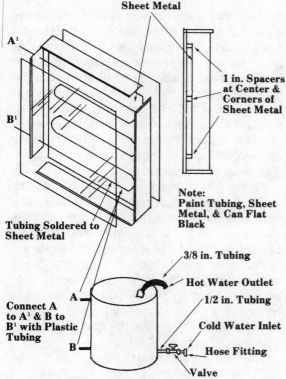

Sheet Metal

A¹

B¹

1 in. Spacers at Center & Corners of Sheet Metal

Tubing Soldered to Sheet Metal

Note: Paint Tubing, Sheet Metal, & Can Flat Black

3/8 in. Tubing

Hot Water Outlet

1/2 in. Tubing

Cold Water Inlet

Hose Fitting

Valve

Connect A to A¹ & B to B¹ with Plastic Tubing

A

B

FIGURE 2-5. Details of Small Thermosiphoning Solar Water Heater

scribed and illustrated at the end of this chapter as well as in Chapter 3—it is easy, using hand tools, to build your own thermosiphoning solar heater.

The dimensions of the heater described in subsequent paragraphs are suitable for a cabin, a camper or trailer, or a portable hot water supply for camping trips. By making a larger collector, and then one or two more panels suitably connected to a considerably larger water tank—say 50 gallons—you can use the same principles in building a permanent hot water source for your home.

You start by making a collector box. The sides are of 1 inch x 4 inch redwood board. Each of the four sides is 2 feet long. At the yard where you buy the 8-foot board, have a groove cut 1/2 inch from one edge of the board. This groove is 1/8 inch wide and 3/8 inch deep.

At the same yard get a piece of 1/2-inch plywood 2 feet square. Assemble three sides of the box by attaching them to this plywood base with wood screws, after you have cemented aluminum foil to the upper surface of the base.

If you plan to make larger collector panels for a permanent installation, first mount a layer of foam insulation on the plywood, choosing polyurethane foam with aluminum foil on its upper surface. This will prevent solar heat from leaking out of your collector somewhat better than the plywood-and-foil base will by itself.

Drill two 1/2-inch holes in the fourth 1 inch x 4 inches side panel. These holes are passages for the copper tubing to be mounted on the absorber plate. Each hole should be large enough to pass 3/8-inch OD copper tubing. The center of each hole is 1-1/2 inches above the bottom of the side piece, the bottom being the side away from the groove previously cut.

Nail in place at the four corners and center of the foil-covered plywood base of the box a series of 5 spacers as shown in Figure 2-5. Spacers are 1-inch cubes, planed down to a height of about 7/8 inches and nailed with finishing nails. These blocks are to hold the copper coil and absorber plate at the correct distance above the plywood base.

Having made the box, you can assemble the collector and coil. The most inexpensive material suitable for the plate is 22-gauge galvanized steel sheet. Get it cut to a square 22 inches x 22 inches, which leaves you plenty of room inside the box. It's a good idea to trim off the corners of the steel sheet to keep from being scratched. Copper sheet is a somewhat better conductor of heat but is more expensive.

Next get 16 feet of 3/8-inch copper tubing. This is flexible and comes in a roll. Start by straightening out the tubing, which is quite soft, so that it lies as flat and true as possible. Now lay one end of the tubing over the flat metal sheet (steel or copper), allowing enough to go through the hole at the end of the box. Mark the pipe at the start of the first bend with a pencil, and then form it into a U-shape as shown in Figure 2-6. By working slowly and carefully, you can avoid flattening the tubing.

Make sure the first U is in the proper place by putting the tubing on the metal sheet. Then mark the second bend with a pencil and carefully form the second U. Continue with this process until you have a serpentine as illustrated. Even out the long ends of the tubing and lay the finished coil on the metal sheet. Make the tubing lie flat, bending it with your fingers or tapping it lightly with a rubber or wooden mallet. The copper tubing must make contact with the metal plate to absorb the maximum amount of solar heat.

Now solder the serpentine tubing to the metal sheet, after cleaning the metal surfaces with emery cloth wherever solder is to be applied. Use either a small torch or a soldering iron, and make your solder joints about 6 inches apart. Hold the tubing flat on the metal sheet. Heat will make the copper distort slightly but it will return to its flat position on cooling.

Clean excess solder paste from the copper tubing and plate, and then paint the assem-

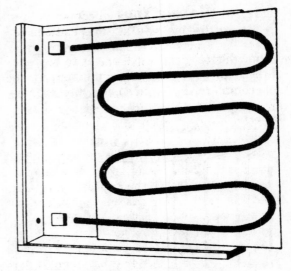

FIGURE 2-6. Partially Assembled Solar Water Heater

bly with flat black paint. It won't hurt to use a second coat of paint, and then let the assembly dry. You could use *selective* black paint—there are several brands formulated for good solar absorption and low reflectivity—but a good quality flat black paint has been found equally effective by many manufacturers of solar collector panels.

Next, mount the metal assembly in the box and nail the sheet to the spacer blocks. Touch up these points with black paint.

Slide a heavy piece of cardboard into the grooves on the upper side of the box, and trim this cardboard to fit the box exactly. Now you can get a piece of glass or transparent plastic (Kalwall and GE Lexan are suitable) cut to the size of your cardboard sample. Slide this transparent cover into position. Then fit the wood end with the holes so that the copper tubing goes through it, and attach it to close the end of the box, using wood screws.

For your portable solar water heater, you can use a 5-gallon metal can, round or square, of the type available at most hardware stores for storing hot water. Solder two short lengths of 3/8-inch copper tubing to the can on one side at the positions indicated in Figure 2-5 to match the inlet and outlet ports of the solar collector box you have just completed. Drill a 1/4-inch hole in each place in the can where you will solder in a length of about a foot of copper tubing. Drive a center punch into the hole to enlarge it, and then insert the piece of tubing, making sure both the hole in the can and the tubing are clean. Using torch or soldering iron, pour solder into the depression around the tubing. Place the can on its side so that the tubing extends vertically from the hole, and the solder will flow smoothly.

In the same way solder a length, perhaps 2 feet, of 3/8-inch copper tubing bent into a U at the upper end, attaching it to the screw-on cap of the 5-gallon can. Solder 1/2-inch copper tubing (instead of 3/8-inch) to the lower part of the can on the opposite side of the ports to be connected to the solar collector. This 1/2-inch tubing should have compression fittings and a shutoff valve obtainable from a hardware store, and then another length of 1/2-inch copper tubing soldered inside a brass garden-hose fitting.

Now cork the outlet ports, connect a cold water hose to the can and make sure all your soldered joints are watertight. Make any repairs necessary.

Your solar heater is ready to produce hot water. Set your collector on a rack with a suitable tilt facing south with an unobstructed exposure to the sun. Install plastic hoses and hose clamps between the solar collector and the 5-gallon can, which should be mounted in such a way that the bottom of the can is level with the top of the collector.

Fill can with cold water. As water flows into the collector coil and is heated, this warmed water rises and is replaced by cool water from the bottom of the can. Soon, on a sunny day, your 5-gallon can will be full of water heated to about 140°F (60°C), a temperature comparable to the average person's setting for a conventional water heater using a fossil fuel or electricity.

Other Homemade Solar Water Heaters

Plans for making solar water heaters are available from many sources. One set of step-by-step directions is contained on pages 40-43 of this author's previous book, *How To Build a Solar Heater*. Included are drawings and directions for making a solar collector 8 feet x 2 feet in area. One panel of this size can be used to heat water in a 50-gallon tank in a warm climate like Southern California's. In New England or other northern states, you'll want more collector area. So if you live in a colder region, build or buy two collector panels, connect them in series to your water tank, and you will have a useful year-round supply of solar-heated water.

If you're going to build your own solar collector panel, there are many designs described both in this book and the author's previous book. One of the most efficient panels is the SolarSan collector, designed by William B. Edmondson, publisher of *Solar Energy Digest*. The inventor is a true solar pioneer, who began his work with solar energy when he was a career engineer in the Marine Corps. He evolved his design for the SolarSan collector during years of experimenting in many climates.

You can get full details on how to build Edmondson's collector and various solar water heaters from *Solar Water Heaters and Their Application*. This 54-page manual provides detailed instructions and sells for $26.50, the price giving you a limited license to use Edmondson's patented design. Using it, and not counting your own labor, you can build a SolarSan panel for about $2.75 per square foot in material costs. This is about half the retail price of the lowest cost solar collector made with quality materials and available commercially. The address of the inventor is P. O. Box 17776, San Diego, California 92117. This is also the address of *Solar Energy Digest*, a monthly news magazine that is one of the best sources of information for anyone interested in using solar energy.

Quoting from a description of the Solar-San collector published in the author's previous book with the inventor's permission:

As a cover material, he uses not glass but 4-mil Tedlar, the clear polyvinylfluoride plastic sheeting (made by Du Pont) which has good durability in all kinds of weather.

Under this plastic cover, Edmondson's solar sandwich has either a 1-inch layer of clear fiberglass filter material or an air space. The filter pad transmits a substantial amount of sunlight and provides a spring-like support for the Tedlar film, as well as trapping some of the heat reflected by the collector plate. The inventor states that even when the absorber plate reaches 300°F, the top plastic film feels cool to the hand.

A novel feature of this design is the use of an 8-mil thickness of soft, highly reflective aluminum foil to which is fastened a serpentine of 3/8-inch copper tubing. Staples are placed at 1-foot intervals and driven through a fiberglass board 1-inch thick, and into a plywood board backing. This presses the copper tubing into the foil and makes a tight contact between the heat-absorbing copper tubing and the reflective foil.

The tubing is coated with a primer, then black graphite paint, and then a selective black such as 3M Black Velvet, which is an excellent absorber of solar energy.

In a typical installation, this section of the SolarSan panel forms the upper part of a shallow wooden box containing a 4-inch insulating layer of foil-faced fiberglass. A completed panel 8 feet long, 2 feet wide, and 5-1/4 inches deep weighs 52 pounds (dry), or 3.25 pounds per square foot. The collector area is almost 15 square feet.

According to Edmondson, this panel will deliver water at temperatures up to 250°F if mounted perpendicular to sunlight striking it at an ambient of 80°F.

As you'll see in later pages, many commercial solar manufacturers are now using similar materials to build collectors that perform very well for solar space heating and cooling, as well as for solar hot water heaters.

Suggestions about Solar Collectors

If you decide to build your own solar collector panel, here are some suggestions that should prove helpful.

- Don't skimp on the quality of your materials. A good solar collector should last for the life of your home.

- Many commercial manufacturers use aluminum as the absorber plate, and attach copper pipes to this base plate. If you use these dissimilar metals, it's a good idea to paint the aluminum and the copper before assembly.

- Paint the absorbing surfaces—base plate and liquid-carrying pipes or tubing—with a primer and then with a good quality black paint. There is some disagreement among solar experts as to the value of *selective* black paint. The term "selective" means a paint that is particularly good as an *absorber* of shortwave solar energy and *reflects* a minimum of the longer waves in sunshine. One good selective paint is 3M Nextel Black Velvet, which is much black paint. While some manufacturers of solar collector panels use a selective black surface, others use an ordinary flat black paint of good quality and claim that their solar panels are equally efficient.

- When mounting your solar panel in a frame, if you are using a wood frame or box to contain the absorber plate and the insulation pad below the absorber, be sure to leave a small space on all four sides of the absorber plate. This is to allow for thermal expansion of the metal absorber, which can get as hot as 450°F when dry and after hours of baking under a hot sun. Normally you will have water or an antifreeze mixture flowing through the pipes of a liquid-type collector, but even so, in the late afternoon of a hot day the absorber plate may well reach a temperature of 350°F, depending on your glazing.

- Many solar collector manufacturers use Tedlar sheeting as a glazing material instead of glass. However to keep this glazing looking good—a smooth sheet without noticeable ripples—a manufacturer such as Reynolds Metals stretches the plastic sheet in a special aluminum frame and bakes the assembly at 300°F. In other words, you may find it easier to use either glass or a solid plastic material instead of the flexible Tedlar. The author's preference is to use solid plastic sheeting of high transparency such as Kalwall's Sun-Lite, discussed later in the book.

- Be sure your liquid-type collector is free from leaks before you mount it in your frame or box. If you are not familiar with brazing and plan to use copper pipes and copper headers, either learn how to braze or get this part of your assembly fabricated by a plumber or sheet metal shop.

- Because you want your solar collector to retain heat as well as absorb it, use a thick insulation pad under the absorber plate. Aluminum foil on top of this insulation is desirable because it reflects heat back to the underside of the absorber and thus keeps your heat-producing assembly hotter. There is a small air space between the lower side of the metal absorber plate and the reflecting aluminum foil. Then use insulation at least 2 inches thick and preferably thicker. The same kind of fiber-glass or polyfoam insulation described in Chapter 1 for insulating your home will help make your solar collector more efficient.

Even if you decide not to build your own solar collector because there are many good commercial panels now available at reasonable prices, you will benefit from the suggestions in previous paragraphs. They will help you in evaluating the features of the solar collectors you buy.

An Inexpensive Solar Heater

If you are a do-it-yourselfer, here are some instructions for building a solar water heater that will add 55 gallons to your present hot water supply as a preheater and put money in your pocket—perhaps $20 a month. The total bill for materials is $214.91, priced in April 1977.

This kind of solar water heater has been assembled by lawyers, doctors, accountants, and school teachers, according to Bob Marks, an owner of American Building Center in Los Alamitos, California. With years of experience running a large building supply business, Marks has been interested in both solar energy and do-it-yourselfers for several years.

So he developed a low-cost plastic solar collector panel and built the solar heater shown in Figure 2-7 for heating the water in his own home. He went a step further and used 10 of his own solar collectors to heat his swimming pool.

Looking at the diagram, you see the solar collector mounted flush on the roof. This is quite satisfactory with a slanting roof like the one at Bob's house. You'll notice that the inclination of this roof is about 30° from the horizontal. In Southern California with a latitude of 32° north—where Marks and the author live—there is a small gain in collector efficiency if the collector angle is about 45° from the horizontal, to capture the maximum amount of winter sunshine. How-

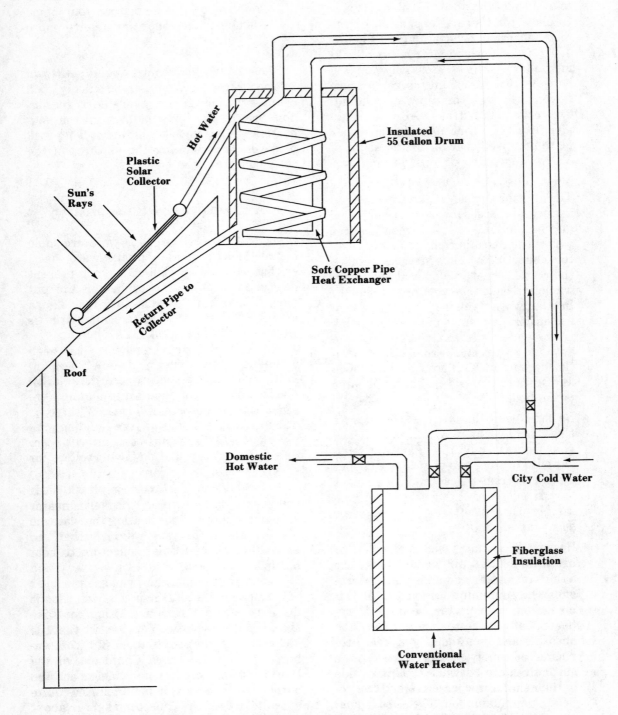

Labels within figure:
- Hot Water
- Plastic Solar Collector
- Sun's Rays
- Return Pipe to Collector
- Roof
- Insulated 55 Gallon Drum
- Soft Copper Pipe Heat Exchanger
- Domestic Hot Water
- City Cold Water
- Fiberglass Insulation
- Conventional Water Heater

FIGURE 2-7.   Low-Cost Solar Water Heater Designed and Built by Bob Marks, American Building Center, Los Alamitos, California

FIGURE 2-8.   Solar Collectors Made by American Building Center

ever a 30° angle for Bob's collector works so well that he and his family get practically all their hot water heated for nothing by the sun throughout the year.

Of course, if your roof is flat or almost flat, you should mount your solar collector panels in a frame made of either metal or wood so as to achieve a suitable slant for your collector array. Remember that a good rule of thumb is to give your solar collectors a southern exposure—10° west of south is even better to get the maximum heating from the afternoon sun. And an inclination of your latitude plus 10° to 15° will make your collector array perform most efficiently during the cold months, when you have fewer hours to collect solar heat.

In this solar hot water heater, designed by Marks, he uses high-quality PVC plastic pipe connected to the plastic headers at the top and bottom of the collector panel. This piping, like the two water tanks shown in Figure 2-7, is carefully insulated with Johns-Manville foil-surfaced fiberglass insulation.

Although Bob Marks originally developed and sold plastic solar collectors made of polypropylene, he is now making metal collectors himself and also selling metal units made by several leading manufacturers. The reason for switching from plastic to metal is that plastic panels occasionally develop leaks, usually because of improper usage. For example, the adhesives used to patch a small leak become tacky at 200°F. If a plastic panel is exposed to bright sunlight on a hot day, with no fluid in the collector, its temperature can easily reach 200°F or higher. When water is again pumped into the hot collector, the patch gives way and the collector leaks.

This has not happened with the plastic panels shown in Figures 2-7 and 2-8 because these collectors contain water all year. If they are drained, they are refilled with water while the surface temperature of the collectors is 100°F or less. As you will find in several discussions in this book, it is quite possible to use plastic solar collectors—hundreds of thousands are in service in Japan and other countries—but you must use care to avoid leaks. (This author's preference is to use metal collectors because of their greater durability, when the collector is carefully assembled of good materials.)

Marks uses an ingenious heat exchanger in the system in his home. The upper tank in Figure 2-7 is a used oil drum, a standard 55-gallon size with a removable lid. It cost Bob all of $15, and of course he cleaned and painted it before installing it in his attic. You can install a drum like this as a preheater in any convenient place—on your roof, with good insulation—just so long as this preheater tank is higher than the top of your solar collector or collectors.

The really ingenious feature, as you'll notice, is that the solar panel draws liquid by gravity from the bottom of the preheater to the bottom header of the solar collector. Then the sun's heat forces hot water up the panel and into the top of the preheater tank. The actual liquid in this system is a 50-50 mixture of water and antifreeze, so it would work quite well in a much colder climate.

Inside the preheater tank are the coils of copper tubing you see in Figure 2-7. Marks uses 3/4-inch tubing that is easy to form. "I simply used the drum as a mandrel to make this inexpensive heat exchanger," he says. "Anyone can do it."

The water to his existing electric water heater comes from the top of the 60 feet of copper tubing, while his normal cold water supply feeds the bottom of this heat exchanger. Thus the solar-heated antifreeze mixture circulates through the preheater tank, warming but never contaminating the water in the copper tubing, which flows into the home water heater.

This kind of heat exchanger brings up an important point for anyone building a solar water heater for home use. If you intend to use antifreeze in your solar collectors, or if the materials used in your collectors may corrode and contaminate your water, or if you're using plastic panels and an unpressurized system, *you must have a heat exchanger* as part of your solar water heater.

Since you need a heat exchanger for an unpressurized solar hot water system be-

cause city water pressure could damage a plastic collector, the unit developed by Bob Marks is both efficient and inexpensive. His copper tubing cost $39.40 and the drum was only $15, so that the total materials cost for this heat exchanger was about $55. These are retail prices at American Building Center as of April 1977. As noted previously, Bob's entire bill of materials for the solar water heater shown in Figure 2-7 amounts to $214.91.

In the same area of Southern California, the owner of a house having an electric water heater serving a family of four will save between $15 and $20 per month by installing a solar water heater—and have the advantage of an extra 55 gallons of hot water available. This means that a do-it-yourselfer will pay for the cost of his Marks-type solar water heater in from 10 to 15 months. And we know that utility bills are bound to go up further, so that the payoff time will be still further shortened.

Low-Cost Solar Water Preheater

Commercial solar water heaters cost from $700 to about $1,200 not counting installation charges. Here is a new low-cost solar water preheater which any do-it-yourselfer can build for a total materials price of about $100. The result appears in Figures 2-9, 2-10, and 2-11. This solar preheater, which produced sun-heated water at about 165°F in July in Southern California, can be particularly useful for installations on flat-roofed buildings.

Start with an old 50-gallon gas-heated hot water tank (costing as little as $10) and strip off the outer insulating shell. If there are a few leaks, they can be repaired with J B Weld epoxy steel mender—retail price $2.95 for a can.

After sealing the leaks with epoxy mender, paint the tank with flat black paint. While the tank is drying, build the remainder of the solar water preheater.

The frame of this first model is made of wood. Subsequent units (when manufac-

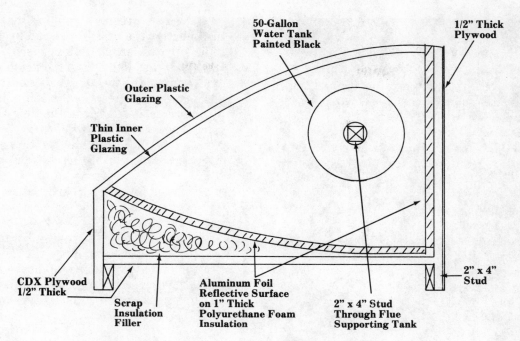

50-Gallon
Water Tank
Painted Black

1/2" Thick
Plywood

Outer Plastic
Glazing

Thin Inner
Plastic
Glazing

CDX Plywood
1/2" Thick

Scrap
Insulation
Filler

Aluminum Foil
Reflective Surface
on 1" Thick
Polyurethane Foam
Insulation

2" x 4" Stud
Through Flue
Supporting Tank

2" x 4"
Stud

FIGURE 2-9.   Cross Section of Solar Preheater

**FIGURE 2-10.   Solar Water Preheater Before Double Glazing is Attached,
Showing 2 x 4 Stud Through Flue of Tank**

FIGURE 2-11.   Completed Solar Water Preheater Built at a Materials Cost
of $100

tured in quantity) will probably have a shell of galvanized steel. About $30 worth of CDX plywood is sufficient to make the ends, floor and back of the shell. This plywood is nailed to 2 inch x 4 inch Douglas fir studs and 3/8 inch x 2 inch battens. Outside corners of the shell are protected by 2 inch x 2 inch galvanized steel angles, using a total of 10 feet costing $1.40.

The black water tank is mounted in this shell ingeniously. If you're working with a used gas heater, there will probably be a circular flue through the long dimension of the tank—a hole just large enough so that you can hang the tank on a 2 inch x 4 inch stud. Attach 2 inch x 4 inch galvanized steel joist hangers, one inside each end of the wooden shell, with a wood block on the outside of the plywood as a stiffener. It is easy to suspend the black tank on its two-by-four support inside the wood shell.

The next step is to line the back and sides of the plywood shell with Technifoam, a polyurethane insulating material 1 inch thick and faced with aluminum foil. Score the lower portion of a Technifoam sheet by cutting grooves on the back side, spaced about 4 inches apart so that you can bend the long side of this reflecting and insulating sheet into the parabolic shape shown in cross-section in Figure 2-12. Before placing this curved bottom sheet in position, fill the space under it with scraps of polyfoam and fiberglass insulation.

As you can see, the whole objective is to provide a highly reflective enclosure *beneath* the black water tank, *behind* it, and *at the ends.* Since this reflective material, the aluminum foil, has an excellent insulation backing, the Technifoam sandwich effectively concentrates sunlight on the black tank and also helps to retain the solar heat, day and night.

The final step is glazing. Stretch ordinary steel baling wire at three points across from one curved plywood end to the other, paral-

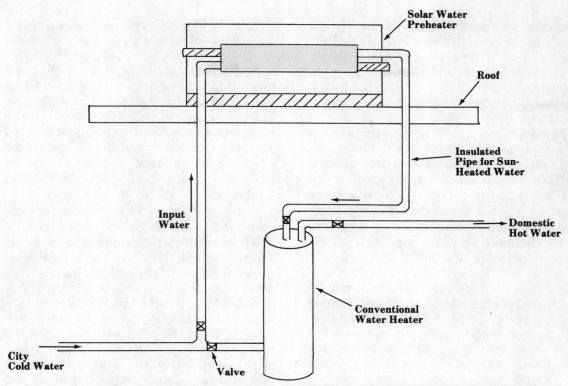

FIGURE 2-12.   Schematic of Solar Water Preheater Connected to Conventional Water Heater

lel to the tank and its supporting two-by-four. Then stretch a sheet of thin transparent polyethylene plastic 0.004 inch thick over these wires for inner glazing. Allowing 1 inch of air space, attach an outer glazing of relatively thick (0.040 inch) fiberglass reinforced plastic sheet (cost: $15). The original model had a single glazing of the heavier plastic, but the inner glazing is worth the effort since it retains more heat overnight.

When this solar preheater was faced south as shown in Figure 2-11, the water temperature in the tank rose from about 120°F early in the morning to about 160°F by noon, and provided 175°F water in mid-afternoon.

Connecting such a solar preheater into your existing hot water system is both easy and inexpensive. You simply run your cold water line from your normal supply by means of a tee and valve, so that you can furnish cold water to the solar preheater on your roof. Or you can shut this valve, shown

in Figure 2-12, and cut the solar preheater out.

City water pressure will bring the cold water up to the solar preheater without a pump. The sun-heated water is brought by gravity into your conventional water heater through a valve. This valve can be manually operated. Or it can be a solenoid valve operated by an inexpensive differential thermostat (see Chapter 9) if you want an automatic system.

The major advantages of this solar water preheater are its low cost and simplicity. It is designed so that you can easily insert it between your cold water supply and your conventional hot water heater. The preheater will keep feeding warm water into your conventional tank every time you use hot water. Thus, it will give you more than an extra 50 gallons of domestic hot water supply.

If you can schedule your home usage of hot water so that you consume most of this

39

heated water for showers or baths and washing clothes and dishes in the late afternoon and early evening, you can probably save about $25 per month if you have an electric water heater. Your savings with a gas- or oil-fired water heater will be somewhat less.

Not everyone will be able to find a used gas water heater. The author is investigating sources for suitable new water tanks—without insulation and without leaks. If you are interested in obtaining a new tank, or want to buy the detailed plans for making this solar water preheater, or would prefer to purchase the complete unit ready for assembly, please follow this procedure:

- *For sources of new water tanks and detailed plans* for building this solar water preheater ($5.95 + 6% tax for California residents), send your check to Ted Lucas, c/o Ward Ritchie Press, 474 South Arroyo, Pasadena, California 91105.

- *To obtain a complete solar water preheater in kit form* ready for assembly, write to Bob Marks, American Building Center, 3626 East Cerritos Avenue, Los Alamitos, California 90720. Estimated price of the kit is $300 plus shipping costs and any applicable taxes. Included are detailed installation instructions so that the solar water preheater may readily be installed by any handy person, or by a licensed plumber where required.

Durable Solar Water Heater

For the do-it-yourselfer who wants to install a durable solar water heater—durable simply because the collector panels are made of metal instead of plastic—here is a step-by-step procedure. This set of instructions is based on an excellent book entitled *Solar Heating—Theory, Equipment and Systems Design*, published by Sennergetics Solar Systems Design & Sales of Northridge,

California. This book represents the distilled experience of James Senn, an electronics engineer who has designed numerous successful solar installations for both space heating and hot water. He uses this book as his text for seminars attended by designers, builders, engineers, and installers of solar heating systems. Senn designs systems and also sells solar hardware. His preference for a solar collector panel is a unit made by Energy Systems, Inc., (ESI) of El Cajon, California.

You may want to make your own solar collector panels using some of the ideas in this book or this author's previous book. Or you may want to purchase commercial solar panels from one of the many manufacturers whose products are described in this book or listed in Appendix 1 of this volume. We have made a sincere attempt to verify successfull installations of every commercial manufacturer's product listed. And unless you are very handy with tools and willing to take account of such simple but important matters as the thermal expansion and contraction of dissimilar materials, our advice would be:

- Buy the commercial solar collector panel you like best, after learning how liquid- and air-type collectors function to absorb solar energy usefully.

- If you are determined to build your own solar collector panels, study the subject first to avoid costly mistakes. We have seen more than one do-it-yourself installation where the collector panels are buckling and leaking because the home owners made beautiful tight fits—too tight, because they didn't allow for the fact that aluminum, copper, and steel have different coefficients of thermal expansion. And in many climates, even the benign ones like those of Arizona, California, Georgia, and Florida, it's not unusual to find day and night temperatures varying by 40° or more during the winter, when you need your solar system most urgently.

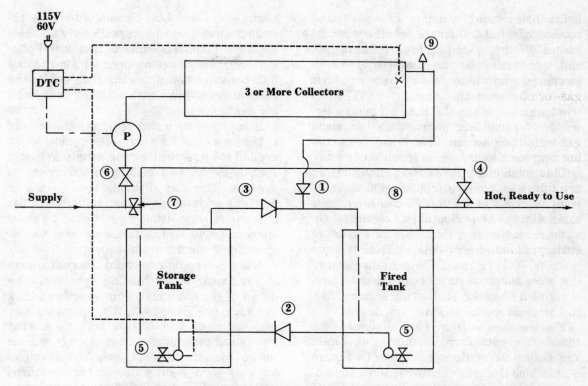

FIGURE 2-13. Solar Water Heating System Designed by Sennergetics

The Sennergetics solar water heater is shown in Figure 2-13. The following is a key to symbols and numbers on this drawing:

DTC: Differential temperature controller or differential thermostat.

P: Circulating pump in the supply line to the solar collectors

X: Thermistor sensors to measure temperatures at the outlet of the collector panels, and at the bottom of the storage tank and the "fired" tank (which is a conventional water heater using electricity or fossil fuel when solar heat is inadequate)

1 1/2-inch swing check valve that prevents thermosiphon loss at night

2 1/2-inch swing check valve that selects water for the solar collector loop from the bottom of both tanks

3 3/4-inch swing check valve that selects user water from the top (hottest) water in the two tanks and prevents bypass of the fired tank by the collector loop

4 3/4-inch tempering valve

5 Tank drain valves

6 1/2-inch shutoff valve

7 3/4-inch shutoff valve

8 3/4-inch relief valve

9 Float air vent, required by building codes and needed for releasing trapped air from the solar collector panels automatically.

DESCRIPTION OF SYSTEM COMPONENTS

Whether you build your own solar water heater or have it installed, it is useful to learn more about the components in the system designed by Jim Senn, who has designed many systems for home owners as well as for architects, builders, and solar installation firms.

The ESI absorber plate consists of 8 longitudinal copper pipes clamped in aluminum fins. This plate is coated on both sides with a flat black paint, using a heavy coating applied carefully. Insulation below the absorber is foil-surfaced 2-1/4-inch fiberglass, and the glazing is two layers of 1/8-inch tempered glass with an air space of about 1/2-inch between the glass layers. The entire assembly is housed in an aluminum extrusion for the four sides, with tempered 1/8-inch composition "hardboard" as the backing for the fiberglass insulation.

This solar collector delivers 130 BTU an hour for each square foot of collector surface, or a total of 2,428 BTU per hour, on a clear winter day in Southern California. On a clear summer day, this collector's average output of heat energy derived from the sun is 2,615 BTU per hour. The manufacturer of this solar collector states that one such panel raised a 40-gallon tank of water from 78°F to 128°F on a typical February day.

These glazed collectors are available with three different arrangements of the inlet and outlet connections as shown in Figure 2-14, which is a view looking toward the upper (glazed) side of the collectors. These variations make it easy to arrange several collector panels in either parallel or series combinations, depending on installation.

It makes good sense to plan your installation carefully before deciding which configuration of collectors to use. Make a scaled sketch, including the plumbing runs to your storage tank and fired tank.

If your installation will be most suitable on the roof of your home, study where you're going to place your solar collectors so that your solar installation won't be hampered by objects already in place and serving a useful purpose. Chimneys, vents, gutters, ventilators, and skylights are examples of things already firmly established on your roof. You need them, and you need a solar heater. With a little advance planning, you can readily avoid unnecessary clashes between inanimate objects.

As everyone who owns a solar installation soon realizes, solar panels collect so much heat that their undersides as well as their sunny sides get hot. People who have installed solar water heaters directly on their roofs get a bonus because of this useful phenomenon: they save on their winter heating bills because their attics are warmed by the solar panels—even with a solar space heating system.

If an object such as a vent is in the middle of the best area for your solar panels, work around it by separating the panels so that a vent between two collectors has room to breathe. You may separate your panels as much as is necessary. Just remember that all runs of connecting pipe should be insulated to avoid loss of the solar heat you're spending your money to collect.

A *tempering valve* should always be used in your solar water heating system at the outlet of the hot water from your fired tank as shown in Figure 2-13. It's quite possible, with efficient metal solar collectors, that your sun-heated water from storage will be too hot for safe domestic use. A good collector may heat your water to temperatures between 180°F and 200°F on a clear summer day. The tempering valve automatically mixes the proper amount of cold water with the hot water to reduce the temperature to a safe level, preset by you.

The *differential temperature controller* is a relatively inexpensive automatic control which is essential to efficient operation of your solar system. More detailed information about these controllers is provided in Chapter 9. Briefly, this unit collects information from the thermistor temperature sensors (marked X in Figure 2-12) at the outlet of the solar panels and in the bottom of the storage and fired water tanks. The controller, having this data, decides when to operate the collector pump—turning it on only when the hot water from the collectors is hotter by a preset amount, determined by you, than the water in storage. This controller can thus be set as an additional safeguard, besides the tempering valve, to make sure the flow from your hot water taps doesn't scald anyone. In cold weather,

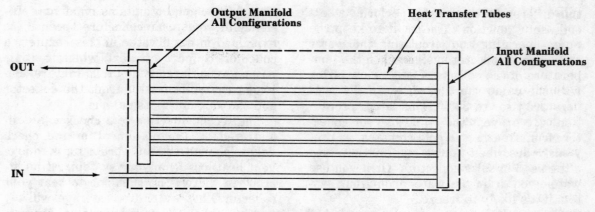

Configuration "A"

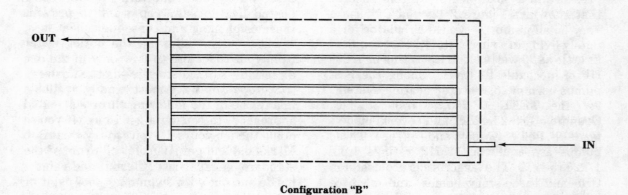

Configuration "B"

Configuration "C"

FIGURE 2-14.   Plumbing Connection Configurations Available for ESI Glazed Collectors

43

this differential thermostat performs a second useful function. You set it to keep the pump operating and circulating the water through the collector system when the temperature of the collectors falls below 36°F, with the pump shutting off when the temperature rises to 37°F. This latter precaution is to prevent the liquid in your collectors from freezing. In cold climates, as previously described, antifreeze mixtures are often used in solar collectors. Or if you use water, you drain the water from your system if it's likely to freeze.

The *circulating pump* for a domestic hot water system must have bronze or stainless steel parts in contact with potable (drinking) water. Since there is no static head pressure in a solar heater system such as that shown in Figure 2-12, you can use a very small pump. A typical circulator for a family living in a single-story house requires as little as 30 watts electrical rating or 1/220 HP of mechanical output. Among the best pumps used in solar water heating systems are the TEEL 1P-760, March 809-DF, Grundfos UPS 25-42SF, and several models made by Bell & Gossett and by Taco. These pumps are available in HP ratings from 1/220 to 1/12. The larger sizes are useful in two- and three-story homes, and in space heating systems where you need many collector panels.

Valves are a most important part of your solar hot water system and should be high-quality bronze or stainless steel shutoff or check valves used as shown in Figure 2-9. Shutoff valves permit depressurizing the solar collectors for service, controlling the flow rate, or replacing a storage tank or backup heater with minimum disruption of your hot water supply.

Check valves are useful because they permit free flow in only one direction. In the Sennergetics system, such valves perform two functions. One is to direct the flow of water from the coldest part of the system to the solar collectors, and then return the flow to the hottest part of the installation.

This flow scheme maintains maximum efficiency of your solar collectors because, as explained in detail later in this chapter, a collector is most efficient when there is minimum difference in temperature between the outlet water from the collector and the ambient (outside) air.

The second function of a check valve, illustrated by the placement of the check valve, labelled "1" in Figure 2-13, is to prevent heat loss from your system. At night, or when there is no sunshine to heat your collectors, hot water from storage will try to rise to the collectors because of thermosiphoning action. Previously, you've seen how thermosiphoning can be useful in liquid-type solar heating systems. In this case, when your collectors are not being heated by the sun, you want to prevent thermosiphoning and consequent heat loss. A check valve, allowing the outlet water from your collectors to flow only in the one direction—toward storage—is the answer.

Storage tanks are most readily available in any one of the following three suggested approaches to getting a good buy. If you're doing the job yourself, you can try what Bob Marks did and get a surplus oil drum of the standard 55-gallon size. Clean it and paint it inside and out with swimming pool paint or some other waterproof finish. A second alternative is to find a used conventional water heater that is still watertight. The third choice for a family-size solar hot water system is to buy a new standard electric water heater. Be sure it is glass-lined. Leave the heating element in place but don't connect it to your power source, since you're using this tank for storage of sun-heated water. Then insulate this tank with at least one layer of fiberglass insulation, available from any building supply store. Although special kits are on sale for insulating hot water tanks, you can do just as good a job and save money by buying standard fiberglass insulation and taping it in place with plastic tape. As described in Chapter 1, be sure to keep the faced side—the side covered either with plastic or aluminum foil—of your fiberglass insulation on the outside of your tank.

Although most hot water tanks contain some insulation, this extra layer of insulation really pays. The author and his neighbors in a large condominium complex with electric water heaters have found that spending about $15 for materials and less than half an hour of labor saves $5 or more a month on each of our electric bills, merely by insulating our water heaters and the exposed hot water feed pipe from this heater, which is in the garage, to the house.

CALCULATING HOW MANY SOLAR COLLECTORS YOU NEED

The number of solar collectors you will need for a hot water system will depend on several factors:

- Your geographic location and the number of hours of sunshine
- The efficiency of design of your solar collector panels
- The number of people in your household
- Whether your home includes such hot water consumers as a dishwasher and washing machine
- Daily variables such as ambient temperature and the temperature of the feed (cold) water.

You can figure that in the typical American household each person uses an average of 30 gallons of hot water per day. This is based on data collected by the U.S. Department of Commerce. It includes hot water used for cooking, bathing, and washing clothes. If you have a dishwasher, the figure may be 35 gallons a day per person—although in many areas people are now trying to conserve water, especially hot water.

The output of an efficient solar collector like the ESI double-glazed unit is about 30 gallons of sun-heated water per sunny day in the winter in an area with good insolation such as Southern California, Arizona, and most of the southern and southwestern United States. In climates like those of Minnesota, Michigan, or Maine, you might use a rule-of-thumb figure of 25 gallons of hot water per sunny winter day produced by one good solar collector.

Now your arithmetic becomes relatively simple. Just keep in mind two other points. You will get more for your money if you don't try to design your solar hot water system to do 100% of the job. In the southern areas, with good insolation, a solar installation that provides 70% to 80% of your family's hot water requirements is economical and should pay for itself in about three years. In northern areas, your solar system may save you only 50% to 60% of your utility bill for a payoff within four or five years. This is on the assumption that utility rates will continue to rise at the rate of only 5% a year. It's quite possible, as of this writing (July 1977), that utilities will be granted much higher rate increases in the next few years because of decontrol of the price of natural gas and other fuels—used by electric utilities as well as home owners and industrial consumers.

If you have a family of four, your installation for solar heating of domestic water may therefore call for two or three efficient solar collector panels. When you are connecting solar panels, use either parallel or series arrangements like those shown in Figure 2-15. If your panels can be placed close together, you can use short pieces of copper pipe and bronze press-fit connectors in an array of collectors. Then wrap these connections with insulation. You can buy press-fit connectors at hardware and plumbing supply stores. An alternative method is to use flexible neoprene hose with clamps at each end like the water in your automobile engine. Again, be sure to insulate. It costs you money and time to get the sun to heat your home supply of hot water, so insulate every length of connecting pipe carrying hot water. And, to repeat, insulate your hot water storage tank and your auxiliary convention-

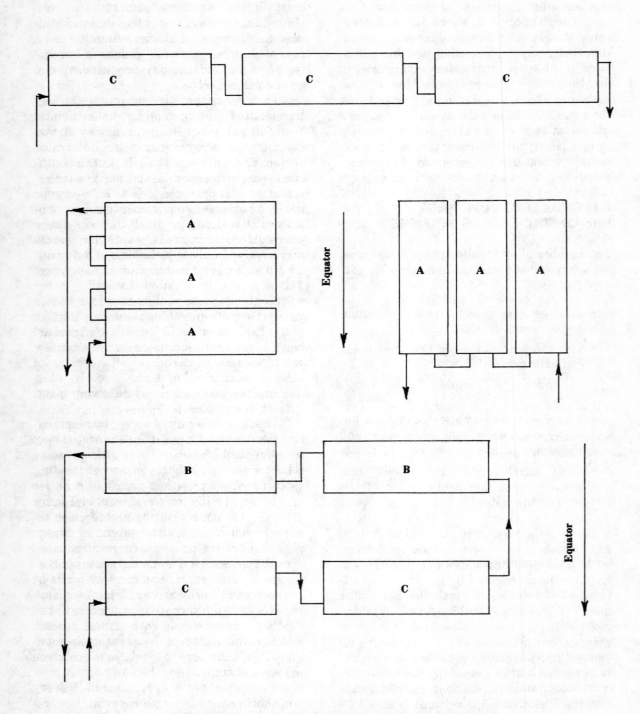

FIGURE 2-15.   Examples of Collector Interconnections

al water heater, whether it uses electricity or a fossil fuel.

As a word of caution, if you are insulating a gas water heater, wrap your blanket of fiberglass insulation around the tank but leave the top or flue area clear. With an electric water heater, cover the top as well as the circumference of the tank with insulation, leaving the electric conduit (if it is at the top of the heater, as is common) open so that it doesn't get too hot.

In warm climates, where there is no danger of freezing, it's unnecessary to insulate your incoming pipes supplying cold water. But wherever there is a possibility of temperatures cold enough to freeze water, wrap your pipes.

In their small mountain cabin, the author and his wife have wrapped all exposed water pipes with an electric heater ribbon and then a thick layer of fiberglass insulation held in place with plastic tape. The heater ribbon, which comes in 15-foot rolls, includes a thermostat that turns it on automatically when the ambient air is 38°F. Since the cabin is at an altitude of 5,700 feet and occupied only on alternate weekends and during holiday periods, this is a very good precaution during the winter—much better than having to drain the system every time we leave, or replacing a burst pipe after a prolonged spell of freezing weather. Needless to say, the water tank is also carefully insulated.

Gravity Drainage Prevents Freezing

The kind of solar water heater designed by Jim Senn is a *pressurized* system, and the liquid used throughout the system is potable water. Therefore, there is no heat exchanger required in the storage tank. If you build such a system, or have it installed in your home, and you live in an area where freezing temperatures are common, then shut off your cold water after sundown or during prolonged cloudy subfreezing weath-

er, and operate your pump long enough to drain your solar collector panels.

In a cold weather area, most experienced solar engineers design water heating systems so that they can be drained by gravity, after the necessary valves have been opened. Another alternative, previously mentioned, is to set your automatic control system up so that your differential thermostat will start your pump circulating water through your collector panels when the outlet temperature drops to 36°F, with shutoff when the temperature of the water coming from your collectors rises to 37°F. This approach is adequate in a mild climate like Southern California's. In areas with more severe winters, you will waste too much solar heat by diluting your sun-heated storage water with cold water. So drain your system.

However there are at least three other approaches to the problem of using liquid-type solar collectors in sustained freezing weather. These techniques may be summarized as follows:

• The most conventional solution, used successfully by designers and manufacturers of solar hot water systems in New England and many other northern and southern areas, is to use an antifreeze solution or a silicone mixture or another suitable heat transfer fluid in the solar collector panels and circulate this sun-heated antifreeze through a heat exchanger in the preheater tank. Usually the heat exchanger is a copper tubing coil like the one described in the Marks system. However another alternative is a tank within a tank, discussed in Chapter 3, where the antifreeze solution heated by the sun circulates through the space between the inner water tank and the outer, insulated steel shell.

• Another way to keep your water carrying pipes in your solar collector panels from clogging with ice and possibly bursting in cold weather is the technique developed by Piper Hydro, Inc. When the temperature of the water coming from the solar collectors drops below 40°F, this hydronic-loop system sends a small amount of hot water through the collectors, warms them up, and automatically keeps them from freezing. The Piper system, described in detail in Chapter 4 has proved effective in the installations in the cold winters of Calgary, Alberta; Boise, Idaho; Spokane, Washington; and the area around Washington, D.C.

• Still a third approach that is easy to drain in cold weather is the trickle system patented by Dr. Harry Thomason, who has built about a dozen successful solar houses in Maryland. In his design the feed water, instead of being pumped into the bottom of the collector panels, is pumped into a pipe running along the top of the collector. This pipe contains a series of 1/16-inch holes spaced so that each hole is above a valley in a corrugated galvanized steel sheet painted black as shown in Figure 2-16. A trickle of water runs down each valley and is heated by the sun. The total runoff is collected in a drain at the bottom of the panel and fed to a hot water storage tank. Thomason uses treated water in his system. He and his son and their families, as well as at least 10 additional households, have enjoyed inexpensive solar water heating for both their domestic hot water and space heating for several years.

Efficiency of Solar Collector Panels in Cold Weather

Solar collector panels of either the liquid- or air-type work satisfactorily under conditions of extreme cold. Figure 2-17 shows a house in Boulder, Colorado, owned by Dr. George Löf, an internationally famous solar

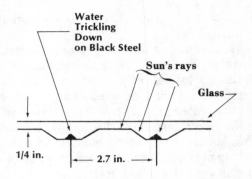

FIGURE 2-16.   Cross Section of Small Portion of Thomason-designed Collector

pioneer. Note the snow on the ground and on the section of roof not covered by solar panels. This home, with space heating and hot water supplied by solar energy, has been occupied longer than any other solar home in the United States. Designed and built by Dr. Löf in 1944, it has a solar system that continues to work efficiently after 33 years of service. This is excellent proof that a well-designed solar heating system, constructed of good materials, should last as long as your house.

You should be aware however, if you're

FIGURE 2-17.   Air-type Solar Collector Panels Have Heated Löf House in Boulder, Colorado, Since 1944

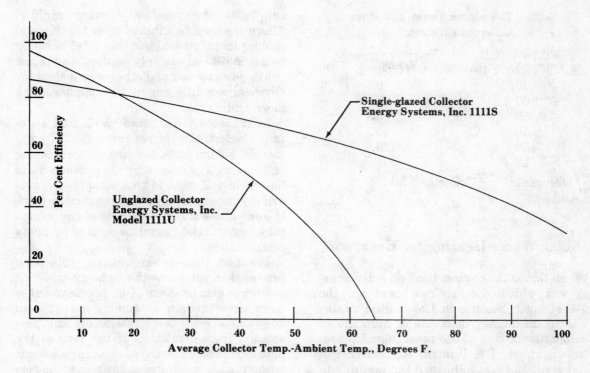

FIGURE 2-18. Comparison of Efficiencies of Unglazed and Single-Glazed Collectors at 250 BTU/H Insolation

planning a solar installation in a cold area, that the efficiency of solar collector panels decreases as the ambient temperature decreases. This fact, shown graphically in Figure 2-18 occurs because of three robbers of heat energy: conduction, convection, and radiation. The solar energy collected by your panels will slip away at an increasing rate as the difference in temperatures between your collectors and the ambient atmosphere increases. Thus, the colder it gets outside your home, the less efficient will your panels become. This effect is intensified by wind: the chill factor affects solar collectors adversely—as a cold wind affects a shivering Chicagoan walking along Lake Michigan in midwinter.

As we've emphasized, all good solar collector panels are carefully insulated, with glazing above the black absorber surface to trap the solar heat and with thick insulation below. By means of this insulation, the heat loss due to temperature difference between the collector and the ambient air is reduced. This is why a well-designed solar collector can do a respectable job in clear sunny weather, even when the outside temperatures are subfreezing.

If there were no losses caused by the three heat robbers, theoretically you would expect your solar collector to perform at 100% efficiency. In practice, the efficiency of a well-designed collector varies, as seen in Figure 2-18. Another good design, Edmondson's SolarSan, shows the variations in efficiency indicated in Table 2. Note that even at 0° temperature difference, the efficiency of a high-quality solar collector is only 70%, largely as a result of radiation from the collector surface if the panel is mounted on a roof. The heat loss from the underside of the collector is relatively small, but it has the beneficial effect of warming your house.

Table 2-1. Ambient Temp. Effect on Collector Efficiency

COLLECTOR EFFICIENCY (%)	$T_{DIFFERENCE}$ (°F)*
70	0
60	32
50	55
40	90
30	125
20	145

*$T_{Difference} = T_{Collector\ Fluid} - T_{Ambient}$

Solar Water Heating for Everyone

When this author's first book on solar energy was published nearly two years ago, the use of solar heating in the United States was in its infancy in terms of numbers of installations. One of the most ingenious solar scientists, Dr. William A. Shurcliff of Harvard, had just published the eighth edition of his informative book, *Solar Heated Buildings—A Brief Survey*, and described 119 buildings. That was in March 1975.

In the thirteenth edition of Bill Shurcliff's book, published in January 1977, there are descriptions of solar heating installations in 38 states of the United States and 11 foreign countries. My friend reports that this is his last edition of this excellent book. He is devoting more time to developing new ways to use solar energy economically. A few of Shurcliff's many inventions are described in Chapter 7.

Meanwhile, commercial manufacturers of solar equipment, after years of struggle and near-starvation (for the small independents), are beginning to go from red ink to black. By early 1977, more than 32,000 solar water heaters were in service in the United States. The installation curve is rising steeply, with one manufacturer selling 1,000 solar heaters a month.

As of the end of 1976, there were some 500 buildings in the United States getting some or all of their space heating from the sun, with the number growing rapidly. There are fewer combined solar heating and cooling installations, but this total is rising because of increasingly widespread solar use in desert areas and other warm climates where air conditioning makes summer living more endurable.

In subsequent chapters you'll find a detailed description of several kinds of commercial solar hot water and space heating and cooling systems, with suggestions as to how to install most of this equipment yourself if your experience in construction work is adequate—and if you obtain the necessary construction permits required by many communities.

The fact that you're reading this book proves that you know the "energy crisis" is no short-term problem. Our predicament is more accurately a continuing struggle to keep our energy costs, nationally and personally, from escalating at the rate of the past four years. For anyone except a hermit without a car and burning firewood, the rise in the price of all kinds of energy is very serious. In areas such as Maryland, people have been forced to sell their homes because their utility bills in winter are $250 a month or more—higher than their mortgage payments in many instances. Fortunately, President Carter, with his excellent technical background, and his new administration are trying diligently to solve our energy problems with many sensible approaches.

One important avenue for short-range improvement of the energy shortage, long recognized by leaders in Congress and now being actively encouraged by the Energy Research and Development Administration (ERDA) with federal funding, is solar heating and cooling. There are now almost 70 million dwelling units in the United States. In a good construction year we'll add about 2 million houses, condominiums, and apartments. By retrofitting existing homes and providing solar water heaters for new buildings, we could eventually save nearly 5% of our national energy consumption of fossil just by heating water with the sun's energy.

Since it is possible to install a solar water heater, even in most older buildings, for less than $1,000, as described in this chapter and the next, and since for a do-it-yourselfer the cost can be less than $500, the goal of sun-heated domestic water for everyone is by no means beyond reach. At present utility rates it costs a typical family of four as much as $35 a month to heat water for showers, baths, dishwashers, cooking, and washing clothes. Your solar water heater will pay for itself in from two to five years.

Solar space heating and cooling, applied to industrial and commercial buildings as well as homes, can eventually cut our consumption of fossil fuels by 10% or more. Recently the Electric Power Research Institute, financed by the public utilities, announced that 116 electric power companies are actively engaged in solar energy research. Many gas utilities are also doing solar work, and the most progressive are selling, installing, and servicing solar water and space heating and cooling systems, supplemented by natural gas energy in bad weather.

With such activity by utilities and consumers, even the most conservative bankers are beginning to provide home loans on favorable terms for solar installations. Your solar heater will add to the value of your home. It will pay for itself in a relatively short time. From then on, your solar heating system will be putting money in the bank for you by slashing your utility bills. And each solar installation conserves useful energy from other sources. When winters as severe as that of 1976-77 strike in the future, widespread use of solar energy will save lives as well as jobs.

3
Installing a Commercial
Solar Water Heater

Solar water heaters are inexpensive. They may readily be installed in almost any home, as well as in commercial and industrial buildings. This author considers that the new status symbol—like an antenna in the early days of television—is a few solar collector panels on your roof, or mounted in racks in an unshaded area of your backyard or at the southern side of your house.

In the previous chapter we discussed several methods of making your own solar water heater. This chapter covers many types of commercial solar water heaters, some of which are suitable—by increasing the size of the solar collection and storage system—for providing a combination of hot water and space heating and cooling.

If you have any doubt about whether a solar water heater is a practical way to save money, consider these facts quoted from "The Solar Water Heater Industry in South Florida: History and Projections," a review paper written by Jerome E. Scott of the University of Delaware (*Solar Energy*, Volume 18, 1976): "Since 1923, energy from the sun has been used to provide hot water for individual residences, apartment buildings,

and other small commercial buildings in Florida. . . . Two [solar heater] manufacturers interviewed estimated that as many as 60,000 installations may have been made in the Miami area. . . . Surveys conducted by the Florida Power and Light Company . . . clearly indicate that many solar heaters were in service before their first survey in 1939 and that by 1951 new installations were exceeded by conversions to conventional electric hot water systems. . . . It is clear that usage of solar water heaters was widespread; and by 1941 as many solar heaters as electric units were in operation."

Most of these Florida systems were of the thermosiphoning type shown in Figure 3-1. Mentioned in this author's first book, *How To Build a Solar Heater*, was W. V. Morrow, Jr., president of Solar Water Heater Company of Coral Gables, Florida. It was pointed out that Morrow's company installed hundreds (actually thousands) of solar water heaters in homes, motels, and apartment houses, as well as trailer parks. This solar pioneer, now semiretired, is a native Californian who found solar gold in Florida. And he still sells three different

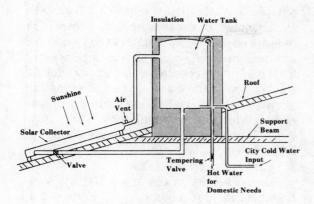

FIGURE 3-1. Layout of Thermosiphoning Solar Water Heater Installation

sets of plans for building a professional quality solar water heater at a reasonable price —for both heater and plans.

As Scott points out in his review paper, although not so numerous today, there are still many of those old solar water heaters operating in Florida. The principal repair needed has been to replace leaking water tanks. The reasons for the decline in use of solar heaters were:

- A rapid drop in electricity rates.

- Higher installation costs for solar systems.

- Many tanks were not as well made as today's glass-lined tanks, were not sufficiently protected against Florida corrosion, and were not insulated on the outside as hot water tanks should be.

- Large builder-developers wiped out choice for the home owner. It was cheaper to install an electric water heater than a solar unit.

The final paragraph of Scott's detailed paper, with research supported by a grant from the National Science Foundation, states: "Recent developments in energy prices and availability, however, have produced an economic environment more promising to a resurgence of solar water heating.

Under certain potentially realistic first-cost estimates and projected fuel price increases, a strong economic argument in favor of solar water heaters can be made. Further, home owner attitudes toward solar units are generally positive and receptive to considering the solar alternatives."

Taking into account the fact that Scott is a conservative economist, and his Florida survey was completed two years ago (October 1975), this is a glowing tribute to solar energy. Since his paper was written, the cost of solar heaters has gone down with mass production while the utility rates continue their inevitable upward climb. Inevitable because utilities are the biggest consumers of fossil fuels and uranium, nonrenewable resources that will keep growing more costly year after year until this planet's supplies are exhausted.

Commercial Solar Water Heaters

Suppose you don't want to build your own solar water heater. Or maybe you're capable of installing a solar hot water system but don't want to make your own solar collector panels. There is a wide variety of solar heaters for domestic or industrial and commercial hot water systems that have been installed successfully in many types of structures. In the following pages some of these systems are described.

But first, paying attention to the suggestions below will save you money and may save you grief:

- Where a construction permit is required, you will need either a suitable contractor's license of your own or the assistance of a professional.

- In building a solar water heater, it would be advisable to follow the Sennergetics layout described in the previous chapter. For an efficient system you will need such items as a differential thermostat, check valves, and a tempering valve.

- You can get complete installation instructions from manufacturers of solar water heaters. Disregard Murphy's Second Law ("If all else fails, read the instructions"). Read and study the instructions first.

- If you intend to have your solar heater system accomplish the dual job of providing hot water and space heating (and perhaps cooling), most manufacturers of solar equipment insist that you hire professional help. Fortunately, in practically all areas of the United States there are progressive plumbing, heating, and air conditioning contractors who have educated themselves in solar installations. There is no mystery, no magic, no danger if the job is done correctly. Most solar scientists refer to domestic solar heating as a "low-technology" business because there are literally no unknown factors in heating your home and your hot water with solar energy.

- Your most economical system will be solar with a backup of electric power, gas, oil, or coal—and perhaps some combination of these conventional energy sources. (Soon, we hope devoutly, solar energy will be also classified as a "conventional" source.)

Reynolds Aluminum Solar Collector

One of the leaders in designing and manufacturing solar collector panels used for heating domestic hot water is Reynolds Metals Company, headquartered in Richmond, Virginia. The pioneering work by Reynolds has been directed by David Laudig, manager of the company's extrusion plant in Torrance, California, a suburb of Los Angeles. Since 1973 Laudig and his associates have developed and tested numerous designs of solar collectors.

At present there are racks containing an array of solar collector panels facing the sun outside the Reynolds plant in Torrance. Performance of these collectors is carefully monitored, and the sun-heated water is pumped into a large, insulated storage tank. This manufacturer uses solar energy for all the hot water and most of the space heating in two large factory buildings and the offices included in one of the buildings. Thus, Reynolds is achieving notable energy savings while testing solar collector panels produced for the commercial market.

A cross section of the latest Reynolds solar collector panel appears in Figure 1-3, Chapter 1. Heart of this collector is an aluminum tube produced as an integral part of the finned aluminum surface of the collector plate. This assembly is made at high speed in a special extrusion machine that turns out long strips of the finned plate containing the tubing. Each strip is 6 inches wide.

Since a typical finished collector is 8 feet x 4 feet in area, the extruded strip is notched on both sides of the tubing in such a way that the tubing can be bent in a serpentine fashion. Thus, the final collector absorber consists of 63.7 feet of extrusion doubled back on itself in the serpentine indicated in Figure 3-2.

Note in Figure 1-3 that there are a main frame and a retaining frame both made of extruded aluminum. These elements provide the sides of the box containing the absorber panel and other elements of the solar collector. The retaining frame is designed so that it clamps into position the two sheets of plastic glazing material that trap the sun's infrared energy. The outer sheet is made of 0.004-inch (4 mil) Tedlar and the inner sheet consists of 4 mil Teflon. It has been found by Reynolds engineers that at times when the solar collector contains no water for solar heating, and the dry panel is in hot sunlight for several hours, the interior temperature may reach 450°F. At this heat the Tedlar develops a ripple that detracts from its appearance and performance. Hence the use of a Teflon sheet as the inner glazing nearest the sun-heated absorber.

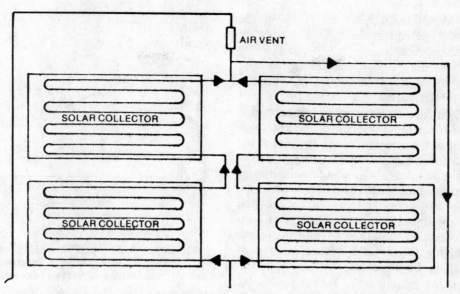

FIGURE 3-2. Serpentine Aluminum Tubing in Reynolds Solar Collectors

You'll also see in Figure 1-3 that there is a layer of aluminum foil bonded to the 1-inch thick polyurethane foam insulation under the aluminum absorber plate or finned tube collector. This foil reflects energy back to the absorber so that heat loss is minimized.

The finned tube collector is painted with a flat black paint. Experience of Reynolds engineers indicates that a good quality commercial paint is as effective as more expensive selective black paints. Frame surfaces are available in either mill-finish aluminum, which should be painted before installation at the site, or anodized or coated aluminum.

The standard Reynolds solar collector is 4 feet x 8 feet in area and 3-5/8 inches thick. It weighs 67.8 pounds when full of water, and its effective collector area is 29 square feet. Because the water flows through a continuous serpentine loop of tubing, users have reported no leaks and excellent heating performance in the field.

After going through several years of development, financed entirely by company funds, Reynolds has achieved both a highly efficient solar collector panel and an efficient process for manufacturing these panels in quantity. According to David Laudig: "We see a great future for solar heating and cooling, and for heating domestic and commercial hot water, as well as for industrial and agricultural applications. People have begun to realize that you can install a solar system, especially a solar hot water heater, in almost any building at quite low cost. In 1977 we're finding very few 'tire-kickers' compared to previous years. Our customers know solar systems work satisfactorily. They ask price and delivery and then they buy."

Reynolds is selling solar collector panels to other manufacturers, including those who build complete solar water heaters. The company also sells through qualified systems installers such as heating, ventilating, and air conditioning contractors; plumbing contractors with suitable training; and general building contractors. Like other collector manufacturers, Reynolds works closely with architects and mechanical and structural engineers who specify solar heating systems.

Retail price in mid-1977 of the Reynolds solar collectors, which are available in 4 feet

55

x 14 feet as well as 4 feet x 8 feet panels, is about $4.50 per square foot. This is a highly competitive price.

Test data on Reynolds collector panels, using methods approved by the National Bureau of Standards, are shown in Figures 3-3 through 3-7. These graphs indicate efficiency of the collectors; show the relationship between solar insolation and collector inlet and outlet fluid temperatures at a normal water flow rate, with the panel tilted at a 45° angle facing south; and depict the temperature rise, ranging from 35°F to 50°F, you can get from two solar collectors connected to an 82-gallon tank in Southern California during the 3-week period from September 27 to October 15.

As a mass producer of metal products, Reynolds furnishes a variety of parts such as collector fins, the absorber plate on which is mounted tubing (often of copper); aluminum reflectors of various shapes to intensify the sun's energy applied to fluid-carrying tubing; frames, mounting brackets, and other metal elements of solar heating systems.

Complete Solar Water Heaters

Two affiliated makers of solar water heaters using Reynolds collectors are Mor-Flo Industries, Inc., of Cleveland, Ohio, and American Appliance Manufacturing Corp. of Santa Monica, California. They supply a simple and efficient system shown in cross section in Figure 3-8. Note that this is a solar system that uses an antifreeze mixture in the collector panels and circulates this fluid, heated by the sun, through a full-surface heat exchanger. That is, there's a tank within a tank. The inner tank is made of Ameriglass-lined steel. Sun-heated fluid circulates around this tank in a heat exchanger jacket of steel surrounding the inner tank. Then there is a layer of insulation 2-3/4 inches thick between the heat exchanger jacket and the outer tank made of steel.

Patents are pending on this design, called "Solarstream," which includes a tempera-

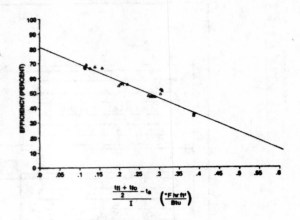

$$\frac{\frac{t_{fi} + t_{fo}}{2} - t_a}{I} \quad \left(\frac{°F\ hr\ ft^2}{Btu}\right)$$

FIGURE 3-3. Jan. 15-Feb. 9, 1976 — Collector Test Results, Virginia Polytechnic Institute and State University

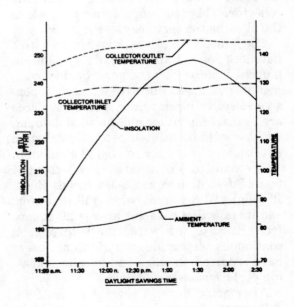

FIGURE 3-4.   June 4, 1975 — .53 GPM per Panel, Richmond, Virginia

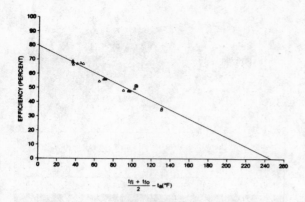

FIGURE 3-5. Jan. 15-Feb. 9, 1976. Collector
Institute and State University
Test Results, Virginia Polytechnic

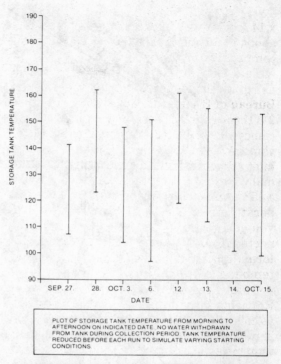

PLOT OF STORAGE TANK TEMPERATURE FROM MORNING TO
AFTERNOON ON INDICATED DATE. NO WATER WITHDRAWN
FROM TANK DURING COLLECTION PERIOD. TANK TEMPERATURE
REDUCED BEFORE EACH RUN TO SIMULATE VARYING STARTING
CONDITIONS.

FIGURE 3-7. Performance for Two
Reynolds Solar Collectors with 82-Gallon
Storage Tank; Wind less than 10 mph

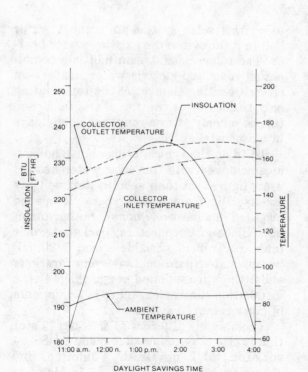

FIGURE 3-6. June 26, 1975 — .657 GPM
per Panel, Torrance, California

ture control so that the solar collector fluid
can be heated to a maximum of 180°F. Since
the fluid is circulated in a closed loop, it
neither boils away nor freezes. A temperature and pressure relief valve as well as a
small expansion tank are provided at the
upper corner of the collector so that the
heated fluid flows through this expansion
tank before going down to the heat exchanger jacket surrounding the water tank.

Shown in Figure 3-9 and the accompany-
ing map of the United States is a method by
which you can calculate how many solar collector panels and what size of water tank
you need, depending on where you live, the
number of bathrooms you have, and the size
of your family. The storage tanks are available in three sizes: 66, 82, and 120 gallons.
There are two alternative models of water
tanks. One is heated entirely by solar energy and is recommended for an installation

57

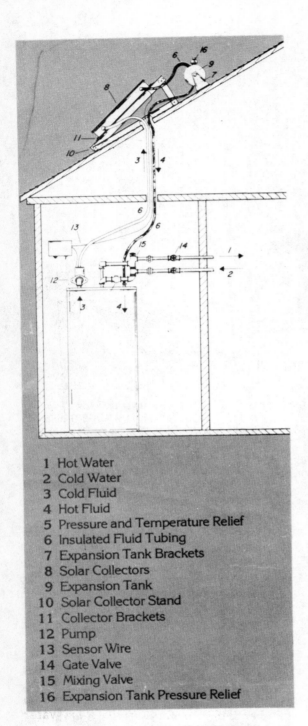

1 Hot Water
2 Cold Water
3 Cold Fluid
4 Hot Fluid
5 Pressure and Temperature Relief
6 Insulated Fluid Tubing
7 Expansion Tank Brackets
8 Solar Collectors
9 Expansion Tank
10 Solar Collector Stand
11 Collector Brackets
12 Pump
13 Sensor Wire
14 Gate Valve
15 Mixing Valve
16 Expansion Tank Pressure Relief

FIGURE 3-8.   A Simple, Efficient Solar Water Heating System

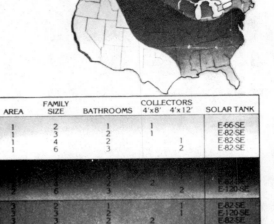

AREA	FAMILY SIZE	BATHROOMS	COLLECTORS 4'x8'	COLLECTORS 4'x12'	SOLAR TANK
1	2	1	1		E-66-SE
1	3	1	1		E-82-SE
1	4	2		1	E-82-SE
1	6	3		2	E-82-SE
2					
2	3	2	2	1	E-82-SE
2	6	3			E-120-SE
3	2	1		1	E-82-SE
3	3	2	2		E-120-SE
3	3	3			E-82-SE
3	4	2		2	E-120-SE
3	6	3		3	E-120-SE

FIGURE 3-9.   A Method of Calculating the Number of Collector Panels and Size of Water Heater Needed in Various Parts of the United States

using this solar system to preheat water before it flows into the existing water heater. The other Solarstream unit is a combination solar and electric water heater—an electric heating element at the top, heating only the water at the top of the tank, and turned on only after a couple of cloudy days in most installations.

Based on the typical utility bills and savings achieved with this solar water heater, users figure that their solar system will pay for itself in from 3 to 5 years. It can be installed in almost any home or other building. Since the collectors, jacketed solar tank, controller, variable speed 1/20 HP pump, and expansion tank, plus brackets and fittings are supplied as a package to the installation contractor, there is a minimum of labor required at the site.

A completely different solar water heater that is also easy to install is made by Solarcoa, Inc., of Long Beach, California, and shown in Figure 3-10 and 3-11. Many of these solar heaters have been installed on the flat-roofed buildings common through-

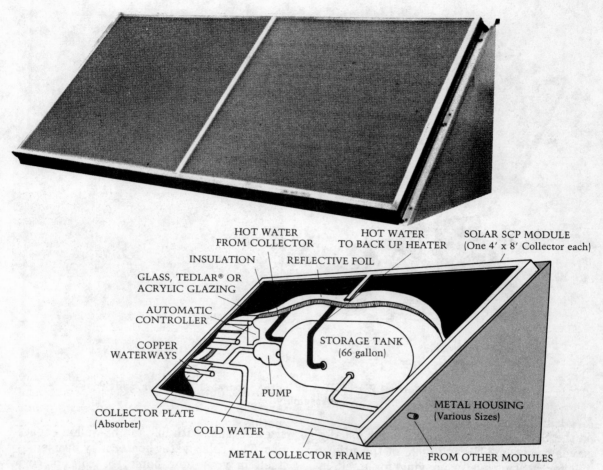

HOT WATER
FROM COLLECTOR

HOT WATER
TO BACK UP HEATER

SOLAR SCP MODULE
(One 4' x 8' Collector each)

INSULATION

REFLECTIVE FOIL

GLASS, TEDLAR® OR
ACRYLIC GLAZING

AUTOMATIC
CONTROLLER

COPPER
WATERWAYS

STORAGE TANK
(66 gallon)

COLLECTOR PLATE
(Absorber)

PUMP

METAL HOUSING
(Various Sizes)

COLD WATER

METAL COLLECTOR FRAME

FROM OTHER MODULES

FIGURE 3-10. Solarcoa Solar Hot Water Heater with Storage Tank and Collector as One Assembly

out the southwestern United States, although one of the two alternative designs of this system is readily adapted to any style of building.

In the version particularly useful where the roof is flat, as shown in Figure 3-10, the solar collector panel provides the hypotenuse, or slanted cover, of a triangular metal structure. Inside this housing, under the collector, are a 66-gallon storage tank, and pump and electronic controller. For a description of the differential thermostats typically used in such solar systems, how they work, and why they are needed in systems with pumps or fans, see the text, illustrations, and graphs in Chapter 9.

This module with the self-contained tank has also been used in some installations without a pump and differential control unit, when a thermosiphoning system was feasible and a very low-cost unit was wanted.

The Solarcoa system, in which you can add collector panels to the unit containing the water storage tank, pump and controls, is designed to provide solar heated make-up water on demand to your existing hot water heater. Solar heated water is stored in the module tank and transferred by line pressure into your water heater. Temperatures between 120° and 160°F are obtained throughout the year in typical installations

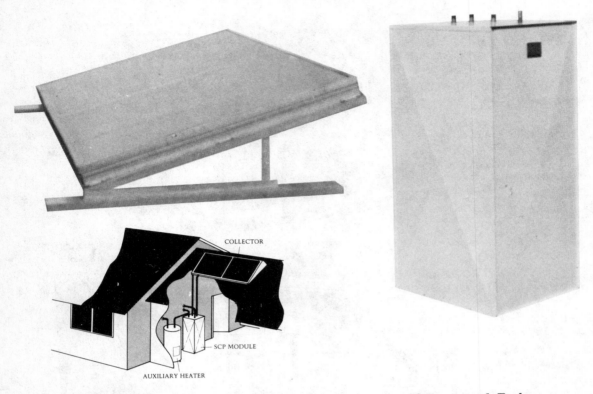

COLLECTOR

SCP MODULE

AUXILIARY HEATER

FIGURE 3-11.   Solarcoa Water Heater with Separated Collector and Tank
Assembly

in the Southwest. This solar heater usually saves between 70% and 80% of the utility bill for heating water, paying for itself in three to five years.

Another version of this system, shown in Figure 3-11, has the solar collector panels mounted on an adjustable metal rack on the roof or attached directly to the roof if its tilt and direction are adequate. Remember in the Northern Hemisphere solar collectors should face south or perhaps 10° west of south for maximum afternoon sunlight, with a tilt equal to your latitude +15° for maximum heating during the winter, when the sun's elevation above the horizon is minimized.

This second Solarcoa system feeds sun-heated water to a tank mounted in any convenient location in your home or other building. This tank is insulated and includes both a pump and electronic controls for the system inside its metal housing. There are two

sizes of tank, with 52- and 82-gallon capacities. This solar water heater may be used by itself in your new home, or to replace a worn-out water heater in your present home if you live in a climate with adequate year-round sunshine. Otherwise, you should mount the solar storage tank near your conventional water heater and use it for preheating.

With either of these designs, because water is the heat transfer fluid, it is necessary to drain the solar collectors when the temperature is likely to go below freezing. This is easily accomplished by shutting off the supply to the collectors and pumping remaining water from the panels into storage.

Construction of the solar collector panel is indicated in the cutaway drawing in Figure 1-8. The water-carrying structure consists of an array of copper pipes brazed to larger diameter copper headers at each end of the panel. These pipes run parallel to each other and are mounted in an aluminum fin plate suitably grooved to hold the pipes in place. Underneath this entire assembly, which is painted black, are 2 inches of polyurethane foam surfaced with reflective aluminum foil. Preferred glazing is 4 mil Tedlar plastic sheeting; and the aluminum frame is so designed that this glazing may readily be replaced if necessary, although no user has had to do this in some 3 years of service experience.

Other Commercial Solar Water Heaters

The business of making solar hot water heaters is expanding so rapidly that this author could not include every manufacturer without converting this book into a directory. One benefit of this expansion of the solar heating industry is that you should be able to save on freight costs by selecting a manufacturer relatively near you. Therefore we have tried to describe some of the solar manufacturing companies and their products in various parts of the United States. This includes both small and large firms. Many of the larger manufacturers, as you might expect, have nationwide distribution. All the companies mentioned will be glad to sell you their products and to furnish detailed installation instructions. Complete addresses are provided in Appendix 1.

In the Pacific Northwest, a relatively small manufacturer has been growing and expanding its product line. Jim Ewbank, president of E & K Service Company of Bothell, Washington, has been building solar collector panels and systems for heating homes and domestic hot water for several years. His liquid-type flat plate collectors are available in four standard sizes: 2 x 4, 4 x 4, 4 x 8, and 4 x 12 (all dimensions in feet). One feature is a panel frame made of treated and coated wood construction to reduce heat loss. Panels are glazed with FRP plastic or 3/16-inch crystal glass, although they are usually shipped without glazing to save shipping costs, since glazing may be done at the site. These collectors weigh about 6.5 pounds per square foot glazed, 4.25 pounds per square foot unglazed. Using single glazing in a typical test, two E & K Sol-R collectors raised the temperature of water in a tank from 50° to 85°F at a rate of 6°F per hour.

California, with its abundant sunshine, is the home of about a hundred solar manufacturers as of mid-1977. Products of only a few are described in this book, with an attempt to select those of most interest from two standpoints:

- Manufacturers with unusual techniques for collecting solar energy, or

- Companies which have made a sizable number of solar installations and generally have both experience and low cost in their favor.

In the category of unusual designs, Solergy of San Francisco deserves attention. The Solergy "fixed concentrator collector" is shown in plain view and cross section in Figure 3-12. The absorber of solar energy is a serpentine of copper pipe painted black. This black pipe is held in bright aluminum paraboloidal extrusions. There are seven of these extrusions, which reflect sunlight on the black copper pipes except at the bends at each end of the collector. The result is concentrated heating of the liquid in the copper piping so that in a pressurized system, water temperatures well in excess of 300°F can be achieved on a hot, clear summer day. This means that with a carefully designed solar water heater using the Solergy panels, fewer collectors will be required than with more conventional designs.

While the Solergy concentrator collector is most suitable for liquid-type space heating/cooling as well as hot water systems, one of its earliest applications is in a home in San Leandro for heating domestic water.

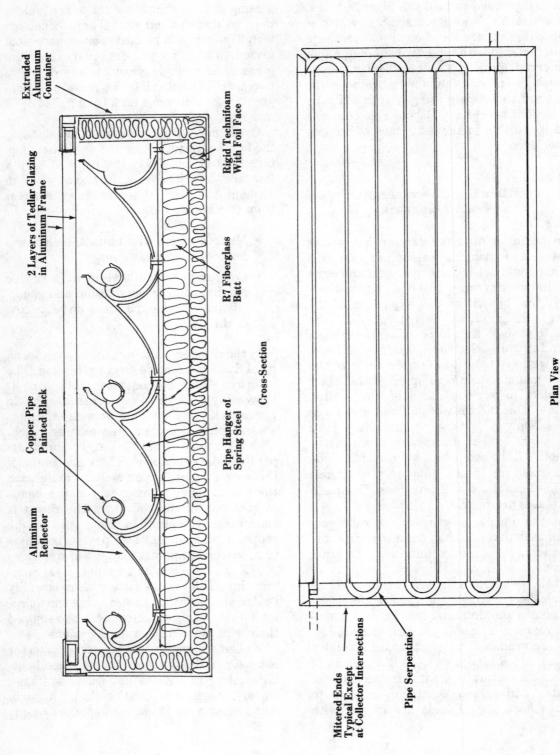

Extruded Aluminum Container

2 Layers of Tedlar Glazing in Aluminum Frame

Rigid Technifoam With Foil Face

R7 Fiberglass Batt

Copper Pipe Painted Black

Pipe Hanger of Spring Steel

Cross-Section

Aluminum Reflector

Mitered Ends Typical Except at Collector Intersections

Pipe Serpentine

Plan View

FIGURE 3-12. A "Fixed Concentrator Collector": Plan View and Cross Section

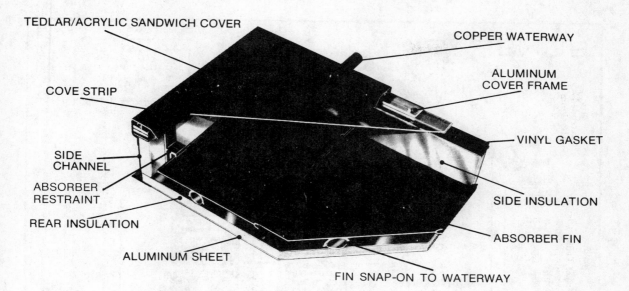

TEDLAR/ACRYLIC SANDWICH COVER

COPPER WATERWAY

ALUMINUM COVER FRAME

COVE STRIP

VINYL GASKET

SIDE CHANNEL

ABSORBER RESTRAINT

SIDE INSULATION

REAR INSULATION

ABSORBER FIN

ALUMINUM SHEET

FIN SNAP-ON TO WATERWAY

FIGURE 3-13.   A Conventional Solar Collector, by Elcam, Inc.

This collector's dimensions are 4 feet x 8 feet x 6 inches and it weighs 5 pounds per square foot—32 square feet of collector area =160 pounds of dry weight. Glazing may be either two layers of 4 mil clear Tedlar heat-sealed over an aluminum frame, or one or two layers of glass installed at the site. Insulation is rigid metal-clad Technifoam, and the extruded aluminum frame is available in anodized or baked enamel of various colors and finishes. Price of this collector, because it concentrates the solar heat on the black-painted copper absorber piping and thus generates hotter liquid temperatures than more conventional designs, ranges from $350 to $384 per panel depending upon quantity, a higher price than for ordinary collectors. However, for a combined water and space heating/cooling application—especially since absorption coolers require water heated to at least 190°F—or for heating large swimming pools or buildings using a large amount of hot water, such as a commercial laundry, the Solergy system is well worth consideration for economic as well as technical factors. Also, in installations where roof area or the unobstructed rack area with a southern exposure is limited,

and therefore only a few solar collectors can be mounted, a more concentrated collector design generating high temperatures may be worth the added cost per panel.

Another unusual collector design has been developed by Applied Sol Tech, Inc., of Long Beach, California. Again, as in the Solergy design, no headers are required. There is a single inlet pipe for fluid supplied to the solar collector and a single outlet for the sun-heated liquid.

A more conventional design is used in the Sunspot solar water heating systems made by Elcam, Inc., of Santa Barbara, California. A cross section of this solar collector appears in Figure 3-13. The absorber surface is Honda black baked on allodined aluminum fins, which snap on the waterways made of 1/2-inch type M copper. All liquid-carrying joints are silver-brazed copper, and the system is pressure-tested to 125 psi. Insulation is 1/2-inch thick isocyanurate, with aluminum foil on the upper surface.

The Sunspot collector is a good structure, having an aluminum sheet bonded to the rear insulation for protection and rigidity. Also the glazing is a Tedlar sheet, called an ultraviolet filter by Elcam, bonded to a clear

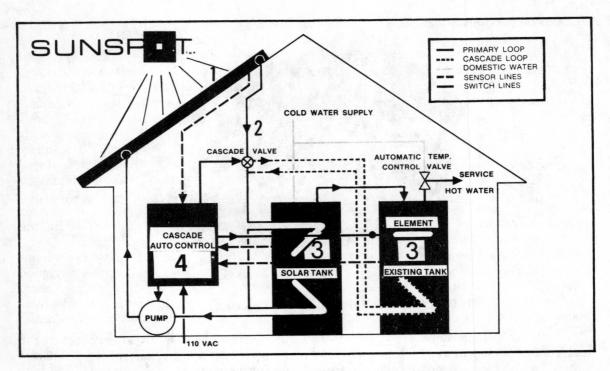

FIGURE 3-14.   The Sunspot Water Heating System and its Components

solid acrylic plastic sheet. This makes a more solid cover than 4 mil Tedlar and the composite transmissivity is 92%. The glazing is held in place by aluminum extrusions and a vinyl foam gasket, with weatherproofing by rubber grommets, silicone rubber, and closed-end blind rivets. Dimensions of the collector are the conventional 4 feet x 8 feet with an absorber area of 30.3 square feet (2.79 square meters). Weight dry is 100 pounds (45.36 kilograms).

A diagram of the typical Sunspot hot water heating system is shown in Figure 3-14. The automatic control system consists of a 3-channel differential thermostat with three solid state temperature sensors monitoring collector outlet temperature, and temperatures of the water in the preheating tank ("solar tank") and the existing conventional tank. The solar preheating tank supplied as a part of this system is available in various sizes: 40- to 120-gallon tanks contain two copper coil heat exchangers; 30-gallon tanks have one heat exchanger. All

tanks are lined with fused glass with double thickness insulation and a stainless steel dip tube for thermal monitoring.

The pump used with this solar water heater draws only 30 watts of electrical power and is a U.L. approved 10.5-foot static head centrifugal pump that will operate satisfactorily at pressures up to 125 psi. Accessories include a pressure and temperature relief valve; a pressure relief valve; automatic temperature control valve; expansion tank; pressure gauge; and thermometer. These are available as a Sunspot accessory kit.

Distilled water is circulated through the closed loop, shown in Figure 3-14, taking liquid from the collector through the cascade valve to the solar preheating tank and back through the pump to the lower end of the collectors. In cold climates this closed loop, shown with solid lines in Figure 3-14, may contain an antifreeze mixture instead of distilled water. Note that there is an alternative path for the sun-heated liquid if desired, on the assumption that the existing tank contains, or can be fitted with, a heat exchanger. In this case the solar collector output is routed via the cascade valve to provide direct solar heating of the electric hot water tank ("existing tank") so that no electricity is required for heating water. The valve labeled "automatic temp. control valve" in the figure is the tempering valve, previously discussed, needed to set the upper temperature limit of domestic hot water provided by the solar system. If the sun-heated water is too hot for comfort, as often happens during the summer in southern climates, this water at 180°F or more is mixed with cold water to bring it down to a temperature of about 140°F.

As with most commercial solar hot water systems, the Sunspot unit's automatic control turns off the conventional heater's electric element whenever there is enough solar energy to keep the water at the temperature you want. Also, by providing a pre-heating tank to supplement the conventional hot water heater's tank, the system doubles your total hot water supply—or adds considerably more, depending on the size of preheating tank you select.

Imported Designs

Quite a number of solar water heaters designed and manufactured in other countries have been imported into the United States despite the fact that solar heater systems include collectors that are relatively large in surface area—to function efficiently—and weigh relatively little since they are mounted on roofs or racks. Thus, the importer of each foreign-made collector must pay a competitive penalty in shipping costs. Even so, several designs are being used in American installations.

In the author's previous book there is a detailed description of the Hitachi solar water heater. This unit was selling in 1975 for about $400 f.o.b. New York City, complete with a small preheater tank and a total hot water capacity of 40 gallons. More than 350,000 of these solar water assemblies, with black plastic collector panel, have been sold by Hitachi; and we are informed that Japanese manufacturers have produced and sold about 2.5 million solar hot water systems.

Your author admits to a preference, however, for water heaters using metal solar collectors. Although these collectors usually cost more, they are also more durable if well designed and fabricated. Because the installation of any solar system costs time and money—even if you do it yourself—the old adage about the best materials being the cheapest in the long run is true.

One excellent solar collector panel imported from Israel is the Miramit, designed by a noted solar pioneer, Dr. Harry Tabor. A company importing this collector is Sunsource, Inc., of Beverly Hills, California. Several installations have been made in the United States. An interesting feature of this collector is that its absorber plate and its piping, both longitudinal waterways and headers, are made of galvanized steel coated with Tabor "selective black," a paint with 92% absorptivity and typical emissivity of 9.4%.

If you add those two percentages and get more than 100%, don't worry about it. The glazing, a "water white crystal" glass 5/32 inch thick, traps much of the solar heat emitted by the selective absorber and piping. Standard materials are used for side and back insulation, and the assembly is mounted in a galvanized steel tray. Dimensions are about 3 feet x 6 feet with a 3.4-inch thickness of the collector sandwich. Although this collector is smaller than most American designs—4 feet x 8 feet is the most popular size because joists are 4 feet apart in standard roof construction—tests by independent laboratories have proven that this Israeli design is efficient as well as sturdily made. Some units like these have been in service along the eastern Mediterranean for 17 years or more. This is a tribute to the patented surface coating process and suggests that more American manufacturers might consider using galvanized steel because of its low cost.

An unusual design is the cylindrical SAV solar heater, imported from New Zealand by Fred Rice Productions, Inc., formerly of Van Nuys and now located in La Quinta, California, in the desert near Palm Springs. Rice, a former vice president of Capitol Records, has been an ecologist for many years. He is a solar pioneer who uses sun-heated water in his own desert home. The design of this solar water heater is shown in Figure 3-15 and a picture of two units in a test fixture in Figure 3-16.

Tests conducted by Stephen A. Vincze, a New Zealand engineer, under the supervision of the national Department of Scientific and Industrial Research, comparing this cylindrical design with a conventional flat plate collector from November 1975 through March 1976, proved some interesting points. The SAV design, which contains 20 gallons (90 liters) of water per cylinder in one model, saved nearly 3 times as much electricity per square meter of collector surface as the flat plate unit.

Fred Rice points out that two SAV cylindrical solar collectors will add 40 gallons to the hot water capacity of your house without the need for a preheating tank. Also, when this cylinder is installed in front of a heat reflecting surface such as a roof, chimney, or wall, reflected solar energy adds to the heat absorption of the collector.

At present the patented SAV units look attractive for someone who wants to install a solar water heater with minimum interconnecting piping and no need for a separate circulating pump and control system. This is because these cylindrical collectors are thermosiphoning and may be located on your roof to feed directly to and from your conventional water heater, as shown in Figure 3-17. Note that you connect to the SAV collector from the bottom (coldest) region of your ordinary heater, and feed into this heater at the top. The smaller SAV model TC10 unit provides 10 gallons (45 liters) of additional hot water storage so that you

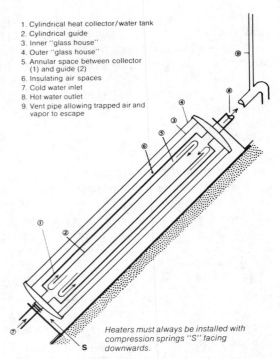

1. Cylindrical heat collector/water tank
2. Cylindrical guide
3. Inner "glass house"
4. Outer "glass house"
5. Annular space between collector (1) and guide (2)
6. Insulating air spaces
7. Cold water inlet
8. Hot water outlet
9. Vent pipe allowing trapped air and vapor to escape

Heaters must always be installed with compression springs "S" facing downwards.

FIGURE 3-15. Construction of SAV Cylindrical Water Heater

FIGURE 3-16. Cylindrical Solar Heater Imported from New Zealand

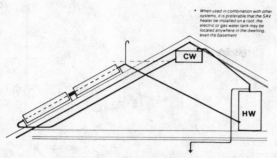

CW

HW

FIGURE 3-17. Typical SAV Solar Water Heater Installation

might want to use three or four such collectors, depending on your family's hot water usage. The one drawback to such a system is that these imported units are relatively expensive because of freight and other charges. Recently, at the Los Angeles Energy Fair, Fred Rice told the author that he would be interested in talking to an American manufacturer about making SAV units, or parts of them, under license to the New Zealand inventor so as to reduce their price in the United States.

Other Good Solar Water Heaters

In Chapter 4 is a detailed description of the Piper Hydro solar heating system, which is being used successfully as a gas-assisted or completely sun-heated hydronic system in installations in 12 states and several foreign countries. This system can be used solely for heating hot water, but it lends itself to both space heating and cooling and warming domestic water.

Another California manufacturer with a long history—26 years is long for almost anything in the Los Angeles area—in water heating and heat transfer is Raypak, Inc., of Westlake Village. This company makes a solar collector panel of excellent quality, shown in cross section in Figure 3-18. Many solar hot water heater installations made as indicated in Figure 3-19 and 3-20 use Raypak equipment, which has been approved by ERDA engineers—like most of the other systems described in this book.

Like many other collector manufacturers, Raypak uses copper pipes as waterways and headers, with the waterways attached to an aluminum absorber plate painted black. Glazing is either 4 mil Tedlar or a solid plastic sheeting like Kalwall's Sun-Lite translucent fiberglass reinforced thermosetting material, or glass. Where two layers of glass are used, the upper layer is tempered to prevent damage from accidents or vandalism.

By achieving a considerable distribution through building supply, plumbing, and hardware outlets, Raypak has been able to bring down the price of its solar collectors while the cost of materials and labor has risen. This is quite an achievement for any manufacturer. Meanwhile the company has made numerous installations, either in conjunction with contractors by supplying engineering help as well as materials, or by furnishing solar heating system components and detailed instructions. Shown in Figure 3-20 is an industrial hot water heating system installed at Aerospace Corporation in Los Angeles, a prestigious technical "think tank" for the U.S. Air Force.

A smaller manufacturer in the same general area is Conserdyne Corporation of Glendale, which has concentrated on solar hot water heaters. Included in this firm's installations is sun-heated water for the Beverly Hills home of writer Howard Fast, as well as for homes and commercial installations from San Diego to Albuquerque. In one large development, components such as those shown in Figure 3-21 and 3-22 show good workmanship.

The Conserdyne collector has glazing of tempered glass over a stainless steel absorber plate painted black and backed by good insulation, with the sandwich in a bronze anodized aluminum frame. Dimensions are 3 feet x 10 feet with a thickness of 3-1/2 inches. The pump used is a 1/2 HP impeller type, and this company offers the user a choice of manual or automatic control.

System design is conventional, with the preheating tank containing a heat exchanger

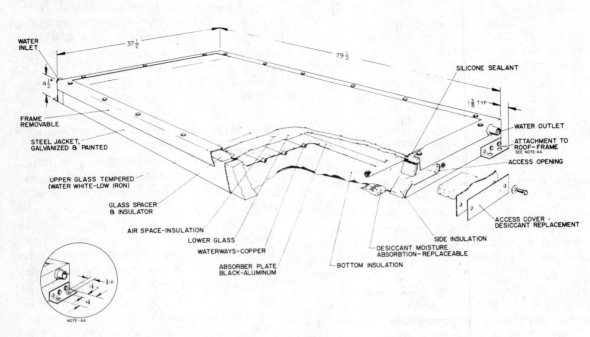

SINGLE GLASS PANEL—3½

WATER INLET

37½

79½

SILICONE SEALANT

4½

1⅜ TYP

FRAME REMOVABLE

WATER OUTLET

STEEL JACKET, GALVANIZED & PAINTED

ATTACHMENT TO ROOF—FRAME SEE NOTE-AA

ACCESS OPENING

UPPER GLASS TEMPERED (WATER WHITE-LOW IRON)

GLASS SPACER & INSULATOR

AIR SPACE-INSULATION

ACCESS COVER DESICCANT REPLACEMENT

LOWER GLASS

WATERWAYS-COPPER

SIDE INSULATION

DESICCANT MOISTURE ABSORBTION-REPLACEABLE

ABSORBER PLATE BLACK-ALUMINUM

BOTTOM INSULATION

NOTE-AA

FIGURE 3-18. **Cross Section of Solar Collector Made by Raypak, Inc.**

so that the hot solar collector fluid travels in a closed loop through the exchanger—which heats potable water in the preheat tank—and then back to the inlet of the collector array as shown in Figure 3-23. According to Howard Kraye, president of Conserdyne, monitoring of various installations indicates year-round savings of 75% to 85% of the fuel bill for heating domestic water. And one reason is the company designs its solar systems with an objective of saving 80%—not 100%—of your bill for hot water.

In one large development where there are several Conserdyne solar water heaters, the cost to the home buyer is about $1,250 installed. The system is being offered by several other builders because of its good quality, reasonable price—and because Conserdyne is a subsidiary of Plast-Alum Manufacturing Company, with a decade of experience as a supplier and subcontractor to California builders. This points up the fact that Conserdyne, like other solar manufacturers, is educating many builders of new homes, as

well as of industrial and commercial buildings, to provide plumbing outlets so that it's easy to retrofit with a solar water heater at any time the owners desire, if they can't be sold on a solar system originally. Offering this solar option simply means installing two feed pipes to the inlet and outlet of the most suitable future location of collector panels, and running this piping to the conventional water heater installation. Cost to the builder ranges from $35 for a one-story house to $50 or less for a two-story house. MORAL: Don't buy a new house without a solar water heater, or at least without the plumbing to add one as soon as you can afford it.

Among many other small California makers of solar water heaters is American Sun Industries of Newbury Park. Their collector panel has copper waterways, an aluminum absorber plate painted black with siliconized polyester paint, glazing of Kalwall Sun-Lite Premium 40 mil sheeting. Insulation is closed-cell plastic foam, and the 4

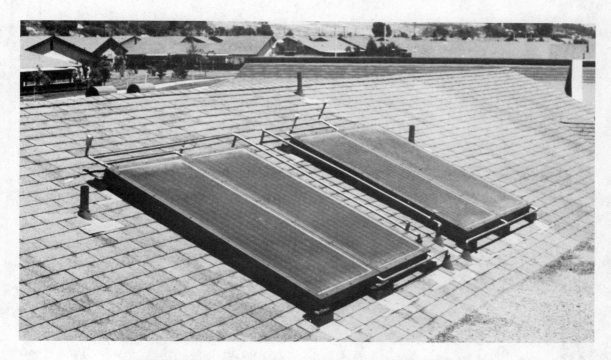

FIGURE 3-19. Solar Water Heater using Raypak Solar Collectors

FIGURE 3-20. Industrial Water Heating System Installed by Raypak, Inc.,
for Aerospace Corporation of Los Angeles

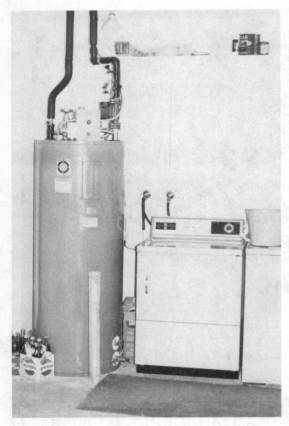

FIGURES 3-21 & 3-22. Solar Water Heater Components Manufactured by Conserdyne Corporation

feet x 8 feet sandwich, 2.625 inches thick, is housed in an aluminum case painted medium bronze. System design is also conventional, as shown in Figure 3-24. If your solar water heating needs are met by a single collector and a 52-gallon preheating tank, you can buy the entire system at a retail price of $917 f.o.b. the factory. Add about $500 if you want two collector panels with an effective area of 58 square feet plus a solar heater system including a 100-gallon thermal storage or preheating tank.

Buying Solar Hardware from a Catalog

Note in the previous paragraph the words "retail price." Most solar manufacturers offer a price to installers about 25% to 30% lower than this retail figure. An installer may be almost any kind of a legitimate contractor holding a permit from the appropriate municipal, county, or state authority to make a solar installation.

Until recently the business of installing solar systems has been so new and so small that the oft-stifling and definitely sticky hands of bureaucracy have let us alone. The general attitude has been, "Let those wild-eyed tinkerers play their silly games." But now, as with every business that shows signs of growing big, regulations proliferate. So far, because most political agencies do realize that we live in a deepening energy crisis, most of them seem to be relatively sensible and not unduly expensive for the installer, whether professional or amateur.

Before continuing with a discussion of commercially available solar water heaters from other areas than California—even this near-native citizen realizes there are 49 other states—consider the fact that you can buy your solar supplies by mail order.

For instance, Solar Usage Now, Inc., Bascom, Ohio 44809, publishes two catalogs annually and will mail you their latest edition, Spring/Summer or Fall/Winter, for $1

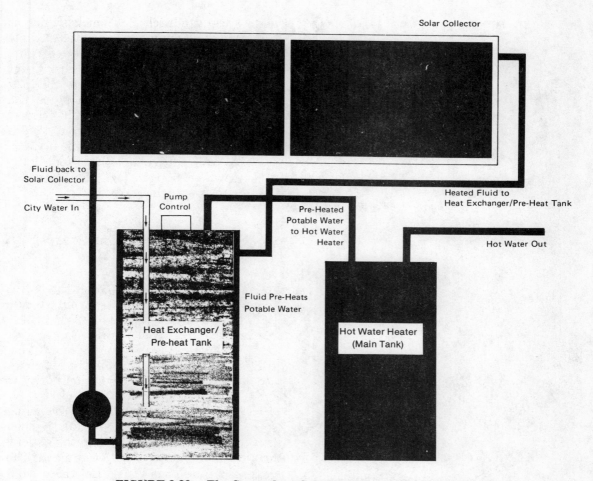

FIGURE 3-23.   The Conserdyne Solar Potable Hot Water System

postpaid. These little catalogs are full of such items as hardware and prices for solar heating of pools and hot water; air heating; pumps, piping, and tanks; even sun dials and solar toys; as well as numerous useful book titles.

Solar Research Division of Refrigeration Research, Inc., Brighton, Michigan 48116, has an even more impressive catalog. It includes a discussion of heat pumps, insulation materials, and many useful solar components and systems.

For instance, you can buy the complete solar water heating kit, Solar Research part number 5847, illustrated in Figure 3-25.

This includes four small solar collectors, each with an area of 10 square feet, for a total area of 40 square feet. The waterways are steel tubes hydrogen-brazed with a copper bond to a steel absorber plate. These tubes and the absorber have three coatings, including a final finish of 3M Nextel Black Velvet, the selective material previously mentioned and found to be an excellent absorber of solar energy. There are 2 inches of insulation in the aluminum case, and the glazing is 4 mil Tedlar thermally shrunk, as is common practice.

The price of this kit, including the 4 collectors, 1 heat exchanger, 1 differential

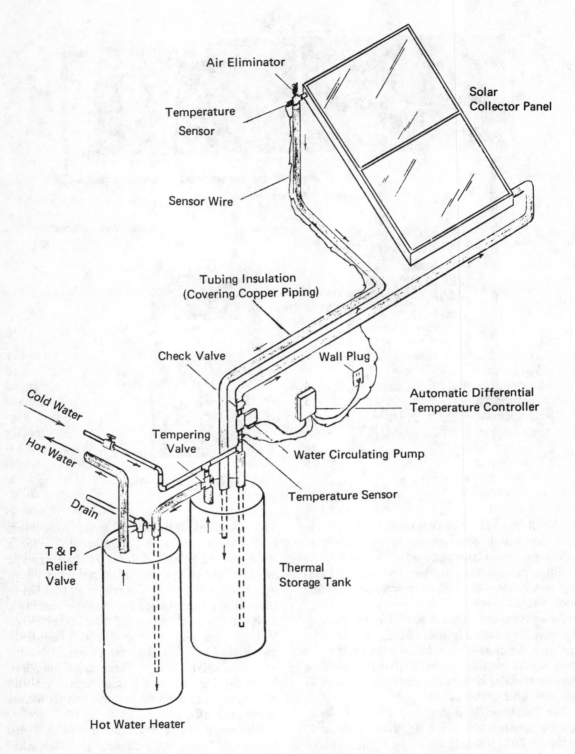

Air Eliminator

Temperature Sensor

Solar Collector Panel

Sensor Wire

Tubing Insulation (Covering Copper Piping)

Check Valve

Wall Plug

Automatic Differential Temperature Controller

Cold Water

Hot Water

Tempering Valve

Water Circulating Pump

Drain

Temperature Sensor

T & P Relief Valve

Thermal Storage Tank

Hot Water Heater

FIGURE 3-24.   American Sun Industries Solar Water Heating System

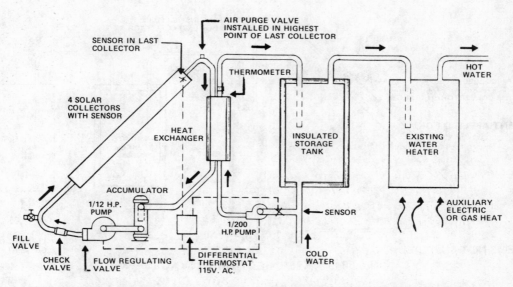

FIGURE 3-25. Diagram of Solar Water Heating Kit Manufactured by Solar
Research Division of Refrigeration Research, Inc.

thermostat, 2 water circulating pumps, 1 accumulator, and 1 check valve—*not* including the preheating tank labeled "insulated storage tank" in Figure 3-25—is $647.88 f.o.b. Brighton. If you are an installer, or get together with a group of your neighbors, and buy 10 or more number 5847 solar water heating kits, the price per kit drops to $555.86 f.o.b. factory.

If you're wondering what an *accumulator* might be, it is a small tank installed in the return line of the water pump. It allows for expansion or contraction of water with temperature changes and eliminates the need for a "pop off" valve (or air vent) at the outlet of the collectors. It also provides a convenient place for air to purge itself from the system and ensures that the pump will always be primed for starting.

Should you prefer to build your own solar collectors, or like another design better than the Solar Research panels, you can buy a domestic water heating package for $367.19, or $330.47 in a quantity of 10 or more, f.o.b. factory. This package includes neither the solar collectors, storage (preheating) tank, nor connecting piping. It

does include 8 components that may readily be connected to your collector panels and conventional water heater. For a typical family of four, you can probably eliminate the "insulated storage tank" shown in Figure 3-26 and connect this package directly to "existing water heater." Connected together at the factory in this package unit are: 1 combination heat-exchanger and expansion tank; pressure relief valve; filler-drain valve; Sundstrand primary pump; March secondary pump; flow regulating valve; check valve; and Rho Sigma differential control unit with one sensor installed. The heat-exchanger expansion tank is insulated. Dimensions are: overall height, 30 inches; overall width, 23 inches. Net weight is 54 pounds and shipping weight, 65 pounds.

Note that both the Solar Research units described are designed with heat exchangers so that your collector fluid operates in a closed loop and therefore should be an antifreeze mixture in a cold climate. Also, if you live in an area with many cloudy days or prolonged bad weather during any season, especially during the winter, you should include an insulated thermal storage

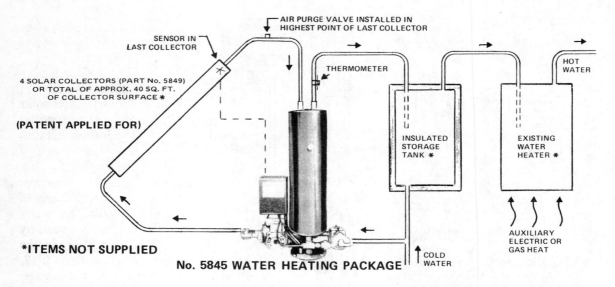

FIGURE 3-26.   Solar Research Water Heating Package, not Including Collectors

tank or solar preheating tank of sizable capacity—100 gallons or more—as part of your solar hot water system.

A third mail order company is A-Z Solar Products, Minneapolis, MN 55404, with an energetic and attractive young woman, Barbara Bayerkohler, as president. This firm has established dealers in about 20 states and in Goteborg, Sweden, and sells both solar hardware and instructive books on solar and wind energy. A suggested solar hot water system, shown in Figure 3-27, includes Waterbank II furnished by A-Z as catalog number 0858 with a price tag of $249.95 f.o.b. an Ohio factory and a shipping weight of 175 pounds. This Waterbank model for cold climates contains a heat exchanger coil and a Sundstrand 456 circulating pump for pumping antifreeze through the collector panels and back to the exchanger coil inside the tank. Standard connections are provided for hookup of the other components of the solar heating system, and this solar preheating tank with heat exchanger and pump adds about 40 gallons to a home water supply when connected as shown to a conventional water heater.

Other Solar Heaters

One of the world's oldest and largest manufacturers of heating and air conditioning equipment is Lennox Industries, Inc., headquartered in Marshalltown, Iowa. With plant facilities in Arkansas, California, Georgia, Ohio, Texas—and in Des Moines as well as Marshalltown—plus factories in Toronto and Calgary, Canada; England; the Netherlands; France; and West Germany, this company has been making heaters for more than 80 years.

Ever since Lennox developed its first steel coal-burning furnace, the firm has pioneered new products. Its solar collector panel, designed by Lennox research and manufacturing engineers working with the Honeywell Energy Resources Center in Mineapolis, is shown in cross section in Figure 3-28.

This LSC18-1 solar collector is somewhat smaller than most commercial panels but its design is good, the choice of materials excellent, and its price should become increasingly competitive because of the mass production facilities established by Lennox to

74

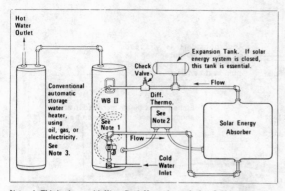

Notes: 1. This hook-up, with WaterBank II, can be used when fluid in solar energy system (passing through the absorber) is not potable.
2. Differential thermostat turns circulating pump on only when water in solar energy absorber is hotter than water in WaterBank II.
3. A conventional water heater of small capacity can be used.

FIGURE 3-27. Waterbank II Supplied as Part of a Solar Water Heater by A-Z Solar Products

manufacture these panels. Area is 18 square feet (1.62 square meters) with an effective absorber surface of 14.7 square feet (1.32 square meters). Glazing consists of two tempered low-iron glass sheets, etched to provide an antireflection surface and transmittance of 96%.

Waterways are 1/4-inch OD copper tubes spaced 3 inches apart and placed in channels on the absorber plate of 20-gauge steel. The copper tubes are solder-sealed in place in a high-temperature oven, and copper manifolds or headers 1.125 inches OD are brazed to the flow tubes at each end of the absorber. Liquid flows through the panel in a Z pattern—in at the left corner of the lower end, out at the right corner of the upper end—at a flow rate of from 0.3 to 0.7 gallons per minute. The recommended solar fluid is a 50-50 mixture of antifreeze and water.

The Lennox collector housing is 22-gauge electrocoated Galvalume, and there are 3 inches of fiberglass insulation under the absorber plate. The plate is coated by a patented black-chrome process in a Honeywell plant, where the glass cover plates are also etched to provide an antireflection surface and transmittance of 96%. A second

collector model, LSC18-1S, has only one sheet of this special glazing and is designed for use in warmer areas.

These Lennox collectors are available through dealers and are used for solar hot water heaters as well as for combined solar heating and cooling and hot water installations. A detailed description of an installation of the Lennox-Honeywell system in a Texas home is provided in Chapter 4.

In Denver and other parts of Colorado, activity in developing useful applications of solar energy has been intense for many years. One reason is the pioneering work by Dr. George Löf, who has been living in the solar heated home shown in Figure 2-17, Chapter 2, since 1944 and has designed many useful applications of solar energy, from home heating to practical solar cookers. Dr. Löf is now engineering vice president of Solaron Corporation in Denver, best known for its development of air-type solar collectors and associated systems for heating and cooling buildings.

More recently, during the past three years, Solaron has developed a "freeze safe" domestic hot water system, diagrammed in Figure 3-29. This approach is quite different from any of the designs previously described in that solar-heated air from the collector panels is used to heat water.

A cross section of the Solaron collector appears in Figure 3-30. A steel absorber panel, coated with a high absorbency black ceramic coating baked on at high temperature, contains steel pipes as air channels. This assembly is mounted in a steel pan insulated with 3-3/4-inch fiberglass batt, covered with a double glass glazing. The collector design is such that panels may be plugged into each other with a minimum of installation time. Air inlets and outlets are cut into each collector array in the field.

In this collector air flows through the channels *beneath* the heated absorber plate and above the thick insulation. Collector efficiency is as high as 64.5%, according to Solaron. As previously mentioned, the effi-

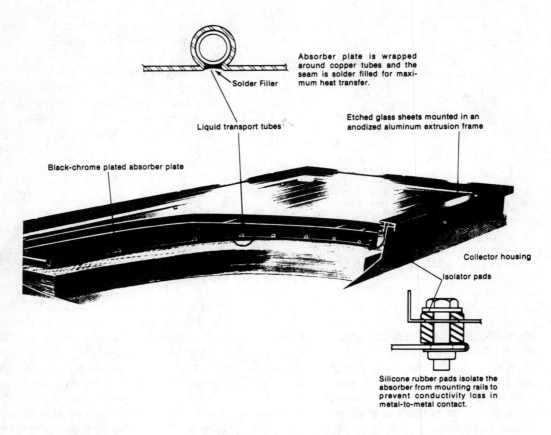

Absorber plate is wrapped around copper tubes and the seam is solder filled for maximum heat transfer.

Solder Filler

Liquid transport tubes

Etched glass sheets mounted in an anodized aluminum extrusion frame

Black-chrome plated absorber plate

Collector housing

Isolator pads

Silicone rubber pads isolate the absorber from mounting rails to prevent conductivity loss in metal-to-metal contact.

FIGURE 3-28. "Freeze Safe" Domestic Solar Hot Water System Developed by Solaron Corporation

ciency of solar collectors as specified by the National Bureau of Standards is stated by the following equation:

$$\text{Efficiency} = k\ \frac{T_{out} - T_{amb}}{\text{Insolation}}$$

where k is a useful constant in converting the numerator (collector outlet temperature minus ambient temperature) divided by solar insolation into efficiency expressed as a percentage of the theoretical maximum that could be obtained.

According to the manufacturer, when $T_{out} - T_{amb}$ equals 120°F and insolation is 300 BTU per hour per square foot of collector absorber, the Solaron series 2000 air-type collector is more efficient than many of

the flat plate liquid-type solar collectors. A temperature difference of 120°F is not unusual, especially in cold weather. Thus, although the Solaron hot water heater involves an air-to-water heat exchanger, which is less efficient than the liquid (usually antifreeze mixture)-to-water heat exchangers described earlier, the total system has merit.

Referring again to Figure 3-29, this solar-heated air-to-water cycle is quite simple. Solar energy is collected by the panels (1), and hot air flows to the heat exchanger (2), where it warms water being circulated by the small pump (6). Solar heated water is continuously circulated into the storage tank (3) so long as an automatic control unit indicates that there is adequate solar heat-

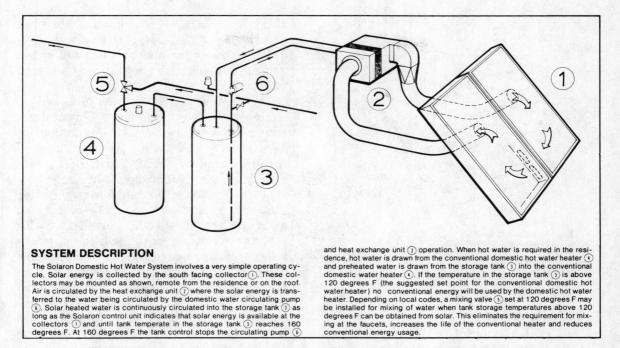

SYSTEM DESCRIPTION

The Solaron Domestic Hot Water System involves a very simple operating cycle. Solar energy is collected by the south facing collector ①. These collectors may be mounted as shown, remote from the residence or on the roof. Air is circulated by the heat exchange unit ② where the solar energy is transferred to the water being circulated by the domestic water circulating pump ⑥. Solar heated water is continuously circulated into the storage tank ③ as long as the Solaron control unit indicates that solar energy is available at the collectors ① and until tank temperate in the storage tank ③ reaches 160 degrees F. At 160 degrees F the tank control stops the circulating pump ⑥

and heat exchange unit ② operation. When hot water is required in the residence, hot water is drawn from the conventional domestic hot water heater ④ and preheated water is drawn from the storage tank ③ into the conventional domestic water heater ④. If the temperature in the storage tank ③ is above 120 degrees F (the suggested set point for the conventional domestic hot water heater) no conventional energy will be used by the domestic hot water heater. Depending on local codes, a mixing valve ⑤ set at 120 degrees F may be installed for mixing of water when tank storage temperatures above 120 degrees F can be obtained from solar. This eliminates the requirement for mixing at the faucets, increases the life of the conventional heater and reduces conventional energy usage.

FIGURE 3-29. "Freeze Safe" Domestic Solar Hot Water System Developed by Solaron Corporation

ing of the air in the collectors, and until the tank temperature reaches 160°F.

At 160°F the control turns off the circulation pump and operation of the heat exchanger. When hot water is needed in your home, it comes first from the conventional hot water heater (4) and meanwhile the solar-heated water is drawn from the storage tank.

If the storage tank's water temperature is above 120°F—a recommended set point for energy conservation—no energy other than solar will be used. A tempering or mixing valve (5) set at 120°F ensures this hot water temperature at your faucets, and helps save water by eliminating requirements for mixing too-hot with cold at the spigots, according to Solaron.

The manufacturer estimates that a home installation for a family of four will cost from $1,500 to $2,100, depending on local weather conditions, and therefore the number of collectors required, and on labor rates. By

making the following assumptions, this type of solar hot water heater will earn you between 10% and 20% return on your investment in savings on your electric bill:

- Federal tax credit will be approved to provide 40% direct tax credit on the first $1,000 invested in a solar system and 25% on the balance up to a maximum of $2,000. No state tax credits are included in the savings estimate, although several states provide them.

- As the buyer, you are in a 30% income tax bracket.

- Electric rates will escalate 10% per year. (In most areas they increased 100% in the past four years, or at an average of 25%.)

- Your family of four uses 14.6 million BTU a year for heating water and you set your solar water heater system for 120°F.

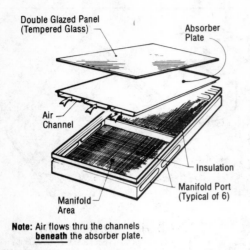

Double Glazed Panel
(Tempered Glass)

Absorber
Plate

Air
Channel

Insulation

Manifold Port
(Typical of 6)

Manifold
Area

Note: Air flows thru the channels **beneath** the absorber plate.

FIGURE 3-30.   Cross Section of Solaron Collector

In Chapter 5 there is a further discussion of the Solaron air-type system for heating and cooling of buildings. This firm's solar hot water heater is neither the highest nor the lowest in cost. It has some marked advantages in simplicity of operation, particularly in cold climates. There is no danger of outdoor pipes leaking, no need to use an antifreeze mixture in the collectors, no requirement for draining the system each night or during prolonged bitterly cold weather as a precaution. On the other hand, air-to-water heat transfer is relatively inefficient. Thus, there are both technical advantages and disadvantages in the Solaron hot water heater. As to its cost in your area, one purpose of this book is to help you make intelligent comparisons among various kinds of solar heaters before you undertake your own installation.

Summary of Other Designs

In Warrenton, Virginia, the Solar Corporation of America (SCA) manufactures the "Joule Box" solar water heater shown in Figure 3-31. The 36-square-foot collector is a conventional design with copper tubing and manifolds, a black aluminum absorber plate and insulated metal housing with insulation at the sides and bottom, and single glazing of high-transmittance tempered glass.

The SCA water heater was designed by engineers of InterTechnology Corporation, which has been responsible for numerous solar heating and cooling projects, most of them financed by ERDA. With SCA a subsidiary of InterTechnology, it has been possible to develop a packaged water heater that can be installed by competent home owners where local codes permit. As with systems previously described, the differential thermostat control plugs into a standard 115-volt AC wall outlet. The storage tank has a capacity of 80 gallons, is stone lined and insulated, and contains a heat exchanger coil. It is connected to the collectors by 3/4-inch flexible tubing covered with 1/2-inch insulation. A useful feature is the 10-gallon accumulator tank containing a float valve. You can drain the water from the collectors into this small tank at night if it's cold and you want to avoid using antifreeze in your closed-loop solar fluid system. Also, this accumulator may be manually filled by opening the valve to the city water supply if you need water to prime the circulating pump.

Estimated cost of the SCA Joule Box solar water heater f.o.b. Warrenton (near Washington, D.C.) without installation ranges from $960 to $2,650 for a family of four, depending on climatic conditions and the size of the house. The low figure is for an installation in the South and Southwest in a one-story home. The top cost is for families in two-story homes living in northern areas with minimum annual insolation.

In the same area as InterTechnology/ SCA is a smaller firm, Solar Comfort Systems of Bethesda, Maryland. According to David S. DeRiemer, president, this company makes collector panels with aluminum absorber plates, copper piping, a lower glazing of Teflon, and an outer window of Lucite acrylic plastic, all contained in an enameled

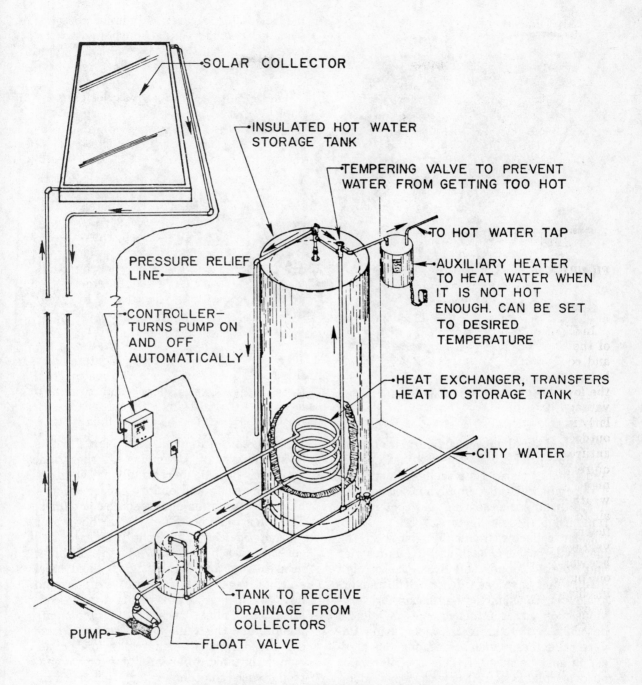

SOLAR COLLECTOR

INSULATED HOT WATER STORAGE TANK

TEMPERING VALVE TO PREVENT WATER FROM GETTING TOO HOT

TO HOT WATER TAP

PRESSURE RELIEF LINE

AUXILIARY HEATER TO HEAT WATER WHEN IT IS NOT HOT ENOUGH. CAN BE SET TO DESIRED TEMPERATURE

CONTROLLER— TURNS PUMP ON AND OFF AUTOMATICALLY

HEAT EXCHANGER, TRANSFERS HEAT TO STORAGE TANK

CITY WATER

TANK TO RECEIVE DRAINAGE FROM COLLECTORS

PUMP

FLOAT VALVE

FIGURE 3-31.   "Joule Box" Solar Water Heater

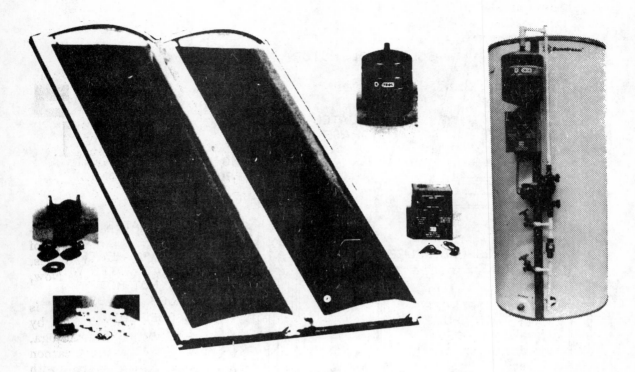

FIGURE 3-32. Components of Sunstream Solar Water Heater Made by Grumman

housing of aluminum, with fiberglass insulation. Size of this collector is 2 feet x 8 feet and 4 inches thick. Its price is competitive. The company is also supplying solar water heaters and space heating and cooling systems using these collectors.

Solar collectors made by giants in the materials business such as PPG Industries and Revere Copper and Brass are of high quality and have been described in numerous publications, including this author's previous book. Later in this volume you'll find a description of solar installations using Revere collectors, which are among the highest in cost because of their use of copper absorber plates as well as waterways, manifolds, all connecting piping, valves, and other hardware. However, there's no question that such installations, well designed and made with excellent materials, will have a life equal to that of the structures they heat and usually cool.

Sunstream of Ronkonkoma, New York, is a subsidiary of Grumman Corporation, which has become increasingly active in solar engineering and energy conservation—like many other major aerospace companies. The Sunstream 50AST is a solar hot water system provided in kit form. It includes two collectors, each about 3-1/2 feet x 9-3/4 feet in area, and an 82-gallon glass-lined steel storage tank with integral wrap-around heat exchanger (tank-within-a-tank construction) plus necessary components mounted on this tank at the factory. These components include an expansion or accumulator tank; differential thermostat controller with tank temperature sensor; circulating pump; check valve; and 2 hose bibs for easy filling and purging of the system shown in Figure 3-32.

This Sunstream kit provides a sensor for installation at the outlet of the collectors, as well as special installation fittings, and even

4 gallons of antifreeze to use in the closed-loop solar heating system. Like other manufacturers in the Northeast, this company encourages use of antifreeze wherever there is any danger of subfreezing temperatures. Price of the system described, with two collectors and all the other items, is about $1,000 f.o.b. factory. Manuals with complete installation instructions are provided, and even with professional help you should be able to install such a system for approximately $200 in labor cost.

Among Pennsylvania manufacturers of good solar collectors, many of which have been used in hot water systems, is Ametek Power Systems Group, Hatfield. This unit has an absorber area of about 2 feet x 8-1/2 feet, with a total collector thickness of 6-3/4 inches. The absorber plate, coated with a proprietary black coating having 98% absorptivity, is Olin Brass Roll-Bond design with integral tubes and headers, and all waterways and absorber surfaces made of copper. Fiberglass insulation plus mineral wool, forming a particularly thick padding underneath and at the sides of the absorber, are contained by a corrosion-resistant steel housing, with tempered glass or high-impact plastic for the glazing. A useful feature is a synthetic rubber gasket with integrally molded zipper to hold the glazing in place securely, but permit easy replacement if necessary.

The collector made by Heliotherm, Inc., of Lenni, Pennsylvania, has a raised cover window of Plexiglas bonded to the metal housing with silicone sealant. An Olin Roll-Bond absorber plate made of aluminum with copper-surface integral waterways and manifolds is mounted over Technifoam isocyanurate insulation, which has structural rigidity as well as high temperature stability. Cross section of this collector, 3 feet x 8

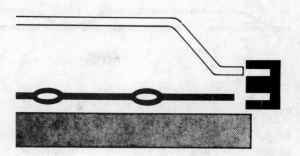

FIGURE 3-33. Heliotherm Solar Collector

feet and 2-1/2 inches thick, is shown in Figure 3-33. The Heliotherm collector is one of many sold by such mail order companies, previously described, as Solar Usage Now, Inc.

What is called "aluminum tube sheet" is also used as the absorber plate material by Energy Converters, Inc., of Chattanooga, Tennessee. ECI has developed a thin carbon particle coating for its absorber that, with other features, has enabled its solar collector to reach temperatures of more than 300°F. This panel has a galvanized steel housing, uses fiberglass insulation and single glazing of Tedlar. ECI engineers have taken considerable data and do a conscientious job so that anyone in the Southeast looking for a solar heater would find this company to be a good source of information.

An unusual design of quilted steel is used as the absorber plate made by Tranter, Inc., Lansing, Michigan. These Econocoil plates, with cross section shown in Figure 3-34, have been tested by NASA Lewis Laboratory, Cleveland, using an assembly with double glazing of glass; efficiencies from 38% to 70% were reported. The standard model has 19.5 square feet of heat transfer surface.

FIGURE 3-34. Cross Section of Quilted Steel Absorber Plate Made by Tranter, Inc.

FIGURE 3-35. Cross Section of Ilse Collector

A solar collector with somewhat similar steel sandwich construction, except that the lower plate of the absorber is flat and the upper plate has long plateaus and narrow valleys as shown in Figure 3-35, is made by Ilse Engineering, Inc., of Duluth, Minnesota. The sandwich panel made with an absorber of this design is priced at $3.25 per square foot f.o.b. factory, a very favorable price indeed.

Low-Cost Solar Water Heater

One of the lowest priced solar water heater kits is the package offered by Sol-Therm Corp. of New York City. According to Itamar Sittenfeld, vice president, the solar system shown in Figure 3-36 is priced at about $700 f.o.b. New York. This is a thermosiphoning system with neither circulating pump nor differential thermostat control, which is one reason for the low cost. Also, as has been pointed out in Chapter 2, if you have a solar system relying entirely on thermosiphoning, the storage tank must be placed as shown in Figure 3-37 so that the tank inlet for the sun-heated water is higher than the top of the collectors.

This heater package includes two flat plate collectors, a 32-gallon storage tank, all

FIGURE 3-36. Solar Water Heater Kit by Sol-Therm. Lack of Circulating Pump and Differential Thermostat Helps Keep Price of This Kit Low

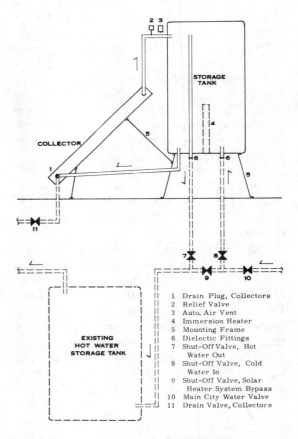

1 Drain Plug, Collectors
2 Relief Valve
3 Auto. Air Vent
4 Immersion Heater
5 Mounting Frame
6 Dielectric Fittings
7 Shut-Off Valve, Hot Water Out
8 Shut-Off Valve, Cold Water In
9 Shut-Off Valve, Solar Heater System Bypass
10 Main City Water Valve
11 Drain Valve, Collectors

FIGURE 3-37. Storage Tank Placement in System Relying Wholly on Thermosiphoning

the pipes and nipples to connect the tank to the collectors, a mounting frame to permit installing the collectors and tank on a flat roof, plus detailed instructions on installation, operation, and maintenance of the solar heater. The collectors are 3 feet x 6 feet and 3-1/2 inches thick, with absorber plate, pipes, headers, and housing made of galvanized steel. Insulation is 1-1/2 inches of rock wool, and glazing is a single glass sheet.

A desirable feature of the Sol-Therm tank is that it contains an electric immersion heater, 1.5 kw capacity, and also an auto-matic thermostat control when operating electrically. There is cathodic protection against corrosion with a magnesium rod mounted inside the tank.

With this simple thermosiphoning system, the sun's energy heats the water in your tank so long as there is adequate sunshine. When the tank water gets colder than the temperature at which you've set the thermostat, the electric unit provides supplementary heat. Dimensions of the tank are 2 feet in diameter, 3-1/3 feet high.

Collectors on Roof of Solarmate Home, Plano, Texas

Installing Collector Plates on Roof of Solarmate Home, Plano, Texas

83

4
Solar Space Systems, Liquid-Type

"If we can put a man on the moon, why can't we solve some of our major problems here on earth—hunger, overcrowding, pollution?" How many times have you heard that question, particularly during the worldwide economic recession of the early seventies? It's as if the astronauts and the remarkable technical teams associated with these manned space programs were transformed from heroes into somewhat dubious characters almost overnight.

If you're wondering what connection the United States space program has with solar energy, the fact is that literally thousands of highly trained space scientists, engineers, and technicians have turned their talents to practical applications of solar energy. That's one reason why our national solar programs are advancing so rapidly.

Early in the development of solar techniques, federal funds amounting to less than $5 million a year were doled out to a few research groups in universities and private industry by the National Science Founda-

tion. Then in 1974, the Energy Research and Development Administration (ERDA) was created by Congress. ERDA awarded substantial federal funding to the National Aeronautical and Space Administration (NASA) to accelerate solar progress. It made sense to use the highly qualified technical agencies to channel taxpayers' dollars, amounting to $281 million in fiscal 1976, into the most productive avenues of solar energy research.

Thanks partly to the vigilance of informed senators and representatives from many states, it appears as though most of this growing federal funding is being spent wisely. The biggest emphasis is on practical applications of solar energy to solve immediate problems: using the sun's power for heating water, for heating and cooling buildings, and for industrial and commercial uses where process heat up to about 500°F obtained from the sun is economically justified right now and will save increasing amounts of fossil fuels.

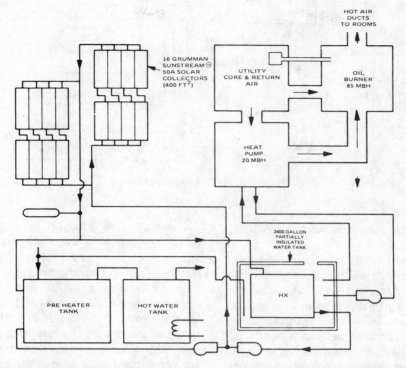

FIGURE 4-1.   Queechee Lake House—Heating and Domestic Hot Water System

Solar Engineering by Grumman for Vermont House

In subsequent chapters you'll find descriptions of useful solar research being performed by organizations formerly known almost exclusively for aerospace expertise: Sandia, McDonnell-Douglas, Martin Marietta, Boeing, Lockheed, and others. As mentioned in the previous chapter, Grumman Corporation—which built the lunar landing vehicle (LEM)—is now building and selling solar water heaters. Grumman is also experimenting with a commercial business in family-sized wind generators as described in Chapter 12.

One of the interesting applications of the Grumman solar collectors and energy system is the "Energy House," built in the town of Quechee Lake, Vermont. As shown in Figure 4-1, solar energy is used there for both space heating and domestic hot water.

There are several features worthy of comment about this 3-story, 2,300-square-foot house. It is in a cold area with much winter snow and an average of 7,500 degree days. A *degree day* is a term widely used by solar engineers. You merely perform a simple multiplication: the average 24-hour temperature in degrees below 65°F x 1 = the degree day value of any specific day. That is, if the average temperature on January 25 is 10°F, this is a 55 degree day.

As pointed out previously, solar collectors lose efficiency when they are much hotter than the ambient air. For this reason, Grumman engineers have chosen a solar system shown in the simple diagram of Figure 4-1. Treated water, including a specially formulated antifreeze, is circulated by means of a 1/3 HP centrifugal pump through 16 Sunstream panels. Solar heat is delivered to the 2,400-gallon insulated concrete water

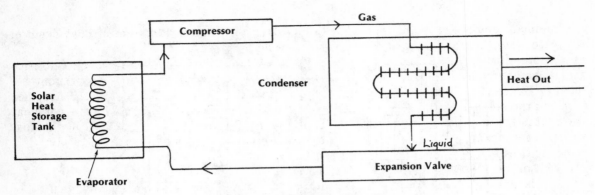

FIGURE 4-2. Operation of Heat Pump

tank in the basement by a coiled copper pipe heat exchanger.

The solar-heated antifreeze mixture is also circulated through an 80-gallon preheating tank of the tank-within-a-tank design described in Chapter 3, where the entire wrap-around space between the outer shell and the inner water tank acts as a heat exchanger. This 80-gallon solar heated tank is connected to a conventional electric water heater, and thus furnishes an ample additional supply for domestic hot water.

Sun-heated water in the large basement storage tank is used by a water-to-air *heat pump* as an energy source when the rooms in this Vermont house need warming. The heat pump is a York Triton Model DW-20H-B, which has a high coefficient of performance (COP) and an operating cost very much lower than an electric baseboard heating system. That is, solar-warmed water in the Quechee Lake big storage tank can be used, when this water temperature is as low as 45° to 80°F, for forced air heating of this house. This is because the heat pump, while performing the water-to-air heat transfer, also adds heat quite efficiently.

Figure 4-2 is a diagram showing the operation of a heat pump. Operating characteristics of a heat pump are similar to those of your refrigerator or air conditioner. In this sketch the process of heating the water in the storage tank via hot liquid (or hot air) from solar collector panels is ignored since it is described many times in this book.

Concentrating on the heat pump, relatively low-temperature water heated by the sun warms the evaporator coil of the heat pump. This evaporator is part of a closed loop containing a vapor pumped through cycles of evaporation and condensation, continually going from vapor to liquid and back to vapor so long as the heat pump is operating. The solar hot water causes the liquid (or condensed gas) to evaporate. Then, by means of an electric motor, mechanical work is applied to the compressor to raise the pressure and temperature of the gas from the evaporator. Now the gas, when it cools to a liquid in the condenser, gives off more heat than was provided by the water in the solar storage tank.

In the Quechee Lake house example, when the temperature of the solar-heated water is 70°F, the heat pump can provide nearly 3 BTU of hot air at a relatively high temperature (110°F or higher) for every 1 BTU of electrical energy used by the compressor. This is what a coefficient of performance (COP) of 3 signifies. The heat pump uses far less electricity than an electric baseboard heater, and enables the Quechee Lake home owner to use relatively cool solar-heated water in midwinter to keep the house comfortably warm at a small fraction of the cost of electric space heating.

Where summer cooling is necessary, a heat pump used with a solar system for space heating and cooling is very efficient and economical.

Grumman engineers point out that a water-to-water heat pump would have been even more efficient if they had been able to find a commercially available unit for this Energy House.

When the solar-heated water assisted by the heat pump does not supply enough BTU to keep the house warm, an oil-fired furnance is turned on to heat the air supplied through ducts to all heated areas. This oil burner is activated only when the heat pump can't meet the home owner's needs, or when the temperature in the big storage tank drops below 45°F. Temperature sensors in the collectors' output and in the storage tank, a typical Rho Sigma differential thermostat system, automatically control the pumps which circulate solar-heated antifreeze through the heat exchangers shown in Figure 4-1.

Energy conservation features included in this Vermont house by the architect, Blue/Sun Ltd., and the builder, Terrosi Construction, Inc., for the land developer, Quechee Lake Corporation, are good examples of modern design in New England. The house is well insulated, with insulation equivalent to the following number of inches of standard fiberglass: walls, 6 inches; roof, 9 inches; basement outer walls, 3 inches. All walls are specially sealed against air infiltration, using a post-and-beam construction with siding sprayed with 1-3/8 inches of urethane. The roof is vinyl-covered homosote 2-3/8 inches thick, which also provides a finished inside surface. The outside surface of the homosote is covered with 1-3/8 inches of overlapped urethane and then covered by asphalt shingles.

There are no windows on the north wall, but loss of light there has been overcome by using skylights. Windows on the east, south, and west walls are triple-glazed with a sealed gas sandwich and minimum crack dimensions. A solarium on the south side has 50 square feet of window and skylight area; these windows are covered at night by insulating shutters. Thus, the solarium provides solar heating passively during sunny days and loses a minimum of heat even on cold nights.

At the main door there is an entrance alcove, acting as an airlock to prevent escape of warmed air. A Heatilator fireplace with glass screen also provides a net heat gain to the house—in contrast with most fireplaces, which are inefficient.

Substantial Solar Savings

Although winter temperatures drop as low as -30°F at this Vermont site, the Energy House has given even better results than predicted. It was *not* designed to provide 100% of requirements for solar space heating and hot water. In a climate like that of northern New England, a solar collector system meeting 50% of those energy demands is economically justified. There is no need for summer cooling at Quechee Lake, and from late Spring to early Fall the solar system provides almost 100% of the energy to heat domestic hot water.

An analysis shows that the added cost of the solar space heating and hot water system compares with conventional systems as follows:

- Solar heating system versus all-electric system pays for itself in annual operating cost savings ($618 as against $2,201) in two years.

- Solar heating system versus oil heating and electric hot water system pays for itself in six years (operating cost $618 as against $1,201 annually).

This analysis is based on assumptions that the added cost of the solar heating system becomes part of a mortgage financed at 8.5%, and that fuel costs escalate at 7% a year. On this basis, the solar installation over a 25-year period saves the home owner $24,500 compared with oil-and-electricity heating, and $87,500 in net savings compared with an all-electric system. By "solar heating system" we mean the solar plus fuel oil plus electric system installed in the Energy House.

Commentary

The Quechee Lake house has an efficient solar heating and hot water system. Collector efficiency ranged from 45% to 50% during the cold winter months of January through March 1976. Installed cost of the total system, solar plus oil plus electric, came to $9,410.

This is by no means an unreasonable cost for a 3-story home as large as the Energy House, although the hydronic systems described later in this chapter, using solar energy assisted by gas, demand considerably less in initial investment, even in cold areas such as western Canada and Idaho.

Also, the cost savings arrived at in the analysis of the Quechee Lake house compare conventional heating installations in a house with "reasonably tight" standard insulation with the carefully designed and extremely well-insulated Energy House. There is no question, as Grumman solar engineers are the first to state, that good design and good insulation are just as important as a solar installation in conserving energy—and saving money for the home owner.

Even so, it is evident that solar-assisted savings will help you pay for a new home. And, as described later in this and subsequent chapters, you can install a solar system in most existing houses, condominiums, and apartment buildings.

Heat Delivery and Distribution

Although this book makes no attempt to serve as a manual on heating and air conditioning systems, it may be helpful to the average home owner to consider briefly some of the most common residential systems for delivering heat. This is also a good introduction to solar space heating systems described on the new few pages. Remember, too, that you can use your solar space heating system, whether of the liquid- or air-type (Chapter 5), for providing your home with hot water as well as comfortable living quarters in cold weather.

A central forced air furnace is the most common residential heater. Usually a centrifugal blower draws air from a return air register or duct, passes this air over an internal heat exchanger in the furnace, and delivers it to the rooms to be heated through ducts leading to registers or grilles in the rooms to be warmed. Heat for the heat exchanger is provided by fuel selected by the builder of the house—sometimes, but not always, the least expensive local energy source. Natural gas, propane, butane, fuel oil, coal, and electricity vary in cost and popularity with the locale.

Simplest control for a forced air system is a single central thermostat. In larger structures there may be two or more zone thermostats, and some have motorized dampers to control warm air flow in individual rooms or areas. When a central thermostat calls for heat, an internal thermostat on the furnace heat exchanger delays turning on the blower until the heat exchanger reaches a preset temperature. This prevents blowing cold air into your rooms before your furnace has reached the temperature you've set. In simple zoned systems, the fuel burner or electric strip heater in the furnace, as well as the blower, are turned on whenever any zone thermostat calls for heat. In more complex (and usually more wasteful) systems, the burner and fan operate continuously and the zone controls operate motorized dampers on the air supply grilles.

Solar conversion with a liquid-type solar collector system is achieved by installing a water-to-air heat exchanger in the furnace plenum or in the return air duct. This is not as difficult as you might think. Standard heat exchangers that will do this job are available from heating equipment and plumbing supply stores, or from the mail order companies listed in Chapter 3. Solar hot water from the storage tank is delivered to the heat exchanger located in a main duct by a small circulating pump, controlled by a central or room thermostat. The furnace fan or blower is controlled by the same thermostat. But the fuel burner or electric heat in the furnace is controlled by a separate thermostat which turns on the supplementary fuel source only when the air from the solar heat exchanger is not warm enough.

Air-type solar collector systems make the solar conversion job still easier when you have a hot-air furnace. See Chapter 5.

Fan-coil systems include one or more assemblies consisting of a coil of metal pipe carrying hot water; a blower or fan to move air over this heat exchanger coil; and a thermostatic control to turn the blower on and adjust its speed to match the heating requirements. The fluid in the heat exchanger coil may be steam, hot water, or an antifreeze mixture if the system is to be used for heating a building. In a cooling application, the fluid is usually chilled water.

There is no burner or furnace of the types used in central forced air systems. In a fan-coil system, when you provide *solar heating* from liquid-type collectors, the hot water is circulated through a hydronic system—a continuous loop of pipe carrying heated water through the coils of various fan-coil units for space heating, and providing direct feeder lines from the main loop for supplying hot water wherever you need outlets. This kind of solar hydronic system may have as a backup either a gas- or oil-fired boiler; or a water heater with electricity, gas, oil, or coal to supply the supplementary energy. It is also feasible to use electric strip heaters in your air ducts as backup to a solar fan-coil space heating system.

When a central fan-coil unit is installed—usually for a small building—a single thermostat controls both the circulating pump for the hot water and the speed of the blower. Hot air is delivered through ducts just as in the central forced air system described above.

If your system includes individual fan-coil units for each heating zone—as, for instance, units for each apartment in a large complex—each fan or blower is controlled by its own thermostat. There is a zone valve, controlled by the same unit thermostat, to regulate the flow of hot water through that fan-coil unit. Since the pumps used in such a system, even in a large apartment or condominium complex, are small and consume little electric power, it is most efficient to keep water circulating through the main hydronic loop.

Forced air convector is a variation of the individual room fan-coil unit, in which the heat exchanger consists of one or more sections of tubing fitted with large metal fins. Hot water circulates through the tubing contained in a baseboard unit or heater cabinet. A fan in this cabinet forces air to flow over the hot fins (around the tubing) and out of a grille into the room.

A further variation of the convector is the type with no fan. There are baseboard units, available by the foot in lengths of finned water tubing controlled by a manual valve or by a thermostat-operated zone valve. Heat is transferred to room air by both natural convection and radiation. A familiar form of such natural convectors is the radiator, steam or hot water, used in public buildings, apartments, and industry for more than a century.

Hydronic radiant panels are waterways of soft copper tubing embedded in floors or ceilings. These panels may be supplied with solar-heated water as shown in Figure 4-3. Usually radiant panels are not incorporated in walls because of the dangers of puncturing the water tubing when hanging pictures or shelves, or of interfering with electrical wiring. Zone controls are desirable with hydronic radiant panels as indicated in the figure.

After *conversion to solar heat*, hot water supplied from a solar storage tank through a tempering valve—"tempered hot water"—

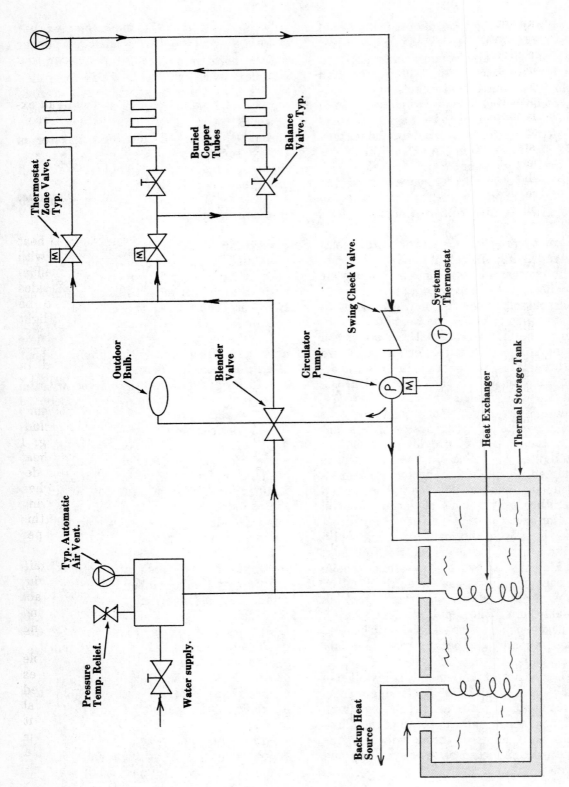

FIGURE 4-3. Simplified Schematic, Hydronic Radiant Heating System

Thermostat Zone Valve, Typ.

Buried Copper Tubes

Balance Valve, Typ.

Outdoor Bulb.

Blender Valve

Swing Check Valve.

System Thermostat

Circulator Pump.

Typ. Automatic Air Vent.

Pressure Temp. Relief.

Water supply.

Heat Exchanger

Thermal Storage Tank

Backup Heat Source

90

goes to radiant panels in each zone through zone valves controlled by individual thermostats. The circulating pump continues to run continuously during the heating season in your area.

Backup heat for hydronic radiant panel systems is supplied by a conventional water heater for most single-family houses. For larger systems, in apartment houses as well as commercial and industrial buildings, a hydronic boiler serves as an adequate backup. There are numerous commercial hydronic boilers available as a package with circulator pump, expansion tank, and controls.

How Many Solar Collectors Are Needed

In Appendix 2 is an estimate of the number of solar collector panels per person required to supply most of the hot water needs of households in many communities in the United States and Canada. This is on the assumption that you install a reasonably flat-plate solar collector with the popular area dimensions of 8 feet x 4 feet, such as the Sol-R-Tech design on which the table in Appendix 2 is based.

Thus, with only two people in your household in a very sunny area, two solar collectors will supply most of your hot water needs throughout the year. If you live in Boston and have a family of four, your most cost-effective installation will include four solar collectors to supply about 50% of your annual domestic hot water. In New England, you could install 10 solar collectors and a large thermal storage tank and take care of perhaps 70% to 80% of your annual hot water requirements for the same family of four. But the added cost would probably not be justified—at *present* utility rates. However, it's an excellent idea to design your solar system so that you can readily add to it, because utility rates will keep on going up. You may eventually want that larger solar system.

Calculating the number of solar collectors required for *space heating* of your home or any other building is far more complex than estimating the number of collectors needed for your hot water supply. Consider that you need to know the following:

- Conduction heat losses through all exterior walls, windows, doors and roof
- Edge losses around the perimeter of your floors
- Air infiltration losses
- Floor and basement (if you have one) conduction losses

Typically you might find your total heat losses in a 2,000-square-foot house with good standard insulation, including double-glazed windows on the north and east sides and adequate weather stripping, to be 25,000 BTU per hour on a day with light winds and an outside temperature of 40°F. At this temperature there are 25 degree days (65 - 40 = 25) in a 24-hour period. In the same period your heat losses are 24 x 25,000 BTU = 600,000 BTU.

It is more convenient to express such large numbers as heating engineers, including solar specialists, are used to doing: 1 *therm*=100,000 BTU. Therefore, your heat losses, under the conditions we have defined, are 6 therms during that day when the average ambient air was 40°F. Carrying it one step further, the heat losses from this house are 6 therms/25, or 0.24 therm per degree day.

Your house may have some heat gain from south-facing windows, if these windows are always available (undraped) to absorb sunlight when the sun is shining, and carefully covered with drapes or insulating shutters when it is not.

Then you may be able to construct a table for the 12 months of the year along the lines of Figure 4-4, a heat load worksheet devised by solar engineer Jim Senn for a theoretical house in the Los Angeles area. It turns out that with this load for a combined solar space heating and hot water system of the design shown in Figure 4-5, the total number of solar panels needed is 12 Energy Sys-

Solar Gain Worksheet

Month	Insolation BTU/Day per Sq. Ft., Vert. Surface	Per cent Sunny Days	Solar Gain, South Windows, Therms
Jan	1908	70	62
Feb	1816	69	52.6
Mar	1484	70	48.3
Apr	1004	67	30.3
May	728	68	23.0
Jun	634	69	19.7
Jul	714	80	26.6
Aug	970	81	36.5
Sep	1428	80	51.4
Oct	1754	76	62
Nov	1870	79	66.5
Dec	1908	72	63.9

Solar gain is calculated from the formula:
$I_g = I_v \times PA \times n \times A \times C_s / 100{,}000$ in therms.
I_v = insolation on a south facing vertical surface, BTU/day/sq.ft.
PA = per cent sunny days for the period.
n = number of days in the period.
A = Area of windows in sq. ft.
C_s = Shading coefficient for the glass used, 1.0 for single glass, 0.9 for double glass.

FIGURE 4-4. Solar Gain Worksheet

Estimated Square Feet of Solar Collectors for Liquid-Type Space Heating and Hot Water System

Insolation Area*	Number of Square Feet in Building	Square Feet of Collectors
1	X	0.15X
2	X	0.2X
3	X	0.3X

*See Figure 3-9, page 58.

tems, Inc., (ESI) 3 feet x 6 feet single-glazed collectors.

Unless you intend to make a career as a heating and ventilating specialist, with specific expertise in solar systems—not a bad idea for anyone, female or male, handy with tools—you can try the following rule-of-thumb estimates and be sufficiently close. This table enables you to estimate a solar system which will provide up to 70% of your space heating and hot water at reasonable cost.

Thus, if your home is in Insolation Area 1 and has 1,500 square feet of floor space, you would plan on using 225 square feet of solar collectors. In a New England home, in Area 3, with 2,000 square feet, you will want 600 square feet of solar collectors—but then your savings will be greater with your solar

system because of higher annual heating costs. Using some of the concentrating collectors described later in this book, you can cut the square feet of collectors required by 25% or more.

Efficient Hydronic-Loop System

Most liquid-type solar systems for space heating and hot water recommend using a large insulated tank, placed underground or in a basement, for providing thermal storage. This is a reservoir of heat energy, created by the sun during periods of prolonged clear weather—a "savings bank" on which you can draw during those inevitable rainy days.

The size of this tank for storing sun-heated water varies with all the factors previously considered: insolation area, size of the building, design of the structure, and efficiency of its insulation.

Many air-type solar systems, discussed in Chapter 5, are also designed to include a large water storage tank surrounded by clean rocks in a bin through which heated air is circulated. This gives you the advantage of air-type collectors and several days' supply of domestic hot water.

One of the most successful pioneers in designing and building solar systems, James Piper, doesn't see the need for tanks holding 1,000 gallons or more of sun-heated water. He is the founder and President of Piper

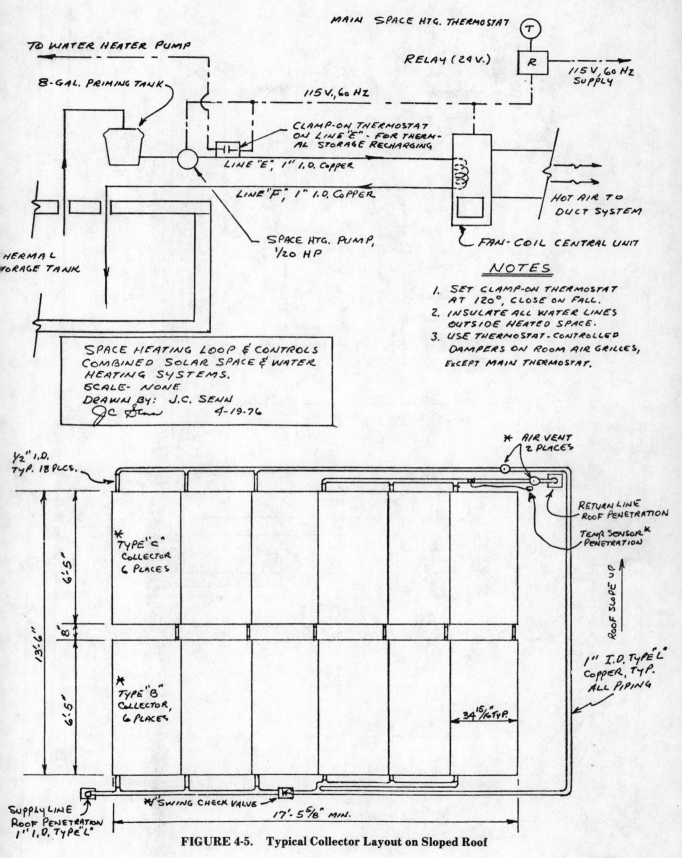

TO WATER HEATER PUMP

8-GAL. PRIMING TANK

MAIN SPACE HTG. THERMOSTAT (T)

RELAY (24V.) R 115V, 60 HZ SUPPLY

115 V, 60 HZ

CLAMP-ON THERMOSTAT ON LINE "E" - FOR THERMAL STORAGE RECHARGING

LINE "E", 1" I.D. COPPER

LINE "F", 1" I.D. COPPER

HOT AIR TO DUCT SYSTEM

SPACE HTG. PUMP, 1/20 HP

FAN-COIL CENTRAL UNIT

THERMAL STORAGE TANK

NOTES

1. SET CLAMP-ON THERMOSTAT AT 120°, CLOSE ON FALL.
2. INSULATE ALL WATER LINES OUTSIDE HEATED SPACE.
3. USE THERMOSTAT-CONTROLLED DAMPERS ON ROOM AIR GRILLES, EXCEPT MAIN THERMOSTAT.

SPACE HEATING LOOP & CONTROLS
COMBINED SOLAR SPACE & WATER
HEATING SYSTEMS.
SCALE- NONE
DRAWN BY: J.C. SENN
JC Senn   4-19-76

½" I.D. TYP. 18 PLCS.

* AIR VENT 2 PLACES

RETURN LINE ROOF PENETRATION

TEMP SENSOR * PENETRATION

* TYPE "C" COLLECTOR 6 PLACES

6'-5"

13'-6"

8"

ROOF SLOPE UP

1" I.D. TYPE "L" COPPER, TYP. ALL PIPING

* TYPE "B" COLLECTOR, 6 PLACES

6'-5"

34 15/16" TYP.

SUPPLY LINE ROOF PENETRATION 1" I.D. TYPE "L"

* SWING CHECK VALVE

17'-5 5/8" MIN.

FIGURE 4-5.   Typical Collector Layout on Sloped Roof

93

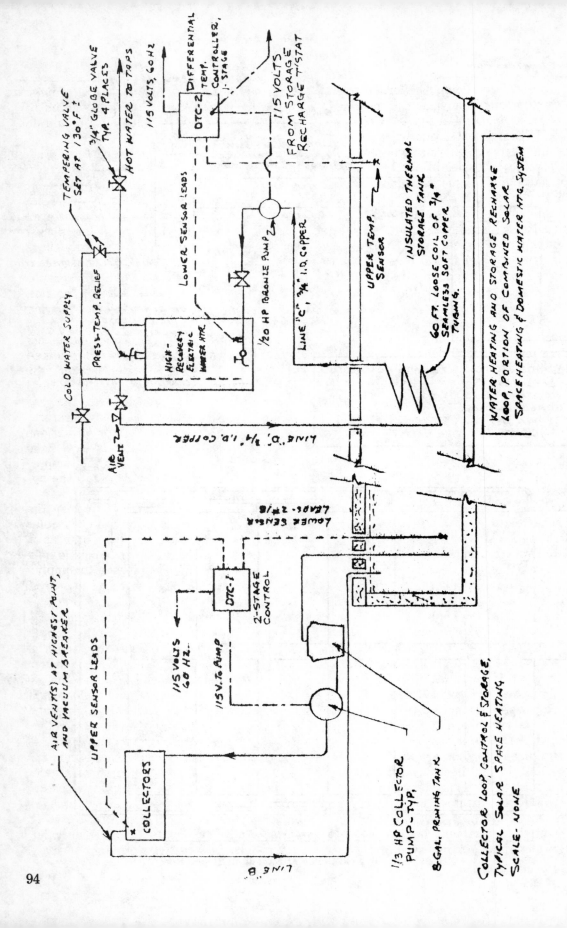

COLLECTOR LOOP, CONTROL & STORAGE.
TYPICAL SOLAR SPACE HEATING
SCALE- NONE

94

Hydro, Inc., of Anaheim, California, with solar installations in many parts of the United States as well as in Canada, Mexico, and Iran. So his arguments, quoted later, for *not* including a large thermal storage tank are well worth considering.

As an additional comment, you would also be wise to design your solar energy system in such a way that, if you decide to get along without a large solar storage tank, you can add it later without great cost. Utility bills are going to soar higher and higher. Piper Hydro has a gas-assisted solar heating system, and natural gas as of July 1977 has been relatively cheap. But as fuels become more costly, added solar heat storage capacity becomes more and more economical.

Interestingly, the Piper hydronic-loop system evolved from a patented concept applied first to a design for saving gas in heating apartment buildings. The company's founder built several large apartment complexes, each with more than 100 units. Piper discovered that by using a continuous loop of copper pipe to carry water heated to a controlled temperature of 140°F, using gas boilers at suitable intervals, he could keep gas consumption very low. Space heating was provided by coiling the main copper pipe at various room locations and blowing air over the heated pipe in a fan-coil arrangement. Hot water was obtained simply by dropping off 3/4-inch copper piping to each hot water outlet, taking these feeders from the main 1-1/2-inch copper pipe loop through the building.

This system proved to be so economical of gas that the bills of individual apartment dwellers averaged only $2.50 to $3.00 per month for space heating and domestic hot water. This was in the period 1970-73. Even though these gas bills might be double or more now, you can see how low they were and how efficient the system was.

By 1973 Piper had become interested in adding a solar collector system to his gas-heated hydronic system. This was before the first major peak of the energy crisis. Owners of the apartment houses weren't interested in solar heating systems. They

required a capital investment, and tenants were paying the gas bills. Who wanted to pay for solar energy—when all it would do was save gas?

Since then the situation has changed drastically. One of the largest solar projects in the United States is a 255-unit apartment complex in Ventura, California. The sun provides space heating and hot water for all 255 units by means of energy centers placed along a Piper hydronic loop. Actually there is a series of hydronic loops and energy centers, described in a subsequent paragraph.

It is easier to start by looking at the simplified diagram of a hydronic solar heating system for a single-family home, indicated in Figure 4-6. Feedwater comes in the cold water inlet to the solar panels and is heated by the sun. From the upper header, the heated water goes to a storage tank, and thence, through an aquastat to the gas boiler. This aquastat is a temperature-controlled valve designed to permit various amounts of sun-heated water to flow from the storage tank, depending on the temperature of the water at the outlet, to the hydronic loop and boiler.

The job of the gas boiler is to keep the water in the hydronic loop at 140°F. Solar radiant energy added to the water as it passes through the collector panels is heat energy the boiler does not have to supply.

The Piper solar panel is 8 feet long by 2 feet wide and includes nine 1/2-inch copper tubes mounted in V-shaped aluminum reflectors or concentrators. These copper tubes, painted black, extend the length of the panel and are brazed to 1-1/2-inch copper pipe headers top and bottom. The assembly of pipes, headers, and reflectors is brazed to a galvanized steel absorber plate, and this entire assembly except for reflectors is painted black. It is mounted on a 3-inch pad of insulation covered, as is common practice, with aluminum foil on the upper surface to reflect heat back into the absorber. Glazing is 4 mil Tedlar sheet, and the collector box is made of galvanized steel. This is one of the most efficient solar collector panels, proved by experience in many

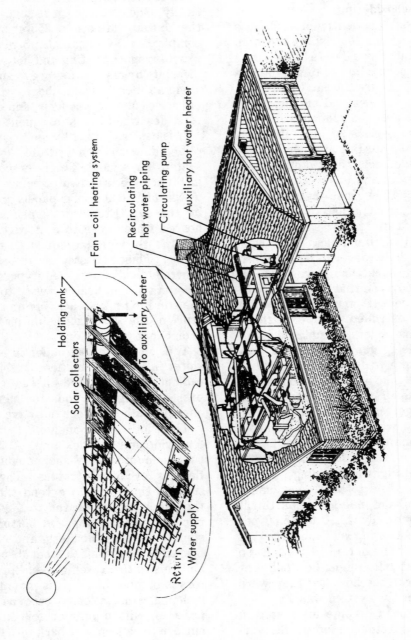

Holding tank

Solar collectors

To auxilliary heater

Return

Water supply

Fan – coil heating system

Recirculating hot water piping

Circulating pump

Auxilliary hot water heater

FIGURE 4-6. Cutaway View of Liquid-type Solar System by Piper Hydro Company

installations and one of the makes approved by ERDA (which has also approved panels made by Reynolds, Solarcoa, and many others).

System Operating Details

In typical operation of this Piper system, the water in the collectors is heated to 140°F within a couple of hours after sunrise, even in cold weather. If no domestic hot tap water is being used—that is, drawn from the main hydronic loop—the solar section thermosiphons. This means that the coolest water in the storage tank returns to the bottom of the solar panels through the line marked "Return" in Figure 4-6.

When water in the storage tank reaches 150°F, the solar pump is actuated by the aquastat in the outlet line from the tank. Water is then drawn up through the line marked "Supplementary" in Figure 4-6 to the bottom of the collector panels. It is again heated by the solar collectors and then returned through the storage tank to the main hydronic loop. In this way the water in the storage tank does not get too hot, and heat is added to the main loop when no hot water is drawn, thus conserving gas.

The same solar pump is actuated by an aquastat at the collector output on cold nights, when the temperature of the water at the outlet of the solar panels drops below 40°F. Then small bursts of hot water are pumped through the collector panels from the main hydronic loop to keep the water in the panels from freezing. This system has worked successfully in homes in such cold locations as Calgary, Alberta; Boise, Idaho, and Spokane, Washington, in the West; Bethesda, Maryland, and other installations in the East. It eliminates the need for a special antifreeze solution in the collector panels, and also for a heat exchanger to heat water in the storage tank.

As indicated in Figure 4-6, space heating is achieved by a small blower moving air through a coil of the main hot water loop, which provides an efficient water-to-air

heat exchanger. This warmed air travels through ducts to any location needing warmth and is delivered to the rooms through conventional registers.

One of the attractive space-saving features of this Piper Hydro system is that there is no requirement for a separate warm air furnace or automatic storage water heater. The space normally occupied by furnace and water heater can be used for storage or living area. This is particularly true when the solar storage tank is placed in an unused space under the roof.

No Large Water Tanks

Another feature of this hydronic solar system is that Jim Piper, unlike most designers of solar heating systems using liquid-type collectors, does not recommend large supplementary water tanks. "With our system," he says, "You don't need a thousand-gallon tank or larger such as some solar homes have installed. It's a matter of economics. Those very large tanks are included to provide carryover of heat for a period of several cloudy days. Experience in our installations in many states, Canada, Mexico and Iran shows that this carryover requirement applies to only a small fraction of a year. In the worst insolation areas, such massive heat storage is useful perhaps 15% of the time. But a large insulated tank and its installation, often in an underground space specially excavated, adds 30% to the initial cost of the solar heating system."

Further details of this hydronic installation in a typical home are shown in Figure 4-7. Note that the heat coils are located in a floor bay or plenum lined with drywall to meet building codes. The fan, controlled by a thermostat, blows air across the heat coil to provide space heating. This variable-speed fan is fused for three amperes and can supply air at rates from 210 to 640 cubic feet per minute. In most houses the only moving parts within the dwelling are fan motor, thermostat, and fan speed control switch. The circulating pump and boiler (heat gen-

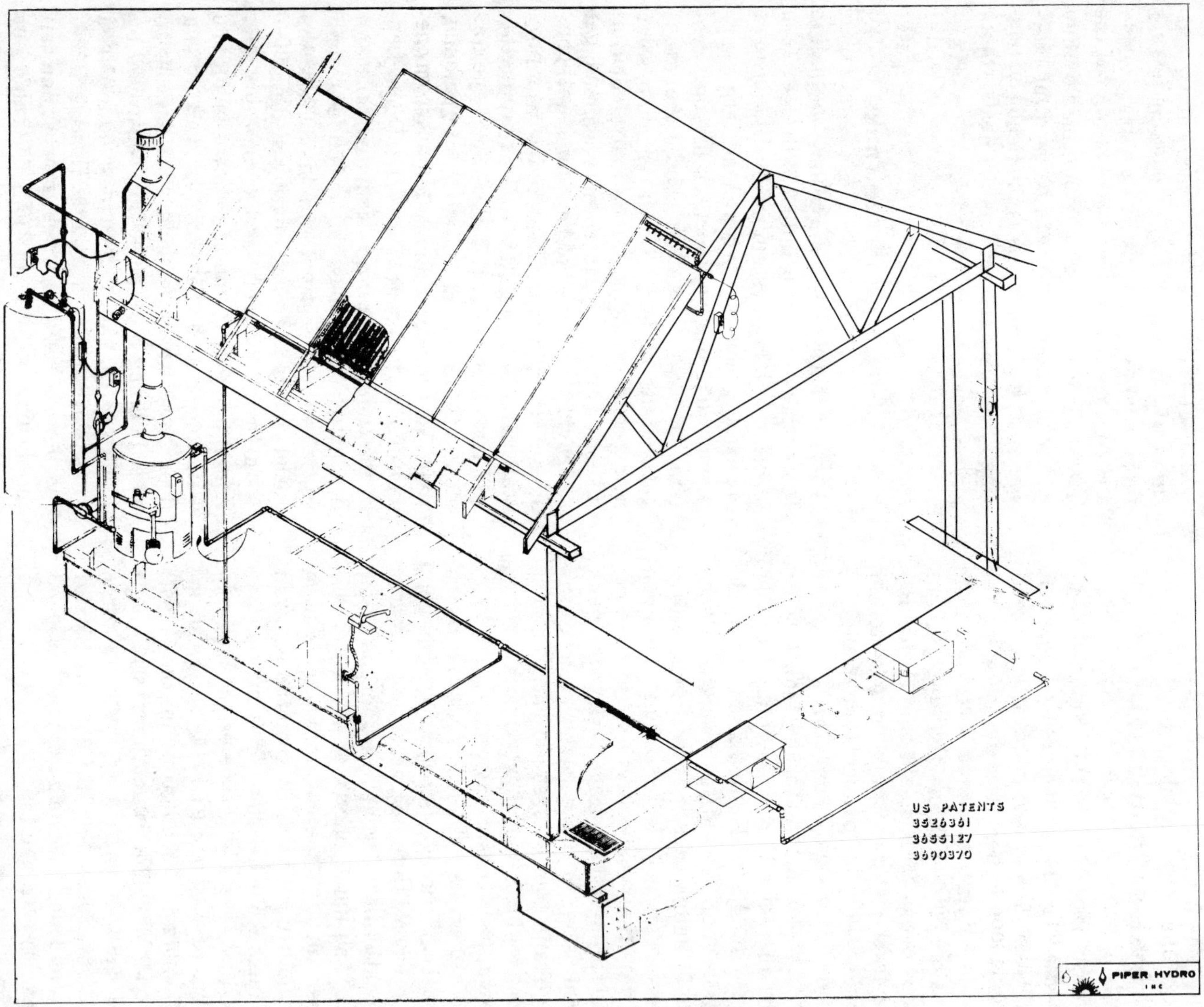

US PATENTS
3526361
3655137
3690370

PIPER HYDRO
INC

FIGURE 4-7.   Details of Piper Hydronic Solar Heating System

98

erator) are usually placed in the garage—or in the case of big apartment complexes or commercial buidlings, in a separate energy center.

The heat generator is an instantaneous copper-tube modulating gas-fired boiler which acts as a supplement to the solar collectors. Piper uses an A. O. Smith Corp. heat generator with a control system that functions with the solar heating controls so that water circulating through the main hydronic loop is maintained at 140°F.

Outlet air temperature is about 110°F so that there is no streaking around outlet grilles. Using the variable speed control and turning the fan to "High" results in warming a cold area in a hurry. Then the control can be turned to a lower speed to match heat gain with heat loss. The thermostat functions in its usual manner to control the cycling of the fan automatically.

With this system heat is available as soon as the switch is turned on since there is no waiting for a plenum to heat. Also, both heat energy and water are saved because there is immediate hot water at any outlet—no wasting of cold water nor waiting for the hot water to reach a remote tap.

The heating coil is sized so that it will fit between ceiling joists or a floor plenum. Approximate outputs of heat from such a fan-coil unit range from 14,500 BTU per hour to 29,500 BTU per hour, with water in the hydronic loop at 140°F.

One additional feature of this system is that it can be installed in many existing buildings so long as the floor is not of slab construction and it's possible to arrange the piping and fan-coil space-heating ductwork as shown in Figure 4-7. In the construction of new homes, the added cost of this Piper Hydro system has amounted to about $3,000 for a residence with 2,000 square feet of living area. Since the fuel savings are between 60% and 70% of the gas bill, the solar system pays for itself in five years or less.

The holding tank for solar-heated water is a glass-lined tank of from 50- to 120-gallon capacity, depending on the size of family and its usage of hot water. Maximum bene-fit can be derived from solar heating by careful spacing of hot water consumption and conservative space heating. In several installations the savings in fuel have amounted to more than 80%.

As with other systems, insulation is very important to conserve heat energy. Note that in Figure 4-7 only a small section of the main hydronic loop is shown with insulation. Actually, every foot of this main copper pipe should be insulated, with the only uninsulated sections at the heat exchangers, where there is a temperature drop of about 1°F with the typical flow of 30 gallons of water per minute at 140°F. Also, the solar water storage tank and the piping bringing heated water to this tank from the collectors, as well as the connecting pipe from the tank to the boiler, and the 3/4-inch hot water feed pipes—all should be insulated to conserve heat.

Energy Centers for Apartment Installations

This hydronic system has been installed, as an efficient combination of solar and gas heating, in a number of apartment complexes of considerable size, including a project with 114 apartments in Farmington, New Mexico. This last is of cluster-type construction with seven to nine units per building, with four types of apartments from one-bedroom efficiencies to two-story, two-bedroom deluxe units. Cost of this New Mexico installation was about $170,000 for both heating and cooling. Thus, the average cost per apartment was approximately $1,500—a figure that compared quite favorably with that for a conventional air conditioning and hot water system. Cooling was accomplished by freon condensing units, using solar- and gas-heated water.

Here is a case where, by careful planning from the start of the project, the apartment house builder has achieved adding a solar heating and cooling and hot water system for essentially the same cost as a conventional air conditioning and hot water installation. There is the enormous advantage that the tenants pay less than 20% of the

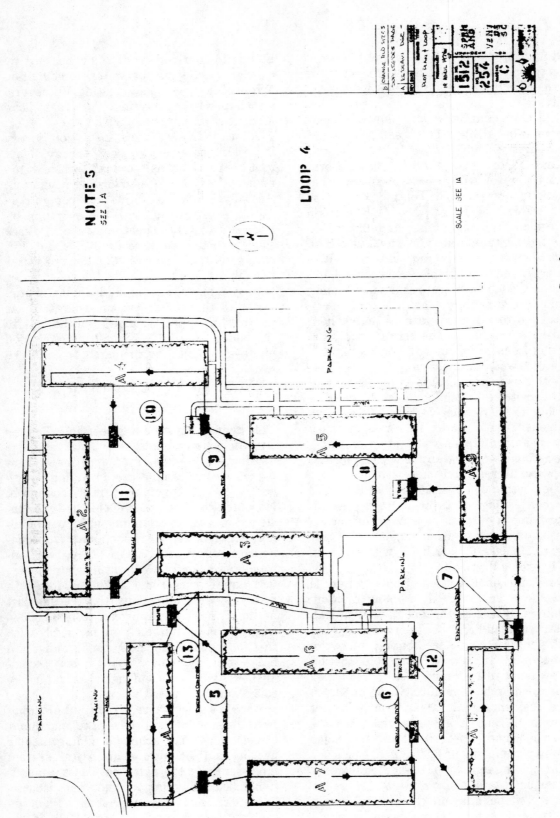

FIGURE 4-8. Diagram of Large Solar-Heated Apartment Complex

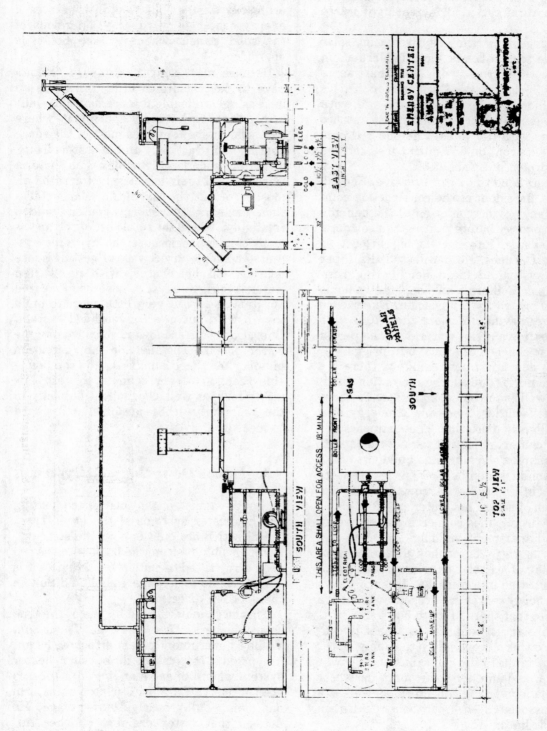

FIGURE 4-9. Plan of Typical Energy Center at Victoria Gardens

ordinary utility bills, and there is a big saving in natural gas, that increasingly scarce fuel.

The largest apartment system using solar hydronic techniques is Victoria Gardens in Ventura, California, with 255 apartments built by Spriggs & Co. Construction. This is a $5-million complex on a 17-acre site, with numerous two-story wood-frame stucco buildings with tile roofs. The one-bedroom apartments contain 684 square feet and the two-bedroom units about 800.

Builders tend to be conservative. But Bill Spriggs, president of the construction company, had convinced himself of the benefits of solar energy before putting the solar hydronic system into such a big project as Victoria Gardens. He had installed a Piper Hydro system in large neighboring residences on a California hillside, his own home and one owned by a physician. Experience in energy savings of more than 70% with solar heating and hot water over the period of a year clinched approval by Spriggs.

In his new apartment complex, there are three laundries and a large recreation building, as well as the 255 apartments. To serve all these facilities, there are 22 energy centers—slightly more than 11 apartments per energy center. A plan of part of this apartment complex showing nine buildings and a corresponding number of energy centers appears in Figure 4-8. Arrows indicate the direction of flow of hot water at 140°F in the main hydronic lines connecting energy centers and apartment buildings.

Each energy center has a slanted roof consisting of six solar panels with the framing illustrated in Figure 4-9. Interior views of the energy center are presented in Figure 4-9. Note that there are two hot water storage tanks and a boiler in each energy center. Also there is one pump to supply water from the tanks to the collector panels' lower headers, and another solar pump for water from the loop to the collectors, as well as a pump associated with the boiler and main hydronic lines.

An innovative design feature places the solar panels directly above the boiler. Spent gases from the boiler contain heat that is ordinarily wasted. This heat is used in each energy center to warm the undersides of the solar panels whenever the boiler is operating.

Because most apartment house tenants have to pay their own utility bills, it's an increasingly valuable feature as utility bills keep rising to have an apartment where free solar energy supplies most of the space heating and practically all hot water. Thus, owners of such large complexes as Victoria Gardens find their vacancy factor to be almost zero. And the cost of the solar installation, including the energy centers, added relatively little to the total cost of the apartment complex. "Because the hydronic system is a simple direct way of getting space heating and hot water, with no wasted water," Spriggs says, "These solar heated apartments cost us very little more to build than if we'd put in a conventional system. Operating costs are lower, since we pay the water bill and the fuel for the recreation building and three laundries. And the favorable reaction of our tenants to very low utility bills, as well as excellent publicity in the community—these are plus factors hard to measure."

Ingenious Do-It-Yourself Systems

Although in most of the solar space heating and hot water systems of the liquid type, the direction of liquid flow in the solar collectors is uphill—from the bottom to the top of an array tilted to match the latitude—it is quite feasible to arrange your liquid flow in the opposite direction.

This has been achieved by one of the true solar pioneers, Dr. Harry E. Thomason. While a government patent attorney, he got his original inspiration for a solar heater system when he was standing in a tobacco shed in North Carolina during a rainstorm one summer day nearly 20 years ago. He noticed that water draining off the "tin" (galvanized steel) roof of the shed was warm.

He put this concept into practice in his first solar house, built in Maryland only 10 miles east-southeast of the center of Washington, D.C. Completed in 1959, this 3-bedroom home and its solar system continue to perform admirably. About 85% of the building is heated by an efficient and inexpensive system.

The design of the Thomason solar heating system, which has now been installed in six homes in Maryland built by the inventor, is covered by several patents. If you want to use this system, you can obtain detailed plans in books available from Edmund Scientific Company, Barrington, New Jersey. For example the sixth house, in Dunkirk, Maryland, is described in Edmund Scientific Book 9487, priced at $24.95.

All six Thomason houses use trickling purified water as the transfer medium for solar heat. His first house has 750 square feet of solar panels on two areas of the roof, both facing south. Slopes of these roof sections are 45° and 60°—resulting in good collector efficiency in the winter because the latitude at this Maryland location is 39° N. Along the ridge of the roof runs 1/2-inch copper pipe with tiny holes, 1/16 inch in diameter and spaced 2-1/2 inches apart. From these holes come trickles of water which flow down the valleys of corrugated aluminum sheet painted black, as shown in Figure 4-10. A sheet of tempered clear white glass is used as the glazing, spaced 3/4 inch above the black absorber panels, to trap solar infrared energy.

Water heated by trickling down the valleys in the aluminum sheets is collected in a gutter and flows to a 1,600-gallon steel storage tank in the basement. Thomason's basement has room enough for a rock storage bin surrounding the tank, which is 17 feet long and 4 feet in diameter. The 50 tons of stones about the size of golf balls are heated by the sun-warmed water. A blower sends air through the bin of warm stones into the ductwork of the house in a conventional forced-air system.

Maintaining a comfortable temperature is accomplished automatically. There are ther-

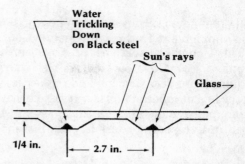

FIGURE 4-10. Cross Section of Solar Panels Designed by Harry E. Thomason

mal sensors to compare the temperature of the roof outlet water from the solar collectors with that of the water in the storage tank. When the outlet water is hotter than the storage water, a pump continues to circulate water from the tank to the pipes, from which water trickles down the collector valleys. When the outlet water is cooler than the storage water, the control system shuts off the pump, and the water from the collectors drains by gravity into the tank. This avoids any problem with the water freezing in Maryland winters.

More recent solar homes built by Thomason Solar Homes, Inc., are larger, but similar in their applications of solar energy for space heating and cooling, as well as domestic hot water. The stone bin surrounding the storage tank is useful in summer as well as winter. In the sixth Thomason solar house, during the summer a small standard room air conditioner, which cost $400, is operated during the coolest part of the night, when it is most efficient, to dry and cool the air in the stone bin. When the house needs cooling during the day, a thermostat turns on the blower so that cool air from the bin is circulated through the rooms.

According to the inventor, the total cost of his sixth house—two stories and a basement, with nine rooms, an indoor solarium, and small indoor swimming pool—was about $65,000 when completed in March 1975. This was the total cost, excluding land. As compared with conventional equipment, the additional cost for a solar system was about $2,000. There is a relatively small (56,000

BTU per hour) oil-fired water heater used as a supplement to the solar installation.

This Thomason solar heating system has supplied from 75% to 85% of the energy required for space heating and domestic hot water in a number of houses. It is a relatively inexpensive installation that has paid for itself in five years or less in each instance.

Economics of Trickle Systems

There is one comment as to this system concerning total area of solar collectors required. As you will readily understand, a trickle system requires a much larger area receiving solar energy than a thermosiphoning system of the various types previously discussed. For example, in his third solar house, Thomason used 900 square feet of collector area to heat 1,500 square feet of house, plus a small indoor pool and game room.

This is because the systems that feed water up through pipes in solar collectors handle a larger volume of water than the amount trickling down the valleys of Thomason's collectors. So if you want to install a trickle system in your home, be prepared to use a considerably greater number of collectors than indicated in the text table on page 00, which is applicable to the more conventional thermosiphoning collectors. If you have sufficient south-facing area on your roof, you should be able to build or buy collectors of the trickle type at somewhat lower cost per square foot than thermosiphoning collectors. Then you should be able to calculate fairly easily which system is most economical for your building.

On pages 29 to 33 of this author's previous book is a description of a solar home built in Snowmass, Colorado, at an altitude of 7,200 feet. The solar system for this house was designed by Zomeworks of Albuquerque, New Mexico, where Steve Baer and his associates have created many ingenious concepts. Several passive systems developed by Zomeworks for using solar energy are described in Chapter 7.

The Snowmass home uses a somewhat different trickle system as well as Skylids, described in detail in our earlier book. R. Shore, the builder and owner of this high-altitude home, gets 100% of his space heating and hot water from the sun. He estimates that his added cost of materials for the solar system was $3,000, with an additional $500 for professional labor beyond that put into the building by Shore and some friends. This solar home is a real achievement in comfortable living plus energy conservation at low cost. It proves that even in a cold climate, a building with 100% of the heating and hot water load furnished by the sun can be designed so effectively that its solar system costs no more than about three years' fuel bills.

Success Stories in New England

Ever since 1939, when Dr. Godfrey L. Cabot made a grant to Massachusetts Institute of Technology to design and build solar houses, there has been keen interest in solar technology—and quite a number of solar buildings constructed—in New England. Development of flat-plate solar collectors owes a great deal to the pioneering work by Dr. H. C. Hottel and B. B. Woertz of M.I.T.

Almost 40 years ago, when M.I.T. Solar House I was completed, there were 400 square feet of collectors on the roof. Each panel consisted of a black copper sheet absorber and black copper tubes under a triple glass glazing. The collector array was installed on a south-facing roof inclined 30°. Sun-heated water filled an underground cylindrical storage tank made of steel and holding 17,400 gallons. Heat was carried to the two rooms of this "house"—actually used as a laboratory—by air, using a water-to-air heat exchanger system. At the end of the first summer of operation, temperature of the water in the huge solar storage tank was 195°F.

Subsequent houses in the M.I.T. series used similar collectors—as you can see, designs in 1977 have changed little since then

—but the inclination of the roofs was greater for more efficient performance in winter. As mentioned previously, the angle of inclination from the horizontal of your collector panels should be your latitude + 15° for best winter performance when you need solar energy at maximum efficiency for space heating.

One feature of M.I.T. Solar House II completed in 1947 was experimental work with storing solar energy using eutectic salts as well as in water storage tanks. This work was done under the direction of Dr. Maria Telkes, a noted physicist and solar pioneer, and several associates.

Eutectic materials have the valuable property of remaining at a constant temperature while absorbing heat energy by going from solid to liquid, or while releasing heat energy when returning from liquid to solid. There are a number of inexpensive chemicals, including Glauber's salt, which are useful in solar thermal storage. The salt is contained in plastic tubes or enclosed trays and many of these units are stored in a bin. Eutectic transformation of the chemical occurs at a temperature easily reached by either liquid or air from solar collector panels. Considerable research on eutectic materials for storing solar energy is being done because a bin of these chemicals occupies a small fraction of the space required by a water tank or a rock bin.

One of the notable success stories in the development of practical solar energy systems in New England is that of Sunworks and Everett M. Barber, a professor at Yale University. The 3-bedroom beachfront solar home in Connecticut occupied by the Barber family for more than two years is shown in Figure 4-11. Designed by Donald Watson, AIA, with solar engineering and collector panels furnished by Sunworks, this modern house has won several awards as a model of energy conservation, with about 70% of its space heating and hot water achieved by its solar system.

Sunworks, founded by Barber, is now a division of Enthone, Inc., of New Haven, Connecticut, a maker of chemicals for the

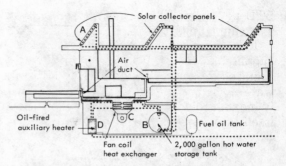

FIGURE 4-11. Cross Section of Prize-Winning House Using a Liquid Heat Transfer System

plating and metal finishing industry. Enthone in turn is a subsidiary of Asarco, Inc., a large smelter and refiner of nonferrous metals. This is merely one example of the keen interest of big business in the growth of solar energy.

Originally Barber and his associates at Sunworks developed good solar collector designs of both liquid and air types. The absorbers and piping were painted with a selective black paint developed by Enthone.

Now Sunworks collectors are manufactured in modern plants in New Jersey as well as Connecticut, with local representatives in many areas. According to Floyd C. Perry, Jr., product manager of Sunworks, "We currently have more business for the first quarter of 1977 than all of 1976 and look forward to a 400 percent increase this year (1977)." Typical installations include a large commercial office building in Stamford, Connecticut, where the performance of liquid collectors is enhanced by reflecting mirrors; a large condominium complex at Grassy Brook Village, Vermont; numerous homes in New England and New York; and the 30,000-square-foot Sunworks manufacturing plant in Somerville, New Jersey.

A cross section of the Sunworks liquid-type collector, now identified by the trade name Solector, appears in Figure 4-12, along with flashing details for roof installation. The surface-mounted panel has an area of 3 feet x 7 feet with an effective absorber area of 18.68 square feet. The absorber consists of copper sheet with six 1/4-inch ID

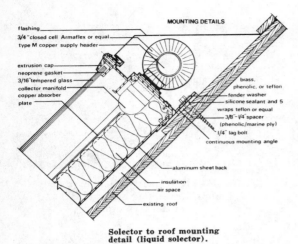

MOUNTING DETAILS

flashing
3/4 "closed cell Armaflex or equal
type M copper supply header

extrusion cap
neoprene gasket
3/16 "tempered glass
collector manifold
copper absorber
plate

brass,
phenolic, or teflon
fender washer
silicone sealant and 5
wraps teflon or equal
3/8 "- 1/4 "spacer
(phenolic/marine ply)
1/4 " lag bolt
continuous mounting angle

aluminum sheet back
insulation
air space
existing roof

Solector to roof mounting
detail (liquid solector).

**FIGURE 4-12. Solector to Roof
Mounting Detail**

(internal diameter) copper tubes solder-bonded to the sheet, and 1-inch ID copper manifolds (1-1/8-inch OD) top- and bottom-brazed to the tubes. Insulation is 2-1/2-inch thick fiberglass (R10), and collectors are available with either single or double glazing of glass.

Enthone has developed a proprietary black selective coating for the copper absorber surfaces, a nonelectrolytic process producing a thin oxide film with solar absorptivity from 87% to 92% and very low thermal emission. There are useful mechanical features in the Solector panels. The liquid unit has a continuous mounting flange integral with the aluminum frame across the top and bottom of the collector to simplify installation. On the air design, preformed U-clips join the keyways of adjoining panels and they also provide tie-down points for mounting.

Typical of most good solar manufacturers, Sunworks guarantees its solar collectors for five years with the exception of cover glass breakage. Actually, as the manufacturer states, panels like this should last "well over 25 years." Dry panels are good for at least 400°F temperatures, and the liquid Solector tubing in assembled collectors is pressure tested up to 250 psi (pounds per square inch). Recommended flow rate of liquid

through each collector is 0.55 gpm (gallons per minute) with negligible flow resistance at this rate.

Because most Sunworks installations are in the Northeast, the fluid recommended for use in Solectors is an antifreeze mixture designated as Sunsol 60. However, water can be used if the pH is controlled within the range of 6.5 to 8 and if the collectors are drained during freezing weather.

Another New England manufacturer of liquid-type solar collector panels with numerous successful installations is Sol-R-Tech, Inc., of Hartford, Vermont. John DeVries, vice president of this company, is responsible for designing collectors as well as solar space heating and hot water systems that use heat pumps efficiently. A typical Sol-R-Tech collector includes an Olin Brass Roll-Bond copper absorber plate with integral expanded channels coated with flat black (nonselective) paint. There is double glazing, with an outer sheet of Alsunite fiberglass-reinforced polyester and an inner sheet of Tedlar. Insulation backing is solid fiberglass board 1 inch thick. The entire assembly, about 3 feet x 8 feet (not counting manifolds) and 3-5/8 inches thick, is sealed in an aluminum frame. A useful feature is the desiccant in the air space between the solid outer plastic sheet 0.040 inch thick and the thinner (4 mil) Tedlar inner glazing as shown in Figure 4-13.

Installations of Sol-R-Tech systems in various parts of northern New England include both residential and commercial buildings. An example of the latter is the Custom Leather Boutique in White River Junction, Vermont, with 1-1/2 stories and 2,100 square feet heated by 910 square feet of solar collectors mounted on a 45° roof. There is a 3,200-gallon concrete tank under a concrete slab near the center of the building, shown in Figure 4-14. This tank is waterproofed on the interior with epoxy and insulated on the top with 3 inches of styrofoam.

In this building three York Triton DW-30H water-to-air heat pumps are used for winter heating and summer cooling. When

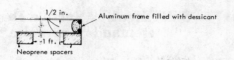

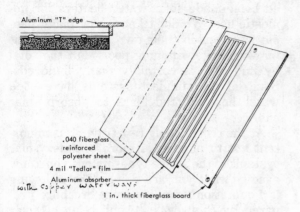

FIGURE 4-13.   Construction of Sol-R-Tech
Solar Collector

FIGURE 4-14.   Even in Winter, Array
of Sol-R-Tech Panels Supplies Vermont
Store with over 90% of Room Heating
and Hot Water

the water in the large storage tank is warmer than 45°F, the heat pumps derive energy from it efficiently and deliver 120°F water in a fan-coil system, as described previously; blowers in conventional ductwork blow air over the coils containing hot water to heat the building. When the thermal storage tank's water temperature rises above 90°F, the heat pumps are turned off and solar-heated water is ciculated directly to coils in the ducts. On the rare occasions when the tank temperature goes below 45°F, electric heaters in the ducts supply backup warming of the air. Solar energy provides about 60% of the space heating requirements with another 20° supplied by energy from the heat pumps, which have a COP (coefficient of performance) averaging 3.

In the summer, cooling of the building is furnished by the same heat pumps operated in a reverse manner. They deliver cold water to the coils in the ducts and dissipate heat from the building by means of a conventional outdoor cooling tower. Meanwhile, in the summer, the solar collectors continue to deliver energy to the big storage tank, from which all domestic hot water for the building is drawn.

Federal Building Tests
4 Different Solar Collectors

An interesting solar installation is the Norris Cotton Federal Building in Manchester, New Hampshire, where ERDA financed the solar heating and cooling system. This is a 7-story building with two levels of underground parking. Energy-saving features in the design of this structure, completed in January 1977, include fixed shading of relatively small windows on three sides with no windows on the north side, and good insulation throughout. Shading is designed to admit winter sunlight and keep out the sun's heat during the summer: effectiveness is estimated by Dr. Shurcliff, Harvard physicist, at 85%.

An unusual aspect of this solar installation is that there are four special racks, at progressively increased heights above the flat roof, to avoid shading of the four different types of solar collector panels mounted on these racks. All collectors use a 50-50 mixture of water and ethylene glycol as the heat transfer medium. Going from south to north atop the building are Sunsav panels with Olin Roll-Bond absorbers on the first rack; Sunworks collectors with copper absorbers and tubing on the second rack;

Ametek panels with copper absorbers on the third stand; and Solargenics collectors with absorbers of aluminum sheet and copper tubes on the fourth (north) stand at the highest level.

Glass is the glazing material used on all four manufacturers' collectors; all are double-glazed except the Sunsav units. In this large installation, with a total of about 4,700 square feet of collector area, it takes a 10-HP centrifugal pump to maintain the average flow rate of 210 gpm of antifreeze mixture through the solar collectors and a 900,000 BTU (9 therms) per hour shell-and-tube heat exchanger.

Solar heat is stored in three 10,000-gallon insulated cylindrical steel tanks in the basement. For space heating of the first three stories, both water-to-air and air-to-air heat pumps are used in conjunction with the solar heating system. The water-to-air heat pumps take heat from the sun-heated water tanks; the other pumps draw heat from room air in any rooms that become too hot. On the fourth story, hot water from the basement tanks is circulated through baseboard radiators. On the top three stories, a fan-coil system is used with solar heated water pumped through the coils. Auxiliary heating, when required, is supplied by a gas-fired boiler, which also drives an electric generator supplying power for a 65-ton electrically operated Trane chiller furnishing part of the extensive cooling needed in this building during the summer. There is also a 25-ton Arkla absorption cooler powered by heat from solar hot water storage. All hot water for this large building comes from solar storage.

Thus, the Manchester federal office building is what engineers call a "test bed" for evaluating the performance of four different makes of liquid solar collectors; scrutinizing techniques for solar space heating, including some with heat pump assistance; and making a comparison of solar cooling with conventional air conditioning equipment.

Solar Heating System Design Demands Expertise

Thousands of do-it-yourselfers have installed home-made solar water heaters for domestic use. We don't know how many people have put in their own solar equipment for warming swimming pools, but the total by mid-1977 is certainly many hundreds. Some of the simplest systems have used water hose painted black to absorb solar energy.

At the risk of being repetitive, it is important *not* to undertake more complex solar systems of the active types unless you know exactly what you are doing. The following is a quotation from a current brochure prepared by Sunworks: "Application of solar energy to space heating or air conditioning in buildings normally requires a system designed by a qualified mechanical engineer who is licensed to practice in the locality of the building. Sunworks architectural and engineering staff, through the local Sunworks representative, is available to provide consulting services to qualified architects, engineers, and contractors involved in solar system design."

Most other manufacturers of solar heating/cooling equipment are following similar procedures. Piper Hydro, on the other side of the continent from Sunworks, has established a dealer system in which each installing dealer must have at least one licensed mechanical engineer in the organization.

In the early days of solar installations, many mistakes were made by nonprofessionals. Examples are building liquid solar collector panels that leak for one reason or another—perhaps because of not allowing for thermal expansion and contraction, as mentioned previously; failure to provide adequate insulation or seals for piping (liquid systems) or air ducts; poor choice of materials.

If you decide to attempt a more ambitious solar system than a hot water heater or a swimming pool installation, the following suggestions will be useful:

- Find out what the building codes are in your area.

- Visit solar installations whose owners are well satisfied with the performance of their systems.

- Consider enrolling in one of the many university and college courses being offered in the design and installation of solar systems for space heating and cooling.

- Many manufacturers will be glad to provide technical assistance, as well as equipment, at reasonable cost. Most companies have descriptive brochures which you can get from a local dealer or by writing to the firm and enclosing a self-addressed stamped envelope. The lists of manufacturers in Appendix 1 at the back of this book are by no means complete, but more information may be obtained from:

Solar Energy Industries Association, 1001 Connecticut NW, Suite 632, Washington, D.C. 20036. Phone: (202) 293-1000.

Offices of the United States Energy Research and Development Administration and the U.S. Housing and Urban Development Department, either in Washington, D.C., or in many principal cities.

- Unless you have considerable expertise in plumbing (for a liquid system), heating and air conditioning, as well as residential and commercial electrical wiring, get the paid help of professionals in installing your solar heating system. In most urban and suburban areas, local ordinances require that you use licensed professionals for this kind of work.

- Since the chances are that you will need professional help in your solar installation, select equipment which will require minimum labor for assembly at your site. Be sure all your materials are on hand before you start paying a contractor $25 to $30 an hour or more for installing your solar equipment.

Other Good Solar Heating Installations

In the following pages are some additional examples of solar space heating and hot water installations which have been carefully designed by licensed engineers and installed by professionals. The final example is a group of 16 houses built in Hemet, California, and sold in late 1976 in the price range from $37,500 to $47,500. You should not have to pay more than 10% (or less) as a premium for a solar home. President Carter's announced goal of 2.5 million solar homes may well be achieved before the target date of 1985.

A trade association long active in developing solar installations is the Copper Development Association, Inc., (CDA) New York City. More than 40 solar collector manufacturers are producing units with absorber plates and waterways of copper, while even greater numbers use copper pipes attached usually to aluminum fins. A showplace built by CDA is a solar house in Tucson, Arizona. This 3,400-square-foot home, shown in Figure 4-15, receives up to 97% of its heating, all its domestic hot water and pool heating, and most of its summer cooling from solar energy.

A plan of this innovative house appears in Figure 4-16, a cutaway view of its solar energy system in Figure 4-17, and a diagram of its solar energy equipment for heating and cooling in Figure 4-18. Practically everything in the house can be run on stored solar energy, from the climate control system to the security system, stereo, clocks, and even the kitchen television set. There is a CDA electric vehicle in the garage, complete with battery charger.

In addition to copper solar collector panels made by Revere Copper and Brass Inc., of Rome, N.Y., there are panels of silicon solar cells on the roof. These solar cells provide power for most of the electric appliances in the house, and are furnished by Solar Power Corporation of Braintree, Massachusetts. A detailed description of how solar cells are made and operate, as

109

FIGURE 4-15. "Decade 80 Solar House" Conceived and Built by the Copper Development Association

well as applications information, is provided in Chapter 11.

Design of the solar collector panels made by Revere is such that they are used as roofing, as shown in Figure 4-19. The absorber plate is a 2-foot by 8-foot copper sheet, 0.016 inch thick, on which are mounted 5 rectangular copper tubes to carry the water. These rectangular tubes are attached to top and bottom headers of 3/4-inch copper pipe with the entire assembly and absorber plate painted black. The lower side of the copper sheet is bonded to 3/8-inch plywood and below this are 3-1/2 inches of fiberglass insulation with alumi-

num foil on its upper surface. Glazing is PPG glass, two panels of clear tempered glass, separated by an insulating air space, which trap the infrared radiation absorbed by the copper.

Windows on the pool side of the house are glazed with special solar bronze-tinted double-glass insulation units that reduce heat gain from sunshine in this desert home by 40%. This cuts the air conditioning load in summer while improving indoor visual comfort. In Michigan, Minnesota, or Maine, you would design your home to bring in as much solar heat as possible through south-facing windows during the winter, covering

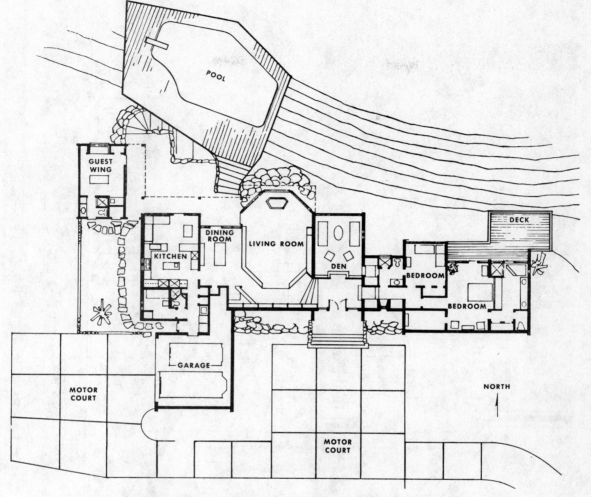

FIGURE 4-16.   Floor Plan of "Decade 80 Solar House"

these windows with drapes or insulation on cold nights; and use overhanging eaves to keep out the summer sunlight.

Other examples of copper absorbers and pipes used in solar systems include:

A handsome modern home in Fort Wayne, Indiana, built by Dave Myers, head of a plumbing and heating distributor firm, includes solar space heating and hot water.

There are 19 collectors mounted on the roof of the Hospitality Inn, located in Temple, Texas, shown in Figure 4-20. This first solar phase provides heating for the motel's domestic water and swimming pool. Next step is to install additional solar collectors

for retrofitting the inn's space heating and cooling system and so cut utility costs substantially.

Also in Texas is the new 50,000-square-foot office building in Houston, shown in Figure 4-21, with a solar system designed by McDermott Hudson Engineering, the firm occupying this modern structure. Solar energy provides 100% of the space heating —with no backup system. And hot water from the collectors is also used to cool corridors and a converted exterior walkway.

One of numerous bank buildings now using solar energy is the Concord National Bank branch in Concord, New Hampshire,

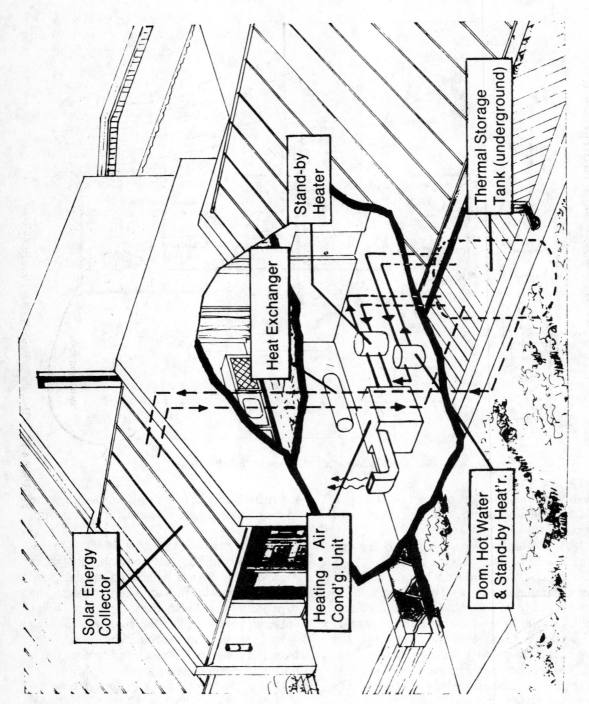

Solar Energy Collector

Heat Exchanger

Stand-by Heater

Thermal Storage Tank (underground)

Heating · Air Cond'g. Unit

Dom. Hot Water & Stand-by Heat'r.

FIGURE 4-17. Cutaway View of Solar Energy System of "Decade 80 Solar House

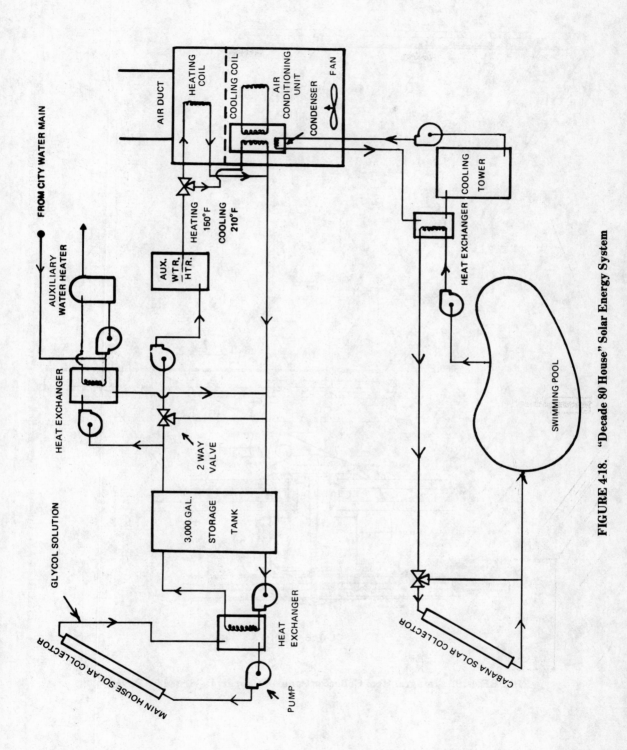

FIGURE 4-18. "Decade 80 House" Solar Energy System

113

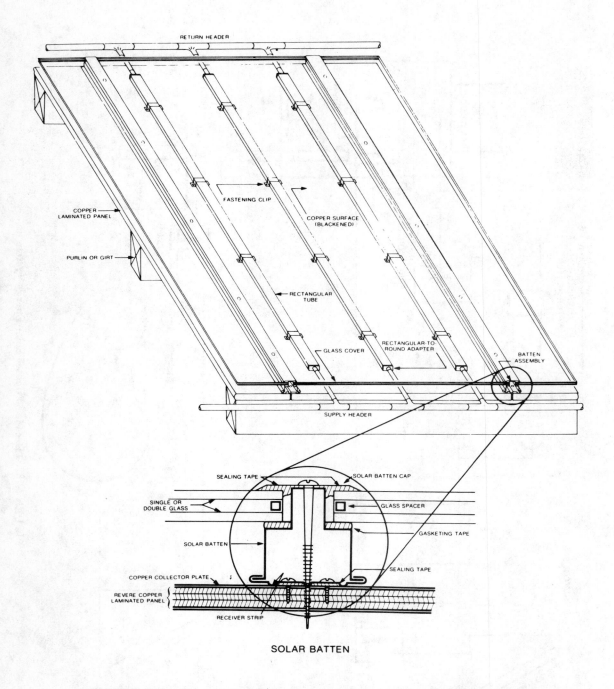

RETURN HEADER

COPPER LAMINATED PANEL

PURLIN OR GIRT

FASTENING CLIP

COPPER SURFACE (BLACKENED)

RECTANGULAR TUBE

GLASS COVER

RECTANGULAR-TO-ROUND ADAPTER

BATTEN ASSEMBLY

SUPPLY HEADER

SEALING TAPE

SOLAR BATTEN CAP

SINGLE OR DOUBLE GLASS

GLASS SPACER

GASKETING TAPE

SOLAR BATTEN

SEALING TAPE

COPPER COLLECTOR PLATE

REVERE COPPER LAMINATED PANEL

RECEIVER STRIP

SOLAR BATTEN

FIGURE 4-19.   Integral Roof Collector Panel of Copper, Designed by Revere

114

FIGURE 4-20.   Nation's First "Solar Motel," in Waco, Texas

**FIGURE 4-21.   McDermott Hudson Office Building in Houston, Texas, Is 100%
Solar Heated, with No Backup System**

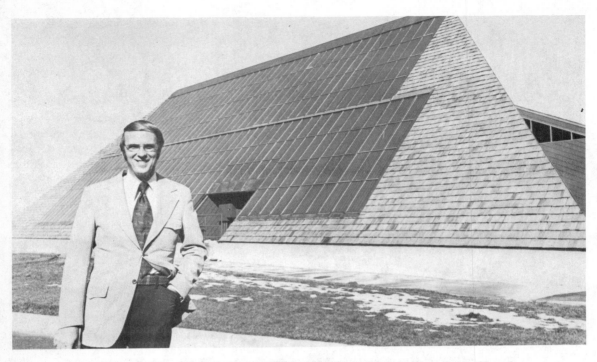

FIGURE 4-22.   Pastor Al Haan Stands in Front of Nation's First Solar Church, Center of Hope Church, in Denver, Colorado

FIGURE 4-23.   Attractive Solar Homes in Hemet, California, Provide both Solar Space Heating and Domestic Hot Water

which gets up to 65% of its cooling and 50% of its space heating from the sun.

The nation's first solar church is the 16,000-square foot structure shown in Figure 4-22. This Center of Hope Church in Denver is equipped with solar collectors from R. M. Products for both space heating and domestic hot water for facilities that include a sizable day care center with classrooms and cafeteria, as well as the church and Sunday school.

Energy Conservation in Reasonably Priced Homes

In Hemet, California, a former wholesale jeweler has built 17 solar homes with many energy-saving features at a price that competes favorably with conventional homes in the area.

"During the few months we showed homes, about 8,000 people came through," says Warren D. Buckmaster, president of Blue Skies Radiant Homes. "Obviously some were just curious to see the Solar Homes but more importantly many indicated concern over the rising cost of utilities. The first group of 17 homes was sold within two weeks of completion and we have reservations on all the 16 new homes we are about to start."

With the help of William McDonald, a solar mechanical engineer formerly in the aerospace business, Buckmaster and his associates in Lauren Construction Company developed attractive designs for single-story houses with 2, 3, and 4 bedrooms. All are priced under $50,000 and provide both solar space heating and domestic hot water.

As indicated in the aerial view, Figure 4-23, the solar collector panels are placed on racks in a recessed area over each attached garage. There is a masonry parapet around the array of solar panels so that when you look at the homes from ground level you can't see the collectors.

Liquid collector panels in a hydronic system deliver sun-heated water to a 1,000-gallon underground storage tank below each home. The differential thermostat and automatic controls are placed in a covered area of a wall in the utility room. Solar energy provides almost all the space heating with a fan-coil system and insulated forced-air ducting; the only supplement is a wood-burning fireplace with gas log lighter in each living room. All hot water requirements for two bathrooms, kitchen (including dishwasher), and clothes washer are met by solar energy.

One reason why these attractive tile-roofed houses are essentially 100% solar for heating and hot water is their excellent insulation. Outside walls have R-21 insulation with a vapor barrier, ceilings have R-25 insulation, windows and double doors are double glazed. "These homes are so well insulated, they are built like a refrigerator," Buckmaster says. For summer cooling a conventional Fedders air conditioner and attic exhaust fan are provided.

Other energy-saving features include indirect fluorescent lighting and electronic ignition (no pilot flames) to save gas in the kitchen range and oven. Even the dishwasher has an energy saving cycle to conserve electricity.

Blue Skies Radiant Homes, designed by the builder and solar engineer for energy conservation, emphasize the fact that solar energy is available to save money for the average American. We see several points worth noting:

- These homes—the first 17 constructed —were built entirely with private capital. No federal subsidy was provided. In the 16 homes of the second development, a relatively small ERDA grant was given to include additional instrumentation and recording equipment so that performance of the solar heating can be monitored. Hemet is at an altitude where occasional winter nights drop below freezing.

117

- Prices of the solar homes are comparable with those of conventional new single-family houses in the area.
- The combination of solar energy and excellent insulation will continue to save the owners of Blue Skies homes as much as $50 a month on each individual's utility bills—more in future years.

Blue Skies Solar Home in Hemet, California, With Collectors Visible During Construction

Solar Collectors are Hidden Behind This Parapet over the Garage of Solar Home in Hemet

**Solar Collectors developed by Honeywell and Made by Lennox Industries
Provide 50% of Space Heating and 67% of Water Heat of Bloomington,
Minnesota, House**

**PPG Industries Solar Collectors Provide Space Heating and Hot Water for
Large Modern Home**

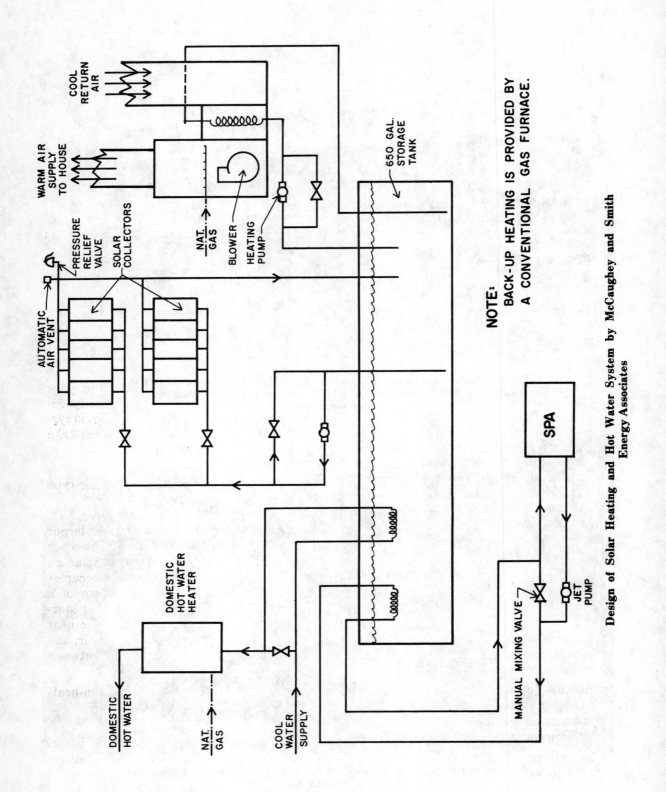

COOL RETURN AIR

WARM AIR SUPPLY TO HOUSE

PRESSURE RELIEF VALVE

SOLAR COLLECTORS

AUTOMATIC AIR VENT

NAT. GAS

BLOWER

HEATING PUMP

650 GAL. STORAGE TANK

DOMESTIC HOT WATER HEATER

DOMESTIC HOT WATER

NAT. GAS

COOL WATER SUPPLY

MANUAL MIXING VALVE

JET PUMP

SPA

NOTE:
BACK-UP HEATING IS PROVIDED BY A CONVENTIONAL GAS FURNACE.

Design of Solar Heating and Hot Water System by McCaughey and Smith Energy Associates

120

5

The Advantages of Air-Type
Solar Collector Systems

While most of the major and minor manufacturers of solar heating systems—and a majority of the early installations—have used water or an antifreeze mixture as the heat transfer medium, there are some real advantages to air systems. This is particularly true in cold areas. That's why you will find an increasing number of air-type solar collectors and associated hardware in solar homes from New England to Colorado.

There are some benefits from using the sun's energy to heat air, which is then circulated through your home.

- You don't have to worry about freezing weather.

- Minor leaks don't cause problems. (Of course, your liquid system should be completely watertight.)

- Because sun-heated air is used directly to heat your house, the total cost of the installation may be lower if your home already contains a forced-air system.

- In extremely hot weather, you don't have to worry about boiling of your so-

lar fluid or pressure buildup in your pipes. (However, with a correctly designed and properly installed liquid system, air vents and relief valves take care of this problem.)

The major disadvantages of an air-type solar heating system are:

- Thermal storage occupies a much larger space. Rock bins are usually used for storing the heat energy from solar air collectors. A bin full of pebbles occupies at least three times the volume of a water tank with equivalent heat storage capacity because the specific heat of water is greater than that of air, and of course there are air spaces between the stones.

- Heat exchangers permitting sun-heated air to provide you with domestic hot water are required.

- Air systems are not economically useful with most conventional solar coolers, particularly the absorption type.

Simple Design of Solar Air Collectors

As many do-it-yourselfers have learned, it is not difficult to build a liquid solar collector. Some designs have been described in earlier chapters of this book, the author's previous book, and many handbooks available from both private and government sources.

It is even easier to make an air collector. A typical design is shown in Figure 5-1. This was developed by the Maine Audubon Society for its headquarters building at Gilsland Farm on the north bank of a river six miles north of Portland.

The whole objective of this project, for which R. C. Hill was the solar consulting engineer, was to design inexpensive but durable solar collectors which could be built by the average home owner. The Society wanted a collector suitable for assembly at the building site by a local building contractor or a do-it-yourself home owner.

As shown in Figure 5-1, this air collector uses both materials and assembly techniques that anyone familiar with ordinary hand tools can readily handle. The top glazing layer of the collector sandwich is a sheet of Kalwall fiberglass-reinforced clear plastic, which has excellent transmission properties (nearly as good as iron-free tempered glass). This solid plastic sheet, called "Sunlite Premium," is easier to work with and cheaper than glass in most areas, and minimizes breakage problems. When you need to fasten the glazing sheet to the collector, you merely drill through it and screw down this cover.

The next items in the Maine Audubon design, created under the direction of W. J. Ginn of the Society, show true Yankee ingenuity. Instead of using a black-painted copper or aluminum or steel sheet as the absorber, this air collector is designed with a sinusoidal structure of ordinary screen window insect mesh painted black and stapled to black-painted plywood. There are nine loops of insect screen per foot on ply-

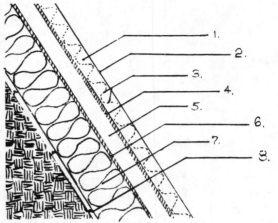

1. Air Intake
2. Kalwall "Sunlite Premium" Collector Glazing
3. Insect Screen At 9 Loops Per 1' - 0"
4. 1/2" CDX Plywood, Painted Black
5. Air Return To Storage
6. 1/2" CDX Plywood
7. 9" Foil-Backed Roll Insulation
8. Roof

FIGURE 5-1. Air Solar Collector Developed by Maine Audubon Society for On-Site Assembly

wood, and 3 feet of ordinary aluminum screen are needed for each lineal foot of the plywood base. The screen, arranged in this wavy pattern in the 3-inch high intake area between the plastic glazing and the plywood, increases the area of absorption of solar radiation and of heat transfer from the absorber to the air passing through. Such a wavy screen also increases air turbulence, an additional factor in making heat collection more efficient.

Under the black-painted plywood absorber is another 3-inch airspace for the return air duct, and then a second sheet of 1/2-inch CDX plywood above a 9-inch thick pad of foil-faced fiberglass batting with the aluminum foil on the underside, next to the roof.

There are 35 of these solar air collectors, each 2 feet x 30 feet, built on the site and covering the south-facing roof. Total net collector area is 2,100 square feet. The roof slopes 50° from horizontal at a site where the latitude is about 44° N, so you can see

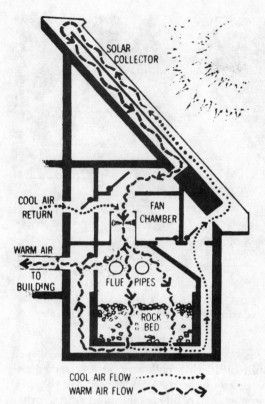

SOLAR COLLECTOR

COOL AIR RETURN

WARM AIR

FAN CHAMBER

TO BUILDING

FLUE PIPES

ROCK BED

COOL AIR FLOW ·······→
WARM AIR FLOW ∼∼∼∼→

HEAT STORAGE AND SUPPLY BY
SOLAR COLLECTOR PANELS

**FIGURE 5-2. Installation of Solar Air
Collectors at Maine Audubon Society
Headquarters**

that the architect, G. B. Terrien, came close
to the most desirable winter inclination for
maximum insolation on the collectors, as indicated in Figure 5-2.

The 2-story wood frame building on
poured concrete slab has an area of 5,500
square feet. The structure is very well insulated, with 5-1/2 inches of fiberglass insulation in the walls, 6 to 9 inches of fiberglass
on the roof, and 2 inches of polyurethane
foam around the perimeter of the floor slab.
Windows are triple-glazed.

Three 1 HP blowers mounted above the
rock storage bin, containing 100 tons of
crushed rock, maintain an airflow of about
11,000 cubic feet per minute (cfm). When
the sun is shining, these blowers force cool

air up through the inlet areas—containing
loops of insect screen. The sun-warmed air
then flows back down the back of the plywood absorbers, through the large rectangular bin full of washed stones (about 1 inch
in diameter on the average). The bin—78
feet long, 9 feet wide, and 3 feet high—is
in a recessed portion of the south floor slab
and foundations. Around this concrete bin is
a layer of 3-inch thick polyurethane foam
insulation.

Solar heat from the rock storage is circulated through the rooms of this Maine Audubon building as required. Domestic hot
water is preheated by the solar system by
means of an air-to-water heat exchanger
and preheat tank. Solar heat is so successful
in this well-designed and well-insulated
building that the sun supplies about 70% of
the energy required for space heating and
hot water even in Down East winters.

Cost of the solar energy system for this
large building was about $11,200. As might
be expected in a timber-rich area like Maine,
supplementary heating was designed with a
wood-burning furnace and a duct system
that supplies standby heat to the rock storage bin or directly to the rooms during a
prolonged period of bad weather.

New Low Cost Air Collector

A new design that's easily built by any do-it-
yourselfer handy with ordinary tools is
shown in Figure 5-3 in cross section. It is
the creation of Keith Poor, owner-partner
with Bob Marks in the American Building
Center, in Los Alamitos, California, and is
illustrated in the foreground of Figure 5-4
with Keith standing beside it.

Construction is very simple. The dimensions are 2 feet wide by 8 feet long and 6
inches thick. Sides and ends are made of 1
inch x 6 inch boards. The bottom of the box
is made of a 2 foot x 8 foot sheet of polyurethane foam insulation with aluminum foil
facing on the upper side. Directly above this
insulation layer is a 2 foot x 8 foot sheet of

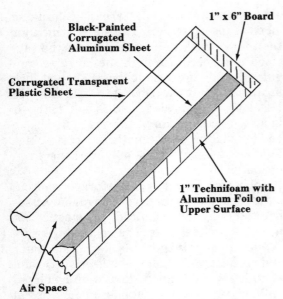

FIGURE 5-3. Cross Section of New Low-Cost Air Solar Collector

FIGURE 5-4. Corrugated Plastic Glazing Over New, Economical Air Solar Collector (Right) Displayed by Keith Poor

corrugated aluminum spray-painted with PPG flat black paint. Then there is an air space of about 3-1/2 inches, and the glazing is a sheet of corrugated translucent fiberglass—the same material you would use to roof a patio.

In fact, Keith Poor suggests that one suitable location for a solar space heater might be doubling as a roof for a south-facing patio area. Rafters or joists of a patio roof—or conventional roofs, for that matter—are 4 feet apart. By placing two of these new solar air collectors side by side, you have a 4-foot width that's just right for mounting on joists.

Poor made a hole about 4 inches in diameter at the bottom of the air collector as an air inlet, and a similar hole at the top as an outlet for the sun-heated air. On a July day, outlet air temperature was 160°F. Fastening several collectors together, side-by-side on a roof, you could use a single input duct at one end and an output duct at the other.

Cost of the materials for this new air collector amounted to about $22.00 at retail, including 6% California sales tax. Thus, you could build this collector at the extremely low price of about $1.25 per square foot. Or, if you want to buy assembled units, get in touch with American Building Center (address in Appendix I at the end of this book).

Air Heating Systems by Solaron

Best-known, oldest, and most experienced manufacturer of solar air heating systems is Solaron Corporation of Commerce City, Colorado, which has provided equipment for a sizable number of residential, commercial, and industrial installations.

Executives of Solaron include John C. Bayless, president and a former aerospace program manager for Ball Bros. Research Corporation; and Dr. George Löf, vice president of Solaron and one of the world's foremost solar pioneers, who is also director of research for Solar Energy Applications Laboratory, Colorado State University.

Löf designed a solar air heating system and installed it in his Denver home in 1944 to supplement a conventional gas furnace used with a forced-air system. This house is

124

considered to be the oldest solar home in the United States continuously occupied and using air collectors successfully for much of the space heating load.

Operation of a Solaron air system is shown in Figure 5-5. Air is drawn through the collector array (1) and heated to temperatures averaging between 120°F and 150°F, depending upon latitude, ambient air, season, and wind conditions. This, of course, takes place during daylight hours when the sun is shining.

The sun-heated air passes through a conventional duct containing an air-to-water heat exchanger (5), which warms the water in a domestic preheater tank. This is the part of the Solaron system described previously in Chapter 3. Water from the preheater tank flows into a conventional domestic hot water heater, which adds energy (gas, oil, coal, or electric) when required.

Most of the solar hot air is pumped through a Solaron air-handling unit (3) and then through a conventionally fueled auxiliary heater via ductwork and appropriate registers to the rooms to be heated. Then return air goes to the solar collectors, which are usually mounted on the roof.

Rock Bin for Heat Storage

There is a large bin full of carefully washed stones—washed so that dust from them doesn't blow through the house—in space (2) of Figure 5-5. Whenever your living area is warm enough, the automatic control system uses motorized dampers in the ductwork to direct the flow of sun-heated air from the collectors to this rock bin via the heat exchanger and air-handling unit. The material in the bin may be pebbles, gravel, or crushed rock about 1 inch in diameter.

The storage bin is large enough to supply useful heat for 24 hours of carryover during the winter. This is the capacity found most economically suitable, according to Solaron, and the dimensions will vary with the size of your house. For a house with 2,000 square

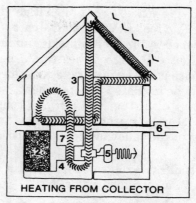

HEATING FROM COLLECTOR

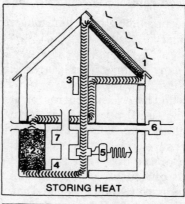

STORING HEAT

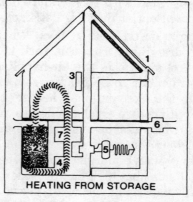

HEATING FROM STORAGE

LEGEND

1. SOLAR COLLECTOR
2. DRY STORAGE UNIT HOT AND COLD
3. CONTROL UNIT
4. AIR HANDLING MODULE
5. HOT WATER UNIT
6. DAY-NIGHT EXCHANGE COOLER
7. AUXILIARY UNIT

FIGURE 5-5. Design for Air-Type Solar Heater

feet of living space, a rock bin with a volume of 500 cubic feet should be adequate. Thus, for instance, a bin whose inside dimensions are 10 feet x 10 feet x 5 feet would be suitable. Since it is a heat storage container, the bin must be insulated to retain heat, with at least R-11 insulation and airtight construction. Materials recommended by Solaron are any of the following (plus insulation):

- Wood frame, plywood on 2 inch x 4 inch or 2 inch x 6 inch studs, or

- Poured reinforced concrete, or

- Concrete block or other masonry materials.

Like many other manufacturers, Solaron insists that this heat storage bin be built and installed by a local contractor according to drawings and specifications furnished by the manufacturer. This is a useful safeguard to make sure you get a satisfactory job. Location of the rock bin is usually in the basement of houses having basements, although any convenient space that can be insulated, filled with rocks, and connected to inlet and outlet ducts is satisfactory.

At night or on cloudy days, when you need to draw heat from this rock storage, the control system in the air-handling unit causes warm air to be drawn from the bin through the conventional heater to the rooms, with return air channeled to the bottom of the bin, as shown in Figure 5-5. Even though your bin is sized for only a single day's carryover, experience shows that rock storage holds heat well and provides useful warmth when the uppermost layer of stones is down to 75°F. When additional heat is needed, the conventional heater cuts in automatically.

Details of the Solaron collector (Figure 5-6) show that air flows through channels under the black absorber plate made of steel with a black ceramic enamel coating under double glazing of tempered glass sealed in place with neoprene gaskets. This assembly

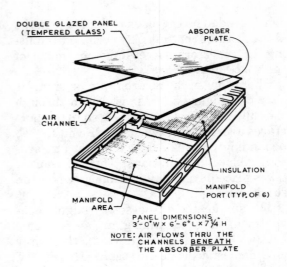

FIGURE 5-6. Details of Solaron Solar Air Collector Panels

is mounted in a painted steel pan having a pad 3-3/4 inches thick on the bottom. Panels are designed with manifold ports for inlet and outlet connections to standard ductwork. There is considerable flexibility in placement of these ports, so that these air collectors may be installed in a variety of vertical or horizontal arrangements depending on the roof space or spaces available with a southern exposure. A typical collector installation appears in Figure 5-7.

160-Unit Installation in Massachusetts

One of the largest Solaron installations provides 70% of the space heating, it is estimated, in a new 160-unit village at North Easton, Massachusetts, built by Friends' Community Development Corporation. Supplementary heating will be furnished by electric strip (resistance) heaters in the hot ducts, one of the typical heating systems described in Chapter 4.

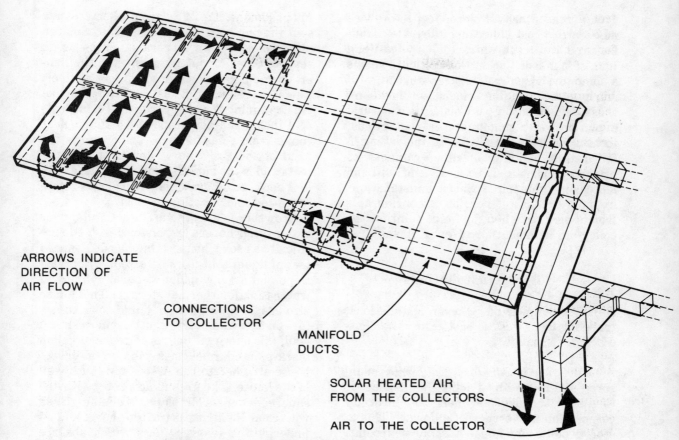

ARROWS INDICATE
DIRECTION OF
AIR FLOW

CONNECTIONS
TO COLLECTOR

MANIFOLD
DUCTS

SOLAR HEATED AIR
FROM THE COLLECTORS

AIR TO THE COLLECTOR

FIGURE 5-7. Typical Solaron Solar Air Collector Installation

Quoting from an article in *Business Week* for October 18, 1976:

Patrick Johnson, a consultant on the North Easton project, concedes that this combination of solar energy and backup resistance heating has a higher capital cost than either an all-electric or an all-oil system—he figures it will add about $3,500 to the cost of each residential unit —but he points out that over the life of a 25-year mortgage homeowners will recoup their expense and eventually start saving money. According to his calculations, the total cost to install and operate the system will range from $335 to $516 a year over 25 years. By contrast, the cost for an oil heating system would range from $382 to $742 and a solar-oil system would range from $551 to $618.

It might be pointed out that this cost advantage in favor of the air solar-electric heating system doesn't take into account possible future tax benefits nor the probable escalation in utility bills. As Dr. James Schlesinger, Chairman of the National Energy Resources Council, has emphasized, without extensive use of solar energy—as well as adoption of other portions of the administration's energy program—our nation will be plunged into a drastic economic recession in the 1980s.

One reason why Solaron collectors are moderate in cost is because they are manufactured by a subcontractor, Choice-Vend Inc., of Windsor Locks, Connecticut. This is a company which makes large quantities of refrigerated vending machines, including those dispensing Pepsi Cola. It is a natural evolution for a manufacturer that bends, forms, and paints steel sheets and tubing in fabricating vending machine cabinets to produce solar air collectors. And with an increasing number of Solaron installations in the Northeast, there is a considerable freight charges when the f.o.b. point for the collectors is in southern New England.

Solaron Installations

A few examples of Solaron installations, traveling from west to east across the United States, include:

A solar house in San Jose, California, sponsored and funded by Pacific Gas & Electric Company, the principal energy public utility corporation in Northern California. This 2-story wood frame house has four bedrooms, a small attic and attached garage, with 2,000 square feet of living space and excellent insulation. On the roof area facing south and with an inclination of 26° from the horizontal are 27 Solaron collectors, each 6-1/2 feet x 3 feet in area. The storage bin in this relatively mild climate contains 16 tons of 1-1/2-inch stones. Volume of the bin is 300 cubic feet and it is made of wood with fiberglass insulation. About 70% of the space heating is furnished by the solar air system, which also preheats domestic water in an 80-gallon tank. A supplementary 40-gallon gas water heater, an auxiliary gas-fired furnace and a highly efficient fireplace are provided as backup for the solar system.

A relatively small house in Denver retrofitted by its owner, the architect who remodeled it, Richard L. Crowther. This 1-story house, with 1,100 square feet and a full basement, has 24 Solaron collectors on a south-facing roof with a 53° slope. Solaron provides collectors in various sizes—as do several other manufacturers—and the panels on the Crowther roof are 2 feet x 8 feet. The storage bin is insulated, a former coal bin containing 20 cubic yards (540 cubic feet) of 1-inch diameter stones. Auxiliary heat comes from a gas furnace. The owner is the head of the Crowther Solar Group/Architects and is the author-publisher of an excellent book, *Sun Earth*. This house was retrofitted for solar heating in 1974.

Crowther is also the architect and owner of two other houses in Denver designed specifically as solar homes. One has 560 square feet of liquid collectors on a roof with a 53° slope and a 1,000-gallon vertical cylindrical water tank for thermal storage. This house also has 24 square feet of liquid solar collectors on a second-story, south-facing vertical wall; this energy is delivered to a 380-gallon black-painted fiberglass tank in a greenhouse attached to the first-story south wall of the house. The greenhouse roof, with 150 square feet and a 30° slope, is double-glazed with clear Plexiglas as the top sheets and an underglazing of gray glass which absorbs about 33% of the solar heat reaching it, transmitting the other 67%.

The third Crowther solar house, on St. Paul Street in Denver, was designed by this outstanding energy-conscious architect to be suitable for row-house or "cluster" projects. It could well be the kind of relatively inexpensive solar home ideal for young married couples, singles, or small families. The floor area at ground level is only 800 square feet (20 x 20) with a 200-square foot loft as the second story. Earth berms on the east, north, and west sides provide natural insulation, with most of the window area (double-glazed) on the south side. There are 10 Solaron 2 foot x 10 foot collectors on the south 50° roof and a 234-cubic foot rectangular plywood bin under the center of the house. This subterranean solar storage is in a special pit—the building has no basement —lined with 6-inch fiberglass insulation; the

FIGURE 5-8. Commercial Installation of Solaron Solar Heating System for
Golden Savings and Loan, Longmont, Colorado

FIGURE 5-9. Industrial Installation of Solaron Solar Heating System for Gump
Glass Company, Denver, Colorado

bin contains 12 tons of stones. Truly well insulated, this comfortable small house has 6-inch rockwool batts in the walls from 3 feet below grade to the roofline, and 12-inch rockwool batts insulating the roof. The roof of the loft is waterproofed and designed to hold a shallow pool of water, which absorbs solar heat in the winter and cools the loft by evaporation during the summer.

In a climate like that of Denver, the air circulation system designed by Dr. Lof of Solaron provides useful summer cooling. At night the air from the wind-chilled collectors is circulated through the rock bin, and then during the day warm air from the rooms is drawn through the cold stones, cooled and returned to the living area. Natural venting of hot air from both stories of this solar house is aided during summer afternoons by a sun-heated chimney on the west wall, which has a vertical solar panel on it. At the top of this chimney is a wind-driven ventilator helping to remove hot air. As reported by Dr. William Shurcliff of Harvard: "Need for cooling is small because of the extensive use of insulation and by reflective blind provided for W window. *Cost:* House $19,000, solar heating system $3,500. Cost would be much less with mass production."

This Crowther house is a splendid example of what can be accomplished by an imaginative architect using both an *active* solar energy system (Solaron) and many *passive* features including insulation, earth berms, and the roof pond.

Golden Savings & Loan's modern building in Longmont, Colorado, (Figure 5-8) and Gump Glass Company's factory in Denver are examples of commercial and industrial Solaron installations. On the Gump Glass Company's building (Figure 5-9) are 760 square feet of collectors, four arrays each having four 10 foot x 11 foot panels. Storage is provided by 60 tons of stones in an 8 foot x 8 foot x 16 foot cement-block bin, insulated and at ground level beside the office area. Solar heating is provided for a 7,200-square foot wing containing showrooms and offices,

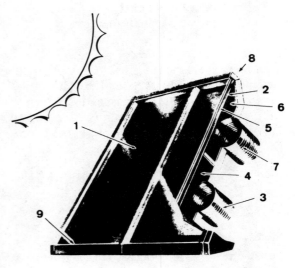

FIGURE 5-10.   Cutaway View of the Sun Stone Solar Air Collector

part of a new large 1-story office building with no basement or attic. Sun-heated air is estimated to provide 75% of the heating load for five zones of the wing, with five gas-fired furnaces (one for each zone) to supplement solar energy during prolonged periods of bad weather.

Scattergood School Recreation Center in West Branch, Iowa, an 8,000-square foot gymnasium complex with 2,500 square feet of Solaron collectors on a south-facing wall sloping 45° from the ground. This is a steel building with good insulation and an air-lock entrance to the locker rooms. Thermal storage is provided by an insulated bin made of steel-reinforced concrete blocks containing about 60 tons of stones in 1,250 cubic feet. Auxiliary heat is provided by a gas furnace and small gas heaters, but solar heating is expected to carry 75% of the load throughout the year in this new building with forced-air heating.

Midwestern Architects Become Solar Manufacturers

In Sheboygan, Wisconsin, a firm of young architects recently became interested in designing solar buildings. Glen F. Groth, Mike Marcheske, and their associates decided they weren't satisfied with any of the solar hardware available a couple of years ago. So they designed air collector panels and other equipment now manufactured under the trade name of Sun Stone solar energy equipment, produced by Sun Unlimited Research Corporation.

A cutaway view of the Sun Stone collector in Figure 5-10 shows (1) single 3/16-inch tempered float glass glazing with an air space (5) over a black-painted aluminum absorber plate (2) with an area of 16.5 square feet. Cold air comes through inlet duct (3) into preheat chamber (4) containing turbulators to increase air turbulence and thereby achieve more efficient solar heating in this space under the hot black absorber plate. Movement of air is past additional turbulators in final heat chamber (6) and then out through the hot air outlet duct (7). There is a removable top cap (8) to permit taking out the glazing and absorber plate to clean the inside surface of the glass when necessary—usually not more often than once a year. At the lower end of the collector (9), there is no bottom glass retainer so that ice and snow slide off the panel, and any dirt is washed off by rain or hosing.

A rule-of-thumb approximation of the number of Sun Stone collectors required in various latitudes is provided in Table 5-1. Note that these estimates indicate that at 45° north latitude, you can achieve about 60% of your annual space heating and hot water requirements with one collector for each 100 square feet of building space. With half as many collectors (1 per 200 square feet), your solar system is estimated to take care of 25% of the load. Probably a good compromise, in both number of collectors and corresponding size of thermal storage, is the middle row of Table 5-1 (1 collector per 150 square feet). Then allow space on your roof to add more collectors as well as more rock bin storage space—usually in a basement or insulated garage—if you find your installation to be undersized.

TABLE 5-1. Approximate number of Sun Stone collectors required for various latitudes.

PERCENT OF ANNUAL ENERGY SUPPLIED (+ −)

BUILDING AREA FOR ONE SUN STONE COLLECTOR PANEL	APPROXIMATE NORTH LATITUDE			
	45°	40°	35°	30°
100 sq. ft.	60%	85%	95%	100%
150 sq. ft.	40%	70%	88%	95%
200 sq. ft.	25%	60%	80%	90%

Although the Sun Stone system is quite similar to Solaron's design, there are some differences. Looking at the schematic diagram of Figure 5-11, you can easily follow the movement of sun-heated air in four basic modes of operation as follows:

Storing Heat. While the sun is shining, a heat sensor on the solar collector array (1) turns on a blower (6) and opens the motorized dampers (2). Solar heated air is drawn from the collectors across a heat exchanger (18), which is an air-to-water exchanger and warms water in a preheating tank for domestic use. The hot air is drawn past the exchanger into the storage bin (5) to warm whatever material is used for thermal storage; the air is then returned through a filter (7) and duct (3) to the inlet or inlets of the collector array.

Storing and Delivering Heat. In this mode, when the building space requires heat and it's a sunny day, control #1 of the room thermostat (14) turns on the blower (12) in the auxiliary forced air furnace (10). Hot air from the solar collectors is drawn from the plenum space above the storage bin (5), then through the auxiliary furnace and into the space to be heated through a hot air register or grille (13). Cold room air is pulled into the bottom of the storage unit via duct

131

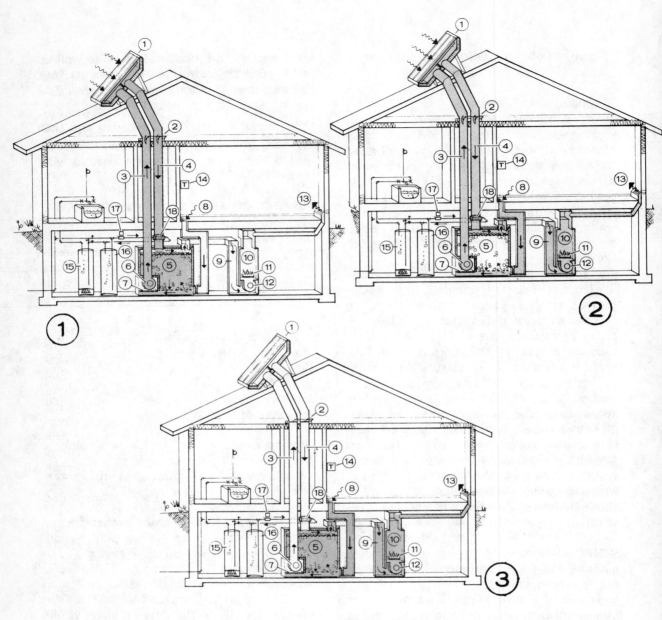

*1. Solar Collector	11. Auxiliary Heater
*2. Motorized Dampers	12. Blower
3. Cold Air Duct	13. Heated Air-to-Room Duct
4. Heat Air Duct	14. 2-Stage Thermostat
*5. Storage Media	15. Water Heater
*6. Blower	*16. Storage
*7. Filters	*17. Pump
8. Room Return Air	*18. Heat Exchanger
9. Heated Air from Storage	
10. Forced Air Furnace	* Sun Stone Solar Energy Equipment

**FIGURE 5-11.   Movement of Sun-Heated Air in Four Basic Modes of Operation:
Storing Heat, Storing and Delivering Heat, Solar and Furnace Heat Combined,
and Passive Delivery of Stored Heat**

132

FIGURE 5-12. Typical Sun Stone Residential Installation

(8) and thus is returned directly by blower (6) to the solar collectors for reheating, in this way bypassing the main storage air. According to designers of the Sun Stone system, this bypass technique is unique, with patent applications pending, because it eliminates dampers beyond those shown at (2).

Solar and Furnace Heat Combined. In this mode consider that the solar collectors are not operating—at night or during bad weather—and dampers (2) are closed and blower (6) is turned off. When the rooms require heat, control #1 of room thermostat (14) activates blower (12) in the auxiliary furnace (10). Hot air is drawn from the top of the storage unit and blown into the rooms, while return cooler air from the living area is brought through (8) to the bottom of the solar thermal storage. Air movement through storage is always upward, using natural convection as well as forced circulation caused by the blower to remove stored heat. When the temperature of air from solar storage drops below a useful

level, control #2 of thermostat (14) automatically senses this point and turns on the auxiliary heater (11) in the furnace.

Passive Delivery of Stored Heat. There are times when the sun is not shining and the auxiliary furnace is turned off. The motorized dampers are closed, no blowers are operating. The only air movement is through natural stratification in the storage unit, causing the hottest air to rise to the top and the coldest to sink to the bottom. Thus the storage unit becomes increasingly efficient, ready to supply stored heat to living areas when required, and to deliver the coldest air for heating by the collectors as soon as the solar array is activated again.

There is an increasing trend among solar manufacturers to supply complete systems carefully engineered for specific installations. Brainchild of architects, the Sun Stone equipment includes collectors, three kinds of heat storage units, automatic dampers, blowers, heat exchangers, circulating pumps and domestic hot water preheating tanks, as well as automatic control equipment including differential thermostats and two-stage room thermostats.

The three types of heat storage provided by Sun Stone include:

- A bin with washed stones wherever space will permit is the favored installation.

- A modular storage unit of a new design described below is applicable to either new or retrofit forced-air systems. This unit is useful where space is limited, since it occupies about one-third the volume of a conventional rock bin and can be installed by a two-man crew.

- Where there is an existing hydronic heating system—see Chapter 4—larger air-to-water heat exchangers make it possible to heat storage water in tanks for space heat as well as domestic requirements. Although air-to-water heat exchangers are not exceptionally effi-

133

cient, for those who prefer solar air collectors this is an acceptable alternative.

Typical Sun Stone Installation

There are several Sun Stone installations, including both homes and office buildings. A typical residence is illustrated in Figure 5-12. This 3-bedroom ranch-style home has 1,550 square feet of living area, a basement and attached garage, with 8 inches of ceiling insulation and 3-1/2 inches of wall insulation. There are 16 two-pass hot air collectors mounted on a rack on the south-facing roof at an angle of about 60°. This home is in Sheboygan, Wisconsin, latitude 44.5° N, so the inclination is ideal for winter solar heating: latitude +15°.

Area of the collectors is 264 square feet and air is circulated through them at 604 cubic feet per minute (cfm). A basement bin of cinder blocks insulated on the inside is 5 feet x 11 feet x 6 feet and holds 351 cubic feet of stones. There is an 82-gallon preheating tank for domestic hot water. Auxiliaries include an oil-fired furnace and an electric water heater. The solar contribution of the Sun Stone system is estimated at about 50% in an area where there are 7,350 degree days, the average January temperature is 21°F, and horizontal insolation varies from 559 langleys per day in January to 2,030 langleys during the average June day.

The Sun Stone equipment installed in this house cost $4,200, including installation. It consists of 16 collectors, 1 end cap, 16 support angles, 12 mounting brackets, 1 motorized damper system, 1 blower unit for the stone storage bin, 1 air-to-water heat exchanger, 1 circulating pump, 1 preheating water tank (82 gallons), as well as the installation of the rock storage bin, ductwork, and controls.

Assuming that the cost of this solar space heating and hot water system is paid for as part of a 20-year mortgage, and that utility bills rise by 12% a year (which may be low as fuel supplies dwindle), this installation

will have paid for itself in 10 years. By the end of 25 years, the accumulated savings are estimated by Sun Unlimited Research Corporation to amount to more than $23,000, or about half the total cost of the house.

In an installation where a rock bin is impractical, the basic Sun Stone storage unit is a rectangular steel bin with suitable ductwork, controls, and blower, insulated with high-density fiberglass insulation board 2 inches thick. At the time of installation this bin is supplied with a large number of plastic containers filled with water. Each container holds about one pound of water. This modular bin provides storage for the solar heat from four Sun Stone collectors. For additional collectors, there are add-on storage modules (without blower and controls); each of these modules has space for solar heat storage from four collectors. Thus, in the house previously described, if there were not room for a stone bin, one basic storage unit and three add-on modules would do the job.

Many Other Air Collector Systems Available

As is the case with liquid collector systems, there are an increasing number of manufacturers of air collectors for solar space heating and hot water. Because installation of an air collector array is not difficult, many types of solar panels delivering hot air through ducts to homes as well as commercial and industrial buildings are assembled at the site.

An example from Dr. Shurcliff's excellent book, *Solar Heated Buildings: A Brief Survey* (13th edition), is a home in Grantham, New Hampshire, designed with a south wall inclined 60° from the horizontal. The surface of this wall is covered with 700 square feet of air collectors—a net absorber area of 640 square feet. The absorbers consist of 0.020-inch thick aluminum sheets with a nonselective black coating. Double glazing is provided by two sheets of Kalwall Sun-Lite Premium fiberglass reinforced translucent plastic. These sheets are 1/2 inch apart, with the outer sheet 0.040 inch thick and the inner sheet 0.025 inch thick. Below the black absorber sheet are about 4 inches of air space and then an insulating layer of 1-inch thick polyurethane foam over the collector's bottom panel. Through the duct formed by the space between the black absorber and the foam insulation, air is driven up the south wall of this house at 3,000 cfm by a 1/3 HP blower in the basement. Header ducts 18 inches x 18 inches in cross section are provided at the bottom of the collectors for inlet and along the top of the roof for sun-heated air outlet.

Solar engineer Dick Gregor designed this system with thermal storage consisting of 1,500 one-gallon plastic bottles—like the ones used for milk, distilled water, or other liquid products you buy at your supermarket. These polyethylene bottles are arranged in a rectangular bin, its top insulated with 6 inches of fiberglass, the sides with 1 inch of polyurethane foam. This 32 foot x 12 foot x 6-1/2 foot bin is the north side of the basement of a split-level wood frame house having 1,536 square feet of living area.

Hot air from the south-wall collectors is brought from the roof-tree outlet duct through an insulated duct to the bottom of the basement thermal storage bin, so that the sun-heated air flows upward through the bin and warms the water in the 1,500 bottles. When rooms need heat, room air is circulated by a blower upward through the bin. If the bottles aren't hot enough, a General Electric air-to-air heat pump is turned on automatically by a thermostatic control. (For a brief explanation of how heat pumps work, see Chapter 4.)

Domestic hot water is preheated by solar energy in a small steel tank inside a stone bin. Auxiliary space heating is provided by a 15 kW electric heater operated during off-peak hours to heat the water in the 1,500 bottles in the storage bin.

A useful feature of this heating system, using a combination of solar energy and a heat pump, is that it can also be a practical method for summer cooling of the house. In the winter, sun heat plus heat pump pro-

vide about 70% of this home's warmth. In the summer, the heat pump is operated in reverse to cool the rooms directly. Also, the second basement storage bin, filled with stones, is cooled at night by outside air circulated through the stones. Then during the hottest part of the day, air from this bin is blown through the rooms for cooling.

Cost of this solar air conditioning system was $4,500 more than an alternative system using electric heaters and a heat pump. The savings in utility bills at present rates should pay for the solar system within 10 years—but the actual payoff will be sooner, since inflation escalates your utility bills along with every other cost of living.

In Chapter 4 the liquid solar system designed by Sunworks is described. Yale professor Everett M. Barber, Jr., founder of this company and owner of an efficient and attractive solar home in Connecticut on Long Island Sound, has also designed air collector systems in collaboration with Donald Watson, AIA, an award-winning solar architect.

One example of their cooperative work is a home in Groton, Connecticut, owned and built by C. Eames. This is a 2-story 1,800-square foot house with both basement and attic. The main collector area is on a south roof with 60° slope, with 18 Sunworks air panels each 3 feet x 7 feet for a total absorber area of 335 square feet. These collectors are made of copper sheets with selective black coating and a single glazing of 3/16-inch tempered glass, a standard glazing material in many applications. There is an air space between the blackened copper absorber and an insulating pad mounted in a frame or container similar to that of the Sunworks liquid collector previously described. Air is circulated at 120 cfm through the space behind the absorber by a 1/3 HP blower.

This house has a supplementary collector consisting of a greenhouse with 60° sloping sheets of acrylic plastic having a total area of 11 feet x 14 feet facing south. Storage is a 1,250-cubic foot stone bin receiving hot air from the main collectors; this bin is beneath

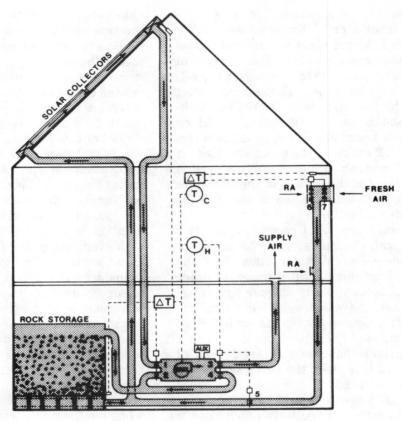

Damper Number (o = open, s = shut)	1	2	3	4	5	6	7	Fan	Back up
Normal position	s	o	s	o	s	o	s	off	off
Solar heating storage	o	s	s	o	s	o	s	on	off
Solar heating house	o	s	o	s	o	o	s	on	off
Storage heating house	s	o	o	s	o	o	s	on	off
Back up heating house	s	o	o	s	o	o	s	on	on
Fresh air cooling storage	s	o	o	s	o	s	o	on	off
Storage cooling house	s	o	o	s	o	s	o	on	off

FIGURE 5-13. Schematic of Jespa Solar House Designed by Donald A. Watson

the floor of the house. There is a second small bin full of stones beneath the greenhouse.

About 80% of the space heating is provided by solar energy, with auxiliary heating from a Heatilator fireplace, which can supply warmth to the larger rock bin. There is also a wood-burning stove in the kitchen-living area.

For domestic hot water there are five Sunworks liquid collectors, arranged so that

their tilt can be adjusted seasonally, supplying hot water to the house with maximum efficiency all year.

Another house with efficient air collectors for space heating and liquid collectors for solar heating of domestic hot water is the Jespa Enterprises solar house in Old Bridge, New Jersey, and shown in Figure 5-13. Frank Lebrato and Eli Lackow are builders under the name of Jespa Enterprises. Their 4-bedroom home with attached 2-car gar-

FIGURE 5-14. Solar House in Old Bridge, New Jersey, Using Air Collectors for Space Heating and Liquid Collectors for Domestic Hot Water

age, served by a hybrid air-liquid heating system, was designed by Donald Watson to use 20 Sunworks air collectors on the steep 60° south-facing roof, while only 3 Sunworks liquid collectors (mounted separately on the stair tower roof) furnish domestic hot water.

About 60% of the space heating requirements is obtained from the solar system in this well-insulated house with energy-conserving features designed by architect Watson and shown in Figure 5-14. Walls contain thick insulation on 6-inch studs, and the major windows face south. A warm-air return at the top of a stair tower recirculates the air from the house. Note that the air system requires only one fan, and that there are 7 automatically controlled motorized

dampers operated as shown in the table below Figure 5-13.

With this system, the warm-air return recovers the heat gained through the south-facing windows and distributes it evenly throughout the house to contribute an additional 15% to the house heating. The rock storage bin is large and well insulated—partly by the foundation walls—and stores enough solar heat for a carryover of "several days," according to the owners.

During the summer, this rock storage bin can be cooled by drawing in night air through the inlet marked "fresh air" in Figure 5-13. Then, during the hottest part of the day, this cool air from the bin is circulated through the house. During the summer additional natural ventilation is pro-

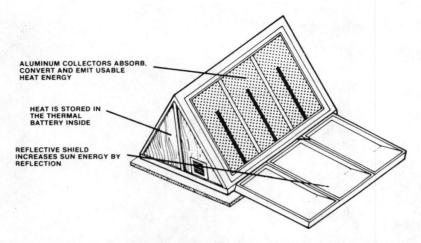

ALUMINUM COLLECTORS ABSORB, CONVERT AND EMIT USABLE HEAT ENERGY

HEAT IS STORED IN THE THERMAL BATTERY INSIDE

REFLECTIVE SHIELD INCREASES SUN ENERGY BY REFLECTION

FIGURE 5-15. A-Frame Shed with Air-Type Solar Collector by International Solarthermics

vided by the stair tower, whose windows at the top are opened to ensure air flow by convection.

Details of the construction of this house and many others, featuring good solar designs, energy conservation, and modern insulating techniques, are provided in Watson's excellent book, *Designing and Building a Solar Home*.

Solar Furnace for Retrofitting Houses

Developed as a design by International Solarthermics Corporation (ISC), Nederland, Colorado, an ingenious A-frame solar furnace which can be connected to homes now using forced-air heating systems is currently being manufactured by four companies under license to ISC. According to John Keyes, chairman of the board of this inventive research firm, some 1,000 solar furnaces had been installed as of mid-1977.

The original design, described in this author's first book, is shown in Figure 5-15. Absorbers are made of aluminum sheets painted nonselective black. On these absorbers are mounted vertical vanes like small cups of black-coated aluminum which cause air turbulence, increase convection, and thus increase heating of the air. Also,

these vanes add to the total area absorbing solar energy.

Covering the absorbers and vanes are two layers of 3/16-inch tempered glass; air is blown between this double glazing and the absorbers in a path from bottom to top of the solar collector—as is common practice with air collectors. The sun-heated air warms a bin of stones contained inside the A-frame structure. The back of the collector panel and the bin are well insulated.

Additional solar energy is gained because of the reflective shield which directs sunlight at the collector panels. This shield is made of bright, highly reflective aluminum foil bonded to a plywood backing. The reflector has a dual purpose. During the heating season it reflects enough solar energy into the absorber plates and vanes to improve their efficiency by an average of 20%. When the solar furnace is not in use—during the summer—the hinged reflector panel becomes a lid to protect the glass cover of the air collector.

One other point, brought out in a May 1977 conversation with Keyes of ISC, is the advantage he claims for placing solar collectors at ground level. "Most solar collectors are mounted on roofs," says Keyes, "while our tests show that you gain anywhere from 5% to 15% in solar energy by having the collector close to the ground as in our A-

FIGURE 5-16.   Champion Air-Type Solar Furnace Facing South

frame design. This is because solar energy is reflected by grass, weeds, shrubs, trees, and walls. You'd be surprised how much heat gain you get with your solar furnace on a lawn when the grass is several inches high."

There are three standard sizes of collectors, with areas of 96, 128, and 160 square feet, depending upon the size of house to be heated. Corresponding reflector areas are somewhat larger: 108, 144, and 180 square feet, respectively.

A fan inside the A-frame pulls air from the outside through the collector vanes and over the absorbers. Then this sun-heated air is blown through internal baffles in the thermal storage area full of small washed stones, averaging an inch in diameter. A load of stones, gravel, or crushed rock ranging in volume from about 230 to 400 cubic feet (8.5 to 15 cubic yards) is placed in the A-frame after it is installed in your yard. This corresponds to from 12 to 22 tons of stones.

According to ISC, this type of bin has a practical heat storage capability from 75°F to 175°F. Because the bin is well insulated, heat loss from it should not be greater than

a few degrees in 24 hours except under conditions of extreme cold and high winds. Average carrythrough has been found to be anywhere from two to four days, depending upon the upper temperature achieved in the bin and the weather conditions. One useful feature of every insulated rock bin in a solar air collector system is that stones retain heat for many days; consequently even when temperatures at the top of the bin are as low as 75°F, it's possible to get useful space heating from this kind of solar thermal storage.

Behind the collector plate is a sandwich structure of thick insulation. Backing the absorber is laminated 3/8-inch plywood, 4 inches of polyurethane foam, and then 3/8-inch insulating board. The same insulation is used on the opposite (north-facing) wall of the A-frame, while the base has a floor of 1/2-inch plywood over 6 inches of polystyrene foam and 3/8-inch insulating board. Below that is a foundation having 6 inches of polystyrene foam with a 6 mil polyethylene vapor barrier. Framing the structure is 24-gauge galvanized steel.

From the rock storage bin, a second fan exhausts warm air through conventional

FIGURE 5-17.   A-Frame Solar Furnace Occupies Little Space

ductwork to the house. In its original specifications ISC called for two Lau Industries model FCP106A centrifugal fans powered by GE 1/2-HP motors.

Licensees of ISC have made their own variations in the original design. Solar Store of Parker, South Dakota, makes the entire A-frame structure of wood. NRG of Napoleon, Ohio, uses bricks as the thermal storage material. Future Systems in Denver has an ingenious variation of the internal design for moving air so that only a single electric motor is required and both blowers are inside the east end of the A-frame.

Champion Home Builders of Dryden, Michigan, one of the nation's largest builders of mobile homes, has also produced by far the greatest number of A-frame solar furnaces as an ISC licensee. Their total was about 800 in May 1977. This company's modifications of the design include a unitized monolithic construction suitable for mass production, with aluminum framing and corners made of molded fiberglass. Polyurethane foam insulation is sprayed on the interior walls, including the underside of the absorber plates. Where ISC made the vanes mounted on the absorbers in the shape of cups, in the Champion design these

vanes are vertical fins like the slats of an open venetian blind. See Figures 5-16 and 5-17.

Keyes is one of many designers of solar collectors, air and liquid, who sees no measurable advantage in using selective black paint. His firm's tests prove that nonselective flat black paint on aluminum sheets and vanes is equally as good as any of the selective materials. This is also the conclusion of David Laudig, manager of the Reynolds Metals extrusion plant, who has been designing solar collectors for several years and whose company supplies components and assemblies to many solar manufacturers of both liquid and air systems.

Do-It-Yourselfers Use Old Cans

In the *Los Angeles Times* of May 9, 1977, an article by Charles Hillinger headed "He Warms up to Old Beer Cans" tells of an ingenious do-it-yourselfer who has used much the same solar heating principle as that of ISC.

Cal Midgley, the 67-year-old operator of a 17-acre flea market in the small town of Sebastopol, California, warms a snack bar in one corner of his property with solar energy. On the south-facing wall of a wood frame structure 16 feet long, 8 feet high, 6 feet wide at the base and slanting upward to a roof tree 2 feet wide, he has mounted 1,200 empty beer cans in holes in plywood. This plywood facing for his trapezoidal structure is covered with aluminum foil—except where the beer cans face the sun. See Figure 5-18.

He uses a single sheet of glass to cover each section of his homemade collector, and the beer cans are painted black, with the popout side of each can facing inward to the rock storage bin inside his structure. No blower is necessary. Thermal convection delivers the sun's heat absorbed by the 1,200 black cans to the rocks.

When Midgley needs heat in his 22 foot x 40 foot snack bar adjacent to his solar heater, he opens the vents in two 8-inch diameter pipes wrapped in fiberglass insulation connecting his solar heater with the snack bar. He turns on a fan driven by a 1/6-HP motor. This blower, located in one of his ducts, draws warm air from the heated rocks inside his solar furnace.

From Hillinger's story it appears that this DIY inventor is quite unaware of the similarity between his design and the A-frame solar furnace developed by ISC. The reporter quotes Midgley as saying: "I built my first solar heating system in 1932. I've been

tinkering with solar heater[...] ancestors were all Scotch. I[...] saving money."

A similar homemade solar fu[...] both soft drink and beer cans, help[...] a mountain home built by a friend[...] author. Others have been built in Oh[...] Illinois. It would be interesting to know[...] many other do-it-yourselfers whose hom[...] have forced-air heating systems are using[...] sun-heated air and rock-bin thermal storage[...] to save substantially on their fuel bills.

FIGURE 5-18.   Painting Beer Cans Black for a Solar Heater (Los Angeles Times photograph)

6
Solar Heat for Summer Cooling

Recently Charles E. Backus, a noted solar authority and professor of mechanical engineering at Arizona State University, made the following comments in a speech before the American Petroleum Institute in Chicago: "Utilizing solar energy to cool buildings is not yet economically competitive in the U.S. However the Japanese, who are far ahead of us in terms of such things as total number of solar water heaters installed, are working hard on solar air conditioners. Maybe they'll come up with a better answer than American manufacturers have so far."

In a brochure issued by the Space Division of General Electric Company, which has developed solar heating and cooling systems and has installed liquid-type solar space heating and hot water devices in such large projects as a 20,000-square foot portion of the Grover Cleveland Middle School in Boston, and a large building at the GE Space Center in Valley Forge, Pennsylvania, there is the following statement:

General Electric has investigated many concepts for using solar energy systems to produce air conditioning such as ab-

sorption chillers, Rankine engine-driven compressors, and chemical dessicants, and has concluded that solar air conditioning requires further development before it will be economically attractive for widespread use.

One of the concepts under investigation uses solar heat to generate a vapor, which is used to drive a Rankine cycle engine. This engine uses a highly efficient expander, developed by General Electric, which drives an air conditioning compressor. When there is either insufficient sunshine or stored thermal energy, an electric motor drives the compressor. Still in the laboratory stage, the principle has been successfully demonstrated.

Since this book is not a text on thermodynamics, if you'd like to know how Rankine cycle engines operate, a good explanation is provided in *Introduction to Thermodynamics: Classical and Statistical* by Richard E. Sonntag and Gordon J. Van Wylen, both professors at the University of Michigan, (John Wiley & Sons), Chapter 10. It is sufficient to say that a Rankine cycle engine is an efficient way to generate electric power from steam in one application; and a similar Rankine cycle, operated in reverse, is used in the vapor-compression technique which cools your electric refrigerator.

Simple Approaches to Solar Cooling and Heating

Although there are a number of ways in which solar energy can be used for cooling your house, it is quite true that none of the conventional approaches appears to be very cost effective. But several simple methods work quite well.

- As mentioned in the previous chapter on air collector systems, in an area where the night air is cool enough—as in mountainous sections of Colorado and other western states, northern New England, and parts of Canada as examples—you can use your blowers at night to cool the rock bin in your house. Then the warm air from your living area is circulated through the cool bin during the day and back into your rooms to provide natural air conditioning, and a summer use for your solar heating system.

- In Maryland, where Dr. Harry E. Thomason and his associates have pioneered in building several efficient solar homes, this inventor has installed a small conventional air conditioner, operated at night, to bring in cool, dehumidified air into his rock bin in the basement of his sixth solar house. This air conditioner operates at off-peak hours, from 10 P.M. to 4 A.M., which is appreciated by the electric utility company—and saves on the electric bill in some areas. And again, the cool stones in the bin provide a useful source of cooling and dehumidification when room air is circulated through them during hot days.

- Sponsored by the Southern California Edison Company, one of the many utili-

FIGURE 6-1. "Thermostructure Model Home," Cathedral City, California, Structured of Insulating Materials, Uses Solar Energy for Space Heating and Domestic Hot Water, but an Evaporative Chiller for Cooling

ties taking an increasingly active part in solar development, is the "Thermostructure Model Home" in the desert at Cathedral City, a suburb of Palm Springs. Shown in Figure 6-1, this house is designed with insulating materials as the structure. There are no conventional studs, beams, or joists. Instead, the arched structure is fabricated on the site by placing polystyrene panels on wood bracing. Steel mesh is applied over this insulating expanded plastic material, which is then covered by 4 inches of reinforced concrete. Concrete under high pressure is then sprayed on the exterior via the gunite method, and painted for weatherproofing. According to the builder, it takes one day to complete the exterior walls with this efficient modern technique.

When the author visited this solar home, the outdoor temperature was 92°F in the shade. The inside of the house was a comfortable 70°F. "Where's the solar cooling?" we asked.

It turned out that cooling is provided by an efficient Fedders evaporative cooler, drawing only about 160 watts—the kind used for years in many thousands of desert homes throughout the Southwest. The solar portion of this model house is provided by 6 Solarcoa collectors, preheating an 82-gallon water tank and an insulated 600-gallon underground tank of concrete. Solar heat is transferred by means of a heat transfer fluid —50-50 water and antifreeze with a corrosion inhibitor—which circulates through a heat exchanger of copper pipe in the underground storage tank and warms this thermal storage supply. When space heating is needed, heated water from the main storage tank is circulated through a fan-coil unit in the house. A 10 kW electric duct heater is provided for backup on the very rare occasions when it is needed. When domestic hot water is needed, it's drawn from a conventional 52-gallon electric water heater. However, most of the hot water comes from the American Appliance 82-gallon preheat tank, with energy supplied by sun-heated water from the main storage tank pumped through the double-wall heat exchanger of this tank-within-a-tank design.

In other words, a solar home in the desert sponsored by one of the nation's largest and most progressive utilities uses solar energy for space heating and hot water, but finds a conventional evaporative chiller most economical for cooling the building.

Skytherm Design Looks Promising

One of the most ingenious and simple designs for solar homes is the brainchild of Harold R. Hay, president of Skytherm Processes & Engineering, Los Angeles. The first applications of his concept, which employs big black plastic water bags, were in supplying solar heating and cooling for houses with flat roofs. Now his design has been adapted for pitched-roof houses in a concept called Skytherm North.

This technique was first tested in a small building in Arizona, then in a home in Atascadero, California. It is applicable to new structures because the Skytherm system must be designed into the building plan.

Later in this chapter you will find a detailed description of how you can cool *existing buildings* by using solar heat to operate absorption chillers, as well as some promising solar air conditioning techniques which are still under development.

But if you are planning a new building and want both heating and cooling from solar energy, the Skytherm approach is worth considering because of its simplicity and low cost. In a conversation in mid-1977 with the author, Hay reported that 5 houses of this design are underway in Selma near Fresno in central California; a 2-story office building is being built in Austin, Texas; a home is under construction in a cold site near Sioux Falls, South Dakota. The inventor is somewhat dismayed at the slow acceptance of his designs despite favorable reports by such authorities as solar pioneer John I. Yellott, an engineer and professor of architecture at Arizona State University; a research team from California State Polytechnical University, San Luis Obispo; and a federally sponsored study prepared by General Electric. Such is the age-old struggle of the independent inventor.

The Skytherm house in Atascadero is a single-story house with 1,140 square feet of living area, a flat roof, and a slab floor. Both outer walls and inner partitions are made of concrete blocks. For insulation, most blocks of the outer walls are filled with vermiculite, while inner blocks forming the partitions between the seven rooms are full of sand.

The solar collector system consists of four transparent plastic bags lying side by side on the flat roof, each bag filled with water. Imagine waterbeds designed for giants— each "bed" is 8 feet wide and 38 feet long, the length of the house along its north-south axis. The bags are made of PVC (polyvinylchloride), the common plastic material of which millions of feet of pipe are made annually. These bags are 0.020 inch thick and are filled with water to a depth of 9 inches, so that there is a total of 6,300 gallons of water (about 26 tons) on the roof of this Skytherm house.

Above each giant water bag is a transparent sheet of ultraviolet-resistant PVC. This sheet is sealed to the edges of each water bag and is held about 2 inches above the bag by means of air pressure from below. The purpose of this top sheet and the air space is to provide insulation for the water bag.

Beneath each of the 4 water bags is a black PVC sheet which is the solar radiation absorber; it is in contact with the roof, made of ribbed steel with 12-foot spans.

During cold weather, heat is absorbed by the four big water bags on their black bottom sheets throughout each day while the sun is shining. The solar heat is conducted through the metal ceiling and flows downward into the rooms, largely by radiation from the hot steel roof. This radiant heating is so uniform that no fans are needed to circulate hot air. According to the report by Dr. Shurcliff, the thermal capacity of this house's walls and partitions augments that of the 26 tons of sun-warmed water on the roof.

There are 5 longitudinal tracks on the north-south axis of the roof, one at each of the two edges of the roof and the other three placed between the four long water bags. During cold nights these tracks or rails carry an array of 9 large insulating panels made of polyurethane foam 2 inches thick, used to cover the warm water bags. Each panel rides on small nylon-rim wheels with ball bearings—the kind of wheels, costing about 5 cents each, on which many sliding doors for home closets roll. The wheels run on positive-guide rails of extruded aluminum designed to provide three levels of runway.

During the day, these panels are automatically retracted by a 1/4-HP motor and chain drive which propel number 9—the biggest panel (33 feet x 12 feet). This panel pushes numbers 5, 6, 7, and 8 and, through those four, the remaining four cover panels.

Because of the three-level track system, the panels are stacked on sunny days above the carport-patio roof at the north end of this Skytherm house in Atascadero. If the home owner wishes, or if there's any problem with this automatic retraction system, the panels may be moved manually.

On cold nights, the panels are moved automatically by this motorized system so as to cover the water bags. During winter days, the panels are also pulled over the roof as an insulating blanket under either of two conditions:

- The room thermostat (one central unit is enough) determines that the rooms are becoming too hot, or

- A small solar energy sensor outside, a miniature air-insulated solar collector, decides that conditions are unfavorable for collecting useful heat from the sun —not enough insolation, cold ambient air, and chilling winds, for example.

Tests conducted on this house, located about halfway between Los Angeles and San Francisco, showed that the Skytherm system provides 100% of the winter heating, with comfort for the family living there. It is estimated that there is a carrythrough of four cold sunless days in January, provided that the initial temperature of the water in the giant plastic bags is 85°F. There is no auxiliary heat in this house— the sun does the entire job.

How about summer cooling? It is often 100°F in the shade in Atascadero, quite a distance inland from the cooling Pacific. On hot days, the plastic sheets above the four big water bags are no longer held up by pressurization; they are in direct contact with the water bags and provide little thermal resistance. But now the bags are covered during the daylight hours by the panels of insulating foam. At night, the bags full of water are exposed to the sky and lose heat energy by both convection and radiation. By dawn the water and the metal ceiling below are cooled, and air circulating

145

through the rooms in the day is kept comfortably cool.

According to the family living in this Skytherm house, there wasn't a day during the hottest part of the summer when the temperature inside the house climbed over about 72°F. Thus the system truly has provided year-round space cooling as well as heating.

Although the Atascadero house cost more than $40,000 since much of its design was a research project, it is estimated that future houses of the same size could be built for about $27,500, or even less, by using mass production techniques. According to Hay, all that is needed to make Skytherm a big contributor to conserving energy by using the sun is to find more builders with imagination, courage, and money.

Adapting this concept to a northern climate, the inventor mounts his structure of motorized panels and water bags on a south-facing roof pitched for maximum winter insolation. Hay states that his Skytherm North design will do 100% of the building's heating with solar energy even when the ambient air sinks to -30°F.

Sun-Heated Water and Absorption Coolers

A more conventional approach, which has been used in many kinds of buildings equipped with solar space heating systems of the liquid type, is to take advantage of an ample supply of sun-heated water for the necessary heat energy for absorption coolers. This is a technique that is being applied to existing buildings as well as new construction. It is an adequate approach for a small house as well as for a large school, factory, or commercial building.

For example Honeywell, Inc., is a corporation active in many phases of solar research—including collector design in association with Lennox as previously mentioned, and as a competitor for supplying the design and equipment for the nation's first commercial solar power plant described in chapter 10. This firm's new 8-story office building at its Minneapolis headquarters includes 60% of its heating load supplied by liquid solar collectors and a hydronic system, while 100% of the building's hot water is sun-warmed. An estimated 60% of the cooling is also provided by the solar system, using hot water from the collectors to supply energy for absorption coolers.

Among many other examples, some of which are included in the latter part of this chapter, is what the developer, Robert A. Felburg, calls "the world's first shopping center dependent solely on the sun for its heating and cooling." This is an $8.5-million project consisting of 110 shops and restaurants around a sunken area of ponds, waterwheels, waterfalls, bridges, and gardens. Construction is underway in Westlake Village, northwest of Los Angeles, and it is predicted that the entire solar heating and cooling system, with 100% of the energy supplied by the sun, will cost more than $1 million.

Solar heated water will be stored in nine 40,000-gallon tanks, insulated and buried under the ponds in the center's courtyard. The plan calls for 500 solar collectors to supply thermal energy at 200°F for the water in seven of the tanks, while the other two tanks will store cold water maintained at 44°F.

As you will see from the detailed description of how absorption coolers operate, they require both hot and cold water. The leading manufacturer of absorption air conditioning systems is Arkla Industries, Inc., of Little Rock, Arkansas.

In Figures 6-2 and 6-3 are simplified diagrams which show two systems for using water heated by solar collectors to supply energy for both space heating and cooling. The only difference is that in the *direct system*, hot water from the collectors is supplied directly to the large storage tank, whereas in the *indirect system* there is the familiar closed loop described in previous chapters, with an antifreeze mixture flow-

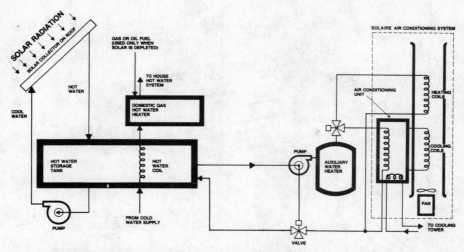

FIGURE 6-2.   Direct Solaire System Provides Sun-Heated Water From Storage to Heat the Chiller's Generator

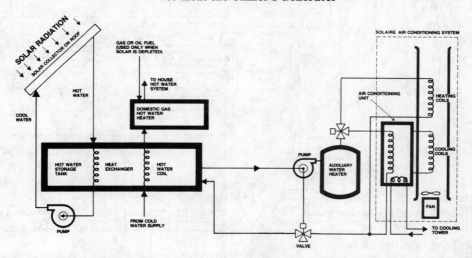

FIGURE 6-3.   In the Indirect Solaire System, a Heat Exchanger Transfers Heat from the Solar Heated Water Storage Tanks and Allows the Use of an Antifreeze Fluid

ing through the collectors and a heat exchanger coil in the big storage tank as shown.

Figure 6-4 is a detailed diagram showing how an absorption cooler works. Older Arkla units require water temperatures higher than 200°F, but the new designs will provide cooling with sun-heated water at 190°F with good efficiency—and can operate on a minimal level at somewhat lower input temperatures, down to 170°F.

The sun-heated water enters the base of the generator (1) and is condensed on the internal heat-transfer surfaces (2) at atmospheric pressure. This part of the generator has a vent (3) at the top of the jacket so that if there is steam mixed with the solar hot water, it will condense before reaching the vent and condensate will drain from the base of the generator by gravity through the outlet port which returns the hot water (cooled somewhat by delivering heat ener-

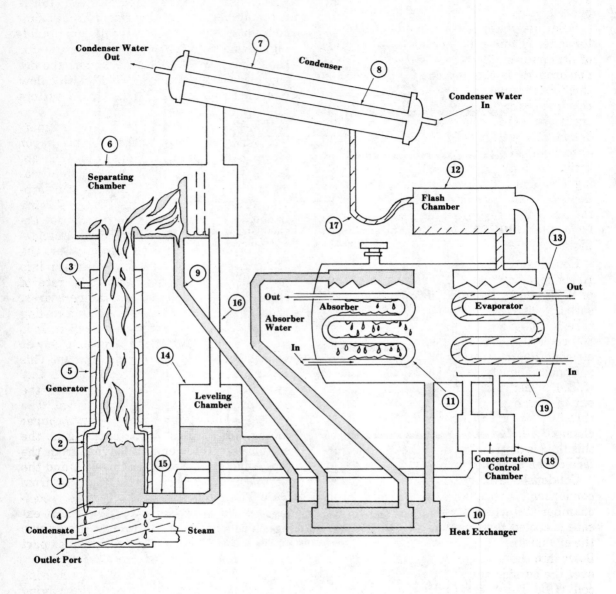

FIGURE 6-4.   Details of Operation of an Absorption Cooler

148

gy) to a large storage tank holding sun-heated water.

Solar hot water flows around the generator inner chamber (4) containing a solution of lithium bromide (LiBr) and water. Lithium bromide is the absorbent and water is the refrigerant. As solar heat is applied to this generator chamber, part of the refrigerant (water) is boiled out of the solution. When this water vapor is driven off, the absorbent solution is raised by vapor lift action through pump tube (5) to a separating chamber (6). The refrigeration vapor flows on from there into the condenser (7) at the top of Figure 6-4, having been separated from the water-lithium bromide mixture (liquid).

Condensing water, supplied according to Arkla specifications at an inlet temperature of 85°F, flows through tubing (8) and absorbs heat so that its design outlet temperature is 102°F for the Solaire Model WFB-300 cooler, with a capacity in conventional air conditioning terms of 25 tons.

Simultaneously, the absorbent solution (LiBr), separated from the mixture, flows out of chamber (6) through tube (9), then through the inner chamber of the heat exchanger (10) and on to the absorber, where this fluid is distributed over the outside surface of the absorber coil (11).

Condensed refrigerant flows from the condenser (7) through tube (17) to a flash chamber (12) where by flashing the condensate is cooled to a temperature suitable for the evaporator. The cooled refrigerant then flows into the evaporator and is distributed over the outside surface of the water chiller coil (13). The water to be cooled flows through the internal passages of the coil and gives up heat, which evaporates the refrigerant (delivered from the flash chamber) on the outside of the coil.

Refrigerant entering the evaporator section vaporizes easily due to the high vacuum —or very low absolute pressure—maintained in this section of the chiller. This high vacuum permits lowering of the boiling temperature of the refrigerant so that it does absorb heat from the evaporator coil (13). It is this chilled water, circulated through fan-coil units generally, that cools your building. Arkla's design inlet temperature for the Solaire 25-ton unit is 55°F, and the design outlet temperature is 45°F, with a flow of chilled water through the closed system of 60 gpm.

Now that the refrigerant has been vaporized again in the evaporator, this vapor flows to the absorber coil (11) and is absorbed by the concentrated solution of water and lithium bromide. The heat of absorption is removed by cooling water flowing through the internal passages of the absorber coil. Because LiBr (lithium bromide) has a strong affinity for water vapor, the refrigerant vapor is readily absorbed into the $LiBr/H_2O$ solution again. The rate of absorption increases at low temperatures, and this is the reason for providing a cooling water coil inside the absorber section. It is also why you must have a cooling tower associated with an absorption chiller. This tower, outside the building, provides a way to cool water from the chiller before the water is returned to absorb more heat. The tower usually contains a long helix of copper tubing, with warm water entering at the bottom of the tower and leaving from the top. A fan directs air over this coil, and the air blown up the tower absorbs heat from the water in the coil. In other words, a cooling tower is a form of water-to-air heat exchanger for you to get rid of heat from some of the water, used in a closed cycle, as part of the absorption chilling process.

In some modern designs of solar heating and cooling systems, engineers are studying how this wasted heat from a cooling tower —at least in larger systems—may be put to use. Certainly it might be useful in the kind of industrial and commercial total energy systems (TOE) described in chapter 10.

The mixture of refrigerant and absorbent drains as a liquid from the absorber section into the outer chamber of the heat exchanger (10) and then into the lower part of the leveling chamber (14). This latter chamber maintains the LiBr/H2O solution at a suitable level for keeping the generator (4) functioning efficiently.

The liquid-to-liquid heat exchanger (10) helps the absorption chiller operate more efficiently. The absorbent solution flowing through tube (9) leaves the generator at a relatively high temperature. Since the affinity of this solution for water vapor increases as the solution temperature decreases, precooling is desirable before the solution enters the absorber.

Conversely, the combined solution of refrigerant and absorbent leaving the absorber and flowing toward the generator is relatively cool. Because sun-heated water (design temperature for the Solaire is 195°F) is used instead of gas to heat the solution (4) in the generator, it's useful to preheat this solution before it goes back into the generator. Thus the heat exchanger, with its counterflow action, serves two useful purposes: *precooling* as described in the preceding paragraph, and *preheating*.

There is a high vacuum maintained throughout all these fluid (liquid and gas) loops in the absorption chiller. But there is a slightly higher absolute pressure in the generator and condenser than in the evaporator-absorber section. This pressure differential between the high and the low sides is preserved by traps in the solution lines and by a trap in the refrigerant line (17).

The concentration control chamber (18) serves to store refrigerant out of the solution when condenser temperatures are high. This results in a more concentrated solution and improves operating efficiency of the entire chiller under those conditions. This concentrating chamber is placed physically at a level such that at lower condenser pressures it will drain and dilute the absorber solution. This prevents the evaporator pressure from dropping too low—close to the freezing point of the liquid—when water flowing through the condenser is at a low temperature. Most of the liquid flowing into this concentrator chamber comes from a pan (19) below the evaporator coil and designed to

catch any overflow of refrigerant cooling that coil.

Summary of Absorption Cooler Operation

When sun-heated water is piped through the absorption unit's generator, the absorbent solution (LiBr/H2O) is raised by this heat to the vapor separator located at the top of the generator. From this point, the solution is able to flow to the absorber by gravity, assisted by the small pressure difference between the generator (relatively high) and the absorber (relatively low).

In the absorber, water vapor is taken into the solution, which then flows back to the bottom of the generator. But we know that pressure in the absorber is a little lower than pressure in the generator. To overcome this obstacle, designers of the chiller unit have placed the absorber higher than the generator so the solution flow is accomplished by the force of gravity overcoming the pressure differential.

The water vapor (refrigerant), which was released or "boiled off" in the generator, rises to the condenser and is condensed there to a liquid. The condenser is placed at a high elevation in the unit so that the liquid refrigerant will flow by gravity to the evaporator. In this case, the flow is further aided because the evaporator is at a lower absolute pressure than the condenser above it.

A net result of careful thermodynamic design, taking advantage of differences in fluid temperatures, density, and the relative height of fluid chambers in the chiller unit, is that this somewhat complex equipment functions without moving parts. So there is no vibration even in a 100-ton absorption cooler of the type used in commercial buildings, factories, and schools.

Many Installations of Solaire Air Conditioners

Most of the Solaire absorption chillers installed now can trace their ancestry to the well-known Servel gas refrigerators—which used gas heat to cool food—and more recently the Servel water-cooled gas-fired absorption units operating with a lithium bromide-water solution. In fact, the Arkla factory where Solaire chillers are manufactured is the former Servel plant in Evansville, Indiana, while the national sales office is in Little Rock.

There is a long list of installations of these absorption coolers in buildings heated and cooled by the sun's energy. Some of the more noteworthy include:

- Shopping centers at Randolph Air Force base, Texas, and Kirkland Air Force Base, Albuquerque, New Mexico, where a combination of solar energy and natural gas is used for both heating and cooling.

- George A. Towns Elementary School in Atlanta, Georgia, with a solar heating and cooling system including 10,000 square feet of liquid collectors and 45,000 gallons of sun-heated water storage for a 32,000-square foot single-story building. Solar engineering was provided by Westinghouse Electric Corporation of Pittsburgh.

- One of three solar houses designed as research projects by engineers at Colorado State University and built in Fort Collins, Colorado. This is a 1-story 3-bedroom house with heated basement and 2-car garage and a heated area (including basement) of 3,000 square feet. Solar heat is provided by a system with 760 square feet of collectors and an 1,100-gallon insulated steel storage tank in the basement. There is a 3-ton Arkla absorption chiller for summer cooling. About 65% of the heating and cooling is provided by solar energy, the other 35% by natural gas.

- NASA solar energy research buildings at Lewis Research Center, Cleveland, Ohio, and at Marshall Space Flight Center, Huntsville, Alabama, where most of the energy for both space heating and hot water and cooling is provided by the sun.

- A solar energy research building with solar heating and cooling at each of the following universities:
  - New Mexico State University, Las Cruces
  - Ohio State University, Columbus
  - University of Texas at Arlington
  - University of Texas, Students' Co-op, Inc., San Antonio
  - Pahlavi University (named after the Shah), Shiraz, Iran

As mentioned earlier, there is growing use of solar energy in the sunny, oil-rich OPEC countries. It's not hard to understand that the intelligent rulers of such countries as Iran and Saudi Arabia are importing American solar technology and equipment in exchange for oil. It wouldn't surprise this author if, in addition to solar heating and cooling for their buildings, at least one of these countries might be one of the first to build a major solar power plant, using their abundant sunlight to generate many megawatts of electric power—and perhaps using some of that electricity to convert salt water into fresh water, urgently needed in desert areas.

Absorption Cooling Requires Very Hot Water

Because heating the generator of an absorption chiller demands water temperatures of 195°F or higher, there has been considerable development of special solar collectors to concentrate the sunlight on the waterways. Here are some examples of designs which ensure a supply of extremely hot water, suitable for reliable operation of absorption units during the summer.

First, it's worth noting that the summer is an ideal season for operating a solar collector to heat water. As pointed out several

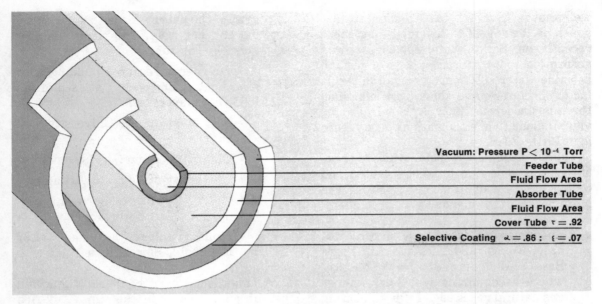

Vacuum: Pressure $P < 10^{-4}$ Torr
Feeder Tube
Fluid Flow Area
Absorber Tube
Fluid Flow Area
Cover Tube $\tau = .92$
Selective Coating $\alpha = .86 : \epsilon = .07$

FIGURE 6-5. Cross Section of SUNPAK Glass Tubular Collector Developed by Owens-Illinois, Inc., for Solar Absorption Coolers

times previously, the efficiency of a collector increases when the difference in temperature between the sun-heated water in the collector and the ambient air is minimal. It's what your common sense would tell you. When it's hot outside, you can expect to get hotter water from your solar collectors. Even so, many installers of absorption chillers have designed their summer-winter solar systems to include special collectors— usually more expensive than the ones previously described in this book—which will provide water under pressure at temperatures over its boiling point (212°F at sea level) or even higher.

One of the solar collectors most widely used to get hot enough water to operate absorption coolers efficiently is the SUN-PAK glass tubular collector, developed and manufactured by Owens-Illinois (O-I), Inc., of Toledo, Ohio. A cross section of this tubular design appears in Figure 6-5. All three of the concentric tubes—feeder, absorber, and cover tube—are made of glass. The glass is a borosilicate with low iron content. According to O-I, this material has good resistance to thermal shock. The vacuum envelope, or cover tube, which has a transmissivity of 92%, is joined to the absorber tube by a flame process to ensure hermetic sealing and a vacuum inside the collector of 10^{-4} Torr.

The outer surface of the absorber tube is coated with a selective coating with an absorptivity of insolation amounting to 86% and an emissivity of only 7%. Inside this absorber is the innermost of the three tubes, the feeder, through which flows either water or an antifreeze mixture (in cold climates). Typical dimensions of the O-I tubular unit are diameter, 2 inches and length, 44 inches. When 24 of these tubes are assembled into a panel, the installation area is 4 feet x 8 feet, with an effective collector area of 27.4 square feet. Manifolds or headers at the top and bottom of each row of 24 tubes are made of 1.125-inch OD copper covered with 1.5 inches of polyurethane foam insulation. Figure 6-6 shows how easy it is to assemble the O-I collectors at the site, inserting the evacuated tubes in the manifolds on the roof.

Outlet temperatures of 240°F or higher are readily achieved with these glass collec-

FIGURE 6-6. Installing Owens-Illinois Collectors on Roof of Mission Viejo, California, Home for Solar Cooling and Heating

tors, which makes them suitable for efficient operation of absorption chillers and for supplying sun-heated water or antifreeze mixture for space heating and industrial process applications. One drawback has been the cost of these all-glass collectors, although the manufacturer has reduced their price from about $25 per square foot of applied area in 1975—when this design was first introduced commercially—to about $15 a square foot in 1977. As production increases, the future price is projected to be under $10 a square foot, according to Richard E. Ford of Owens-Illinois.

One large application of O-I collectors is in supplying solar energy for space heating and cooling of the El Camino Real School in Irvine, California. This system is shown diagrammatically in Figure 6-7.

Designed by an outstanding firm of solar engineers, McCaughey & Smith Energy Associates of Tustin, California, this solar installation provides 5,000 square feet of effective collector area. The evacuated glass tube collectors are mounted on tilted platforms on the roof of the school, which has an interior area of 41,000 square feet.

Water is heated to a maximum temperature of 240° at the collector outlet, where the maximum pressure is 30 psi. This sun-heated water is pumped through the collector flow loop to a heat exchanger in the

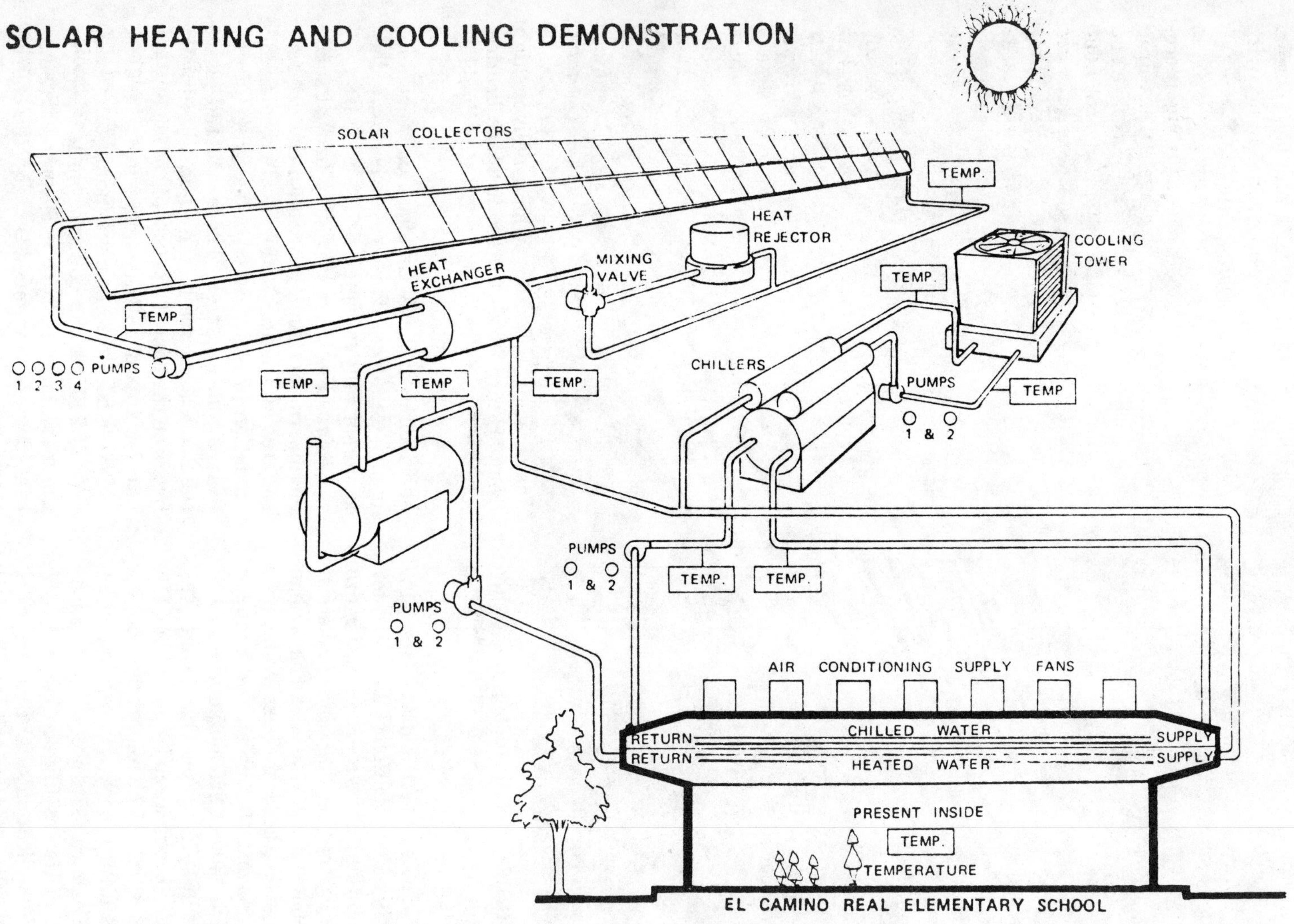

SOLAR HEATING AND COOLING DEMONSTRATION

FIGURE 6-7. Application of Owens-Illinois SUNPAK Glass Tubular Collectors in El Camino Real School, Irvine, California

building equipment room. The exchanger transfers thermal energy to a second high-temperature water loop which includes an auxiliary gas-fired water heater. An automatic control system of the differential thermostat type turns on this auxiliary heater on the rare occasions when there is not enough solar energy to meet the building load.

The high-temperature water in the secondary loop supplies solar energy enough to operate two 100-ton Arkla absorption chillers. These are older air conditioning units, already in the school before the solar installation was made, and require 220°F water for maximum efficiency. Chilled water from the two Arkla units is circulated through fan-coil assemblies to cool the building.

According to the solar engineers who designed this system, such a large building in Southern California normally occupied by many people and with extensive internal lighting the year around—it's a 12-month school—needs much more cooling than heating. However, the sun heated water in the secondary loop is also used in a hydronic system, the same fan-coil units, to heat the building whenever heating is needed.

An interesting feature of this installation, as indicated in Figure 6-7, is that there is a "heat rejector" mounted on the roof. This is a bypass unit used to dissipate excess energy when the number of BTU or langleys being collected from the sun is greater than the amount needed for heating or cooling this large school. "We can't turn the sun off," says Owen McCaughey, "so we had to design a heat rejector which is included in the output line from the collectors to the main heat exchanger whenever our automatic control system says we're collecting too much solar energy."

Shenandoah, Georgia, has a new Recreation Center equipped with a solar heating and cooling system. On the sawtooth roof are mounted 11,200 square feet of Revere Copper and Brass liquid-type panels with double glazing. Installation of these collectors was speeded by using a helicopter to lift them up to the roof. A 15,000-gallon

water storage tank is buried in a berm as part of the insulation, and supplies thermal storage for space heating and cooling (with a 100-ton Arkla chiller). Another 2,300-gallon preheat tank has a heat exchanger coil in it, where the hot water needed in the recreation center is heated. Backup is a gas-fired heater. Total investment is $726,000 and the annual savings are estimated at $77,000 at present fuel rates. Since these rates are bound to increase, the payoff will probably be in about 7 years. After that this large recreation center will have exceptionally low operating costs compared with conventional buildings.

Corning Glass Works of Corning, New York, developed a similar tubular solar collector, made largely but not entirely of glass as is the O-I unit, but is not offering a commercial model in 1977. A research program is continuing, aimed at coming up with a design with good thermal efficiency—which the previous Corning collector had—but one better adapted to mass production at a modest price. General Electric is testing an evacuated tubular collector for introduction in 1978. It makes sense that large manufacturers of fluorescent lights should become interested in using similar techniques to make solar collectors which deliver high temperature fluids for use in space heating and cooling, as well as superheated liquid or steam for industrial applications requiring process heat.

Concentrating Collectors for Higher Temperatures

As a corollary to the need for relatively high temperatures in the fluids heated by solar collectors, there has been an increasing interest in going one step beyond the flat-plate collectors described earlier in this book. This added step also results in higher outlet temperatures than are achieved by the evacuated tube design of Owens-Illinois.

Every high school student of physics—and most elementary school students who have taken a general science course—will recognize the principles on which the de-

FIGURE 6-8.   Northrup Concentrating Solar Collector Using Linear Fresnel Lens

signs of *concentrating* solar collectors are based. On a relatively cool sunny day, you can easily burn a hole in a piece of paper by concentrating the sun's energy, using a simple magnifying glass and placing the paper at the focal point of the magnifier lens.

A modification of this concept is found in the concentrating collector made by Northrup, Inc., of Hutchins, Texas, and shown in cross section in Figure 6-8. Facing the sun, instead of a flat glass cover plate, is a linear curved Fresnel lens made of extruded acrylic plastic. The smooth outer surface of the lens transmits solar radiation with a minimum of reflective losses. As the solar radiation passes through the lens, it is refracted

(bent) by an array of small prisms. These prisms, their shape computer-designed, concentrate the sunbeams so that they are focused on a black-painted copper absorber at the bottom of the trough shown in the figure.

One feature of this Fresnel-type collector cover claimed by Northrup is that the concentration factor is about 10. Sunlight falling on the standard collector with a lens about 10 feet long and 1 foot wide—an effective collecting area of 9.7 square feet—is concentrated on a small black copper tube with a surface area of less than 1 foot. The maker declares that this concentrating collector will collect about twice as much solar energy per square foot (using its 9.7 square feet of lens area) as a flat-plate collector with double glazing, and about 25% more solar energy than vacuum tube collectors. This means that fewer collectors are required to produce the number of BTU you need to heat and cool your house.

Housing for the Northrup collector is a galvanized steel trough insulated with fiberglass. Each group of from 3 to 40 collectors is aimed at the sun throughout the day by a sun-following system. Two silicon solar cells are set on a base at a 60° angle to one another, with both facing the sun. When one cell gets more radiation than the other, the electronic bridge to which the cells are connected becomes unbalanced. This activates a small electric motor attached to a cable-and-pulley system capable of turning up to 40 collectors so that they face the sun.

This sun-tracking mechanism offers a still further advantage of the Northrup energy collection system because it enables each collector to receive nearly direct radiation—minimizing losses from reflection—throughout the day. This is a definite gain over a south-facing tilted flat-plate collector during summer months when this conventional type of collector receives much less direct radiation until the sun's position is south of the east-west line.

According to Northrup tests, if 200°F water is required in the summer to operate an absorption chiller, the Fresnel-type concentrator will supply it at 65% collection efficiency or about 20% higher than the efficiency of an evacuated tube collector system under similar conditions. The conditions cited are an ambient air of 90°F and insolation of 300 BTU per square foot per hour, with the 200°F temperature of collector water being 1/2 the sum of inlet fluid temperature and outlet fluid temperature.

Other collector systems incorporating Fresnel lenses include those of the following California manufacturers:

McDonnell Douglas Astronautics Company, Huntington Beach, California has made large V-shaped collectors about 20 feet long, 3 feet wide at the top, and 6 feet high. A black-surfaced copper pipe at the bottom of the V carries water, which can reach a temperature of 600°F on a sunny summer day. The Fresnel lens was designed jointly by engineers of McDonnell Douglas and Swedlow, Inc., of Garden Grove, California, the plastics fabricator. Each of these large concentrating collectors is aimed at the sun automatically in only a single axis, moving on a north-south axis while the sun's apparent movement is east-west. (We say "apparent" because our planet actually moves around the sun.)

These highly efficient solar collectors have been fabricated by the giant aerospace company as one phase of its program on Total Energy Systems (TES) as a subcontractor to Sandia Laboratories, Albuquerque. Details and illustrations of the TES program financed by ERDA as a means for supplying not only space heating and cooling but also electrical energy, using superhot water, are provided in Chapter 10. Water at 600°F under pressure becomes steam when permitted to expand, and this steam is useful for driving turbogenerators which deliver electricity and also can be used in a variety of industrial applications requiring process heat.

A relatively small company, *Applied Sol Tech, Inc.*, of Long Beach, California, has designed a completely different collector using an array of cylindrical Fresnel lenses as a cover plate over an absorber plate of steel painted black. There are multifaceted plastic lenses, one lens over each of the fluid channels in the multiple sawtooth structure of the absorber, shown in Figure 6-9. Each lens acts as a small prism to concentrate solar energy on one of the absorber channels. With sunlight focused in this way, the designers state that no tracking mechanism is necessary to achieve a high temperature from the sun-heated fluid. Specifications of the ASTI-10 solar collector, which includes 100 concentrator modules and 20 flow channels, indicate a typical output temperature of 302°F (150°C) at a flow rate of 13.3 gallons per hour (14 cubic centimeters per second) with 1 langley of solar flux. This collec-

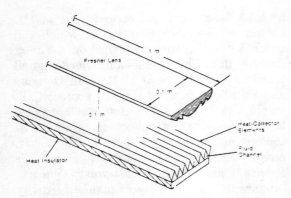

FIGURE 6-9. Concentrator Module Manufactured by Applied Sol Tech, Inc., of Long Beach, California

tor is 16.4 feet x 6.6 feet (5 meters x 2 meters) providing an area of 107.6 square feet (10 square meters). Designer of this unit is Ulf Brynjestad, long an aerospace engineer with Northrop Aircraft. According to Robert N. Woodworth, president of Applied Sol Tech, the first models of this collector are priced at $3,400 each, or about $31 per square foot, but this figure should come down with production quantities.

Advantages claimed for this concentrating collector design, which is also being marketed by Owen Enterprises, Inc., of Wilmington (the harbor area of Los Angeles), include its greater efficiency than flat-plate collectors; delivery of high temperature sun-heated fluid without use of a tracking system; and useful application to solar cooling and industrial and commercial processes. (Owen Enterprises is one of the first solar companies to be owned by American Indian entrepreneurs.)

Efficient Parabolic Collectors

One of the oldest and best ways to concentrate solar radiation is by means of parabolic reflectors which focus the sun's rays. An example of this technique is the tracking collector made by Sunpower Systems Corporation, Tempe, Arizona, and shown in Figure 6-10.

The heat transfer fluid flows through a black copper pipe placed along the long axis of a parabolic trough. This trough is 10 feet long, and there are two versions: one 2 feet wide, the other 4 feet wide—thus having twice as much reflective surface. The trough is made of anodized aluminum with a reflectivity of 85%. Framing for the reflector and absorber pipe is painted steel tubing.

In typical rooftop applications, the Sunpower Systems collectors are made to track the sun by a technique similar to that of Northrup's Fresnel-type concentrating collectors. Two solar cells in a bridge circuit operate a 1/15-HP motor which turns the parabolic troughs so that they collect and reflect a maximum amount of available sunlight. The manufacturer claims a tracking accuracy of ±0.5° and states that the system includes antifreeze protection as well as a high-temperature defocusing circuit. "Storm damage is minimized because in overcast weather or at night, the troughs are automatically returned to their nighttime position," says the chief engineer of this Arizona company.

Installations in Arizona of this concentrating collector system include:

- A number of homes in Sun City, a desert retirement community near Phoenix with solar cooling (3-ton absorption chillers) as well as solar space heating and domestic hot water. Three parabolic trough collectors do an adequate job for the home illustrated in Figure 6-11.

- A solar system on the roof of a coin-operated laundry on the Navajo Reservation of Kayenta. One of the best as well as most obvious commercial applications of solar energy, now being installed in many areas and using numerous types of collectors, is to heat the large amounts of water required by laundry operators.

- A solar cooling and heating system for the Air National Guard building at Sky Harbor Airport, Phoenix.

FIGURE 6-10.   Parabolic Reflectors in Tracking Collector Made by Sunpower
Systems of Tempe, Arizona, Makes Use of One of the Oldest Known Ways to
Concentrate Solar Radiation

- A similar solar system at Dead Horse Ranch State Park.
- A solar car wash in Mesa and swimming pool heating in Fountain Hills.
- A solar-powered irrigation pump used by Arizona cotton growers.

Another interesting development by Sunpower Systems is what the company calls a "Solar Carousel." An array of parabolic collectors is made to travel each day on a circular track—as if they were miniature railroad cars—moving 210° daily while each collector in the array simultaneously tracks the elevation of the sun in the southern quadrant. Steam generated from this array at 400°F is used to operate a steam engine designed by this company. The engine may

then drive pumps or an electrical generator, or perform other useful work.

Sunpower Systems estimates the efficiency of the solar carousel at 79% and states that this dual-tracking solar unit is capable of heating moving water under pressure to 500°F. This approach, where space permits, appears to be an interesting entry in the race to achieve efficient TES designs for many potential applications in industry, as outlined in Chapter 10.

Another parabolic reflector made of brightly polished aluminum focusing sunlight on a 1-1/2-inch black copper tube is produced by ZZ Corporation of Los Alamitos, California. This reflector, 8 feet long and 4 feet wide, is held in a painted steel rack as shown in Figure 6-12. The concen-

FIGURE 6-11. Model Home at Sun City, Arizona, Cooled and Heated with BTU (Sunpower Systems Parabolic Collectors)

FIGURE 6-12. Clock-Driven Parabolic Collector

trating collector will deliver water under pressure heated to about 300°F, according to Fred W. Hottenroth, a veteran mechanical engineer and president of ZZ. Tracking is accomplished by a small 10-watt motor and clock mechanism adequate to keep four solar collectors facing the sun throughout the day. Each collector weighs less than 50 pounds and is considerably more efficient than flat-plate units. An array of four collectors with a single drive is priced at $290 per collector, or about $9.20 per square foot—an extremely competitive price.

Hottenroth has also designed a simple heliometer, consisting of a miniature collector and temperature gauge, to give you a reading of output temperature resulting from solar radiation in a matter of minutes at any site. His company is quoting on solar installations at large industrial plants now using gas for space and process heating, where solar energy during winter months may mean the difference between profitable operation and forced shutdowns in areas such as Ohio and Pennsylvania.

Experimental Solar Air Conditioner from General Electric

Since we began this chapter with a quotation from GE as to the lack of a truly cost-effective solar air conditioner for cooling buildings, it's appropriate to conclude with word from GE on a new development that looks promising. This is a heat pump system driven by solar energy.

According to a recent report at the 1977 annual meeting of the American Society of Heating, Refrigeration, and Air Conditioning Engineers (ASHRAE), the components of the new system include liquid-type solar collectors, a Rankine cycle engine, and a standard heat pump, plus suitable auxiliary equipment such as a centrifugal pumps, valves, and thermostatic controls. The principal new feature of this system, says B. J. Tharpe, manager of Advanced Energy Systems for the GE Space Division in Philadelphia, is a multivane expander as part of the low-temperature Rankine cycle engine. This expander can be slowed down or speeded up without a marked effect on the total system's COP (coefficient of performance.) High efficiency is maintained over a wide range of load, speed, and vapor pressure conditions. The multivane expander may be used with dry or wet vapor without problems of erosion of liquid compression, and operates efficiently at speeds compatible with today's refrigeration compressors.

A prototype of the new GE system has been tested for more than 3,000 hours with an average COP ranging from 0.85 to 1.0. When operated as a Rankine cycle engine with certain conventional refrigerants, including freon compounds, the system can deliver 3 tons of air conditioning—accomplishing this cooling when water at temperatures up to 230°F is supplied. For winter operation, the system can be used like a conventional heat pump and delivers 83,000 BTU per hour for space heating. Tharpe says this kind of system needs more development but "it could become the kind of solar heating and cooling system the American public can afford."

Many other companies, large and small, are working with solar-driven heat pump systems. For a novel technique developed by Solartec, a relatively small firm in San Diego, see the description at the end of Chapter 8 showing how a swimming pool, for instance, along with highly efficient concentrator collectors delivering solar-heated water at temperatures well in excess of 200°F can supply a home with heating, cooling, and domestic hot water.

New GE Collector Supplies High Temperature Fluid

According to GE's Tharpe, the company's new "thermos bottle" solar collector can supply almost twice as much heat energy as a conventional flat plate collector, at liquid temperatures around 250°F. This new model TC-100 collector consists of a parallel array of 10 glass double-walled vacuum tubes mounted in a frame over a metal reflector. The reflector is designed so that practically all the sunlight is either absorbed directly by, or reflected on, the 10 collecting tubes constituting one collector with an area of 16 square feet.

Each collecting tube is formed from two coaxial glass cylinders separated by 0.10 inch, with the intervening space evacuated to a pressure of less than 10^{-4} Torr. This vacuum sealing eliminates most conductive and convective losses.

Solar radiation passing through the clear outer cylinder is absorbed by a black, selectively coated surface on the inner glass cylinder. This inner black surface has an emissivity of less than 10%. The absorbed heat is transferred by thin metal fins lining the inside surface of the inner glass cylinder. These fins are brazed to a small copper tube which is doubled back and serves to carry the heat transfer fluid. In a typical arrangement, the copper tubes carrying the solar-heated fluid in each of the 10 collecting tubes are joined in series, with input and output lines connected to insulated headers or manifolds.

Tharpe says that about 50% of the space heating and hot water needs in a Washington, D.C., home with an area of 1,800 square feet can be provided by 200 square feet of the new TC-100 solar collectors heating an antifreeze mixture to temperatures well over 200°F. Techniques used by the GE fluorescent lamp production operations have been borrowed by the Space Division, with the goal of producing these new solar collectors on a large scale at low cost.

As a corollary, intensive testing of various designs of solar collectors is underway not only by many government and private laboratories but also by such big merchandisers as Sears and Montgomery Ward. Both of these huge chains are testing solar water heaters and will offer them to the public soon—perhaps before you read this page.

7

Passive Solar Techniques — Versatile and Low-Cost

The first inhabitants of the North American continent used passive solar heating and cooling effectively. Particularly in the Southwest, dwellings of many Indian tribes were designed to take advantage of the seasonal positions of the sun in the sky.

Their adobe houses had thick walls which absorb heat during the day, a gradual process taking advantage of the material's thermal lag. As a result, the interiors of these buildings remained relatively cool in the summer heat. Then at night there was enough residual heat, released slowly, to keep the inside comfortable.

Even more primitive dwellings in the cliffs were chosen so that their entrances faced south, for warming by the winter sun. But each cave had an overhang, natural or manmade, providing shade in the summer and keeping the cliffhouse cool when the sun was high overhead.

Similar concepts are being used by modern architects determined to take advantage of passive solar techniques to save energy at low cost. As mentioned previously, a leader in solar design is Donald Watson, AIA, a member of the Yale University architectural faculty, consultant in about 100 solar heating projects and author of several books,

including *Designing and Building a Solar Home* (Garden Way Publishing). He and his associates have used both passive systems and a variety of solar collectors, liquid and air.

For example, in existing homes or apartments, Watson recommends a number of passive techniques for energy conservation. If you have windows facing south, they will provide good heat gain during sunny days in the winter. Insulated glass, with double glazing and weatherstripping, should be used in colder areas—or even triple glazing in exceptionally severe climates. To retain the heat collected during the day, you should cover the windows with some form of insulation at night. Interior insulating shades and draperies are easily installed.

An increasingly popular automatic system, which any handy do-it-yourselfer can apply, is the Beadwall developed by Steve Baer, the highly inventive proprietor of Zomeworks in Albuquerque. Styrofoam beads are blown between two panes of glass to prevent heat loss during wintry nights or heat gain on summer days. This patented system, as well as the same inventor's Nightwall, an insulating cover held in place by magnetic clips and thus easy to install or

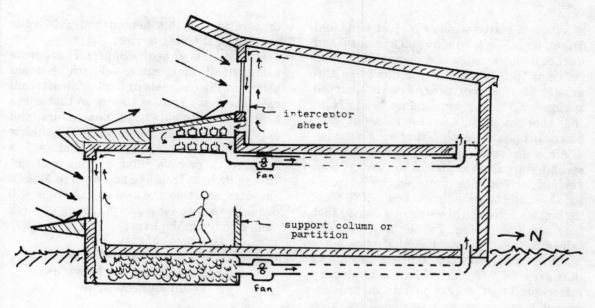

interceptor sheet

fan

support column or partition

N

fan

FIGURE 7-1. Passive Solar Heating System

remove, and Skylids, louvers opened and closed by the sun's heat, are described in detail later in this chapter.

Low-Cost Method of Storing Solar Heat

There is a simple method for obtaining solar heat through a window or french door, preferably facing south, based on Scheme S-110 described by Dr. William A. Shurcliff, noted solar scientist, author, and Harvard University physicist. As he stated to this writer in a recent letter, he keeps "inventing new and cheaper schemes for the solar heating of homes."

You buy a sheet of transparent gray plastic, which Bill Shurcliff calls an interceptor. This sheet should have a transmittance of about 30% for sunlight—slightly more transparent than sunglasses—and an absorption of about 60% of the solar radiation. The other 10% is lost by reflection.

Hang this gray plastic sheet in such a way that it extends from about a foot below your ceiling to about a foot off the floor. Place it as a sunshade and interceptor about 4 inches behind your south-facing window or glass

door. Below the sheet put a double row of plastic bottles filled with water. These are the familiar 1-gallon bottles found in your supermarket and originally containing distilled water, milk, detergent, or some other liquid.

Most of the solar radiation will be intercepted by the gray plastic sheet, and the warm air from this surface will flow over the bottles full of water. During the day these bottles will gradually become warm. At night the sun-warmed water will radiate heat into your room. This is an extremely inexpensive method for adding heat energy to almost any room exposed to sunlight, and storing this energy so that you get useful heat when the sun goes down or the weather suddenly changes to stormy.

Don't expect any miracles from such a simple, low-cost passive system. But it illustrates what a little ingenuity and everyday materials can do to help you gain solar energy—whether you live in a city apartment or a suburban home.

If you are building a new house, you might show the sketch in Figure 7-1 to your architect. Here Shurcliff suggests a south wall on the second story consisting mainly of a double-glazed window 30 feet wide and 5 feet high. This window faces south and next to its lower edge is a sloping aluminum reflector 16 feet wide. If you don't like aluminum on this roof area, a white-painted surface will serve reasonably well. Note that there is an interceptor sheet of gray plastic inside this south-facing wide window.

Air is directed through a duct below the second-story floor as shown so that the convection currents flow between the interceptor sheet and the window to heat 1,500 plastic bottles filled with water in a bin 30 feet long and 8 feet wide. The air flow is maintained by a fan in the duct that runs automatically whenever the temperature in the duct exceeds 75°F. Most of the solar energy intercepted by the gray plastic sheet is directed away from this second-story area and into the storage bin to heat the water bottles. On a sunny day, Shurcliff estimates that the bin temperature will be 10°F higher than the temperature of the upper room.

On the first floor, with a similar south-facing window area, interceptor sheet and outside reflector, warm air is directed to 25 tons of stones in an insulated bin below the floor. The house is well insulated and has massive masonry floors and walls, with insulation outside the walls.

After early May, direct solar radiation is blocked by eaves and awnings. Large portions of the gray interceptor plastic may be unclipped and stored during the hot months. Reflected radiation is blocked by installing a green canvas "fence" about 2 feet high below the big windows on both floors. After midnight each night, an automatic control opens vents and the fans pull in cool night air and circulate it through the two bins—the upper filled with water jugs, and the lower full of stones. Then during the day, when cooling is needed, air circulation through these bins provides chilled air.

Floors and interior walls are channeled to facilitate heat input and output. You can preheat domestic water by running a coil of soft copper in a helix perhaps 60 feet long through one of the heat storage bins, and then returning this heated water to your conventional water heater.

For auxiliary heat, Shurcliff suggests using small inexpensive electric heaters placed in the channels or ducts downstream from the fans. You set timers so that these heaters operate only at off-peak hours, and only when the room temperature falls below 68°F. The inventor's guess is that such a house with passive solar heating will get 75% of its heat from the sun even in Massachusetts, and that the two storage bins will provide warmth for a carrythrough of 1-1/2 sunless days in January.

Ingenious Passive Devices from Zomeworks

One of the most remarkable solar pioneers is Steve Baer, the young Albuquerque inventor and founder of Zomeworks Corporation. Dressed in Levis, this engineer-builder and his associates, Dave Harrison and Brud Grossman, are dedicated to the proposition that everyone should be able to use solar energy at a modest price. They work in an adobe building with a large back yard. Both building and yard are filled with examples of how the sun's heat can be utilized in passive applications—little or no external energy applied—at minimum cost.

One device is Beadwall, an insulating window shown in Figure 7-2. Between the two layers of glass is an air space just like that in a double-glazed storm window. The difference in Zomeworks' patented design is that this air space is filled with tiny styrofoam beads to prevent heat loss during winter nights or in stormy weather, and to block heat gain in the summer.

The complete Beadwall system consists of a motor-storage unit, plastic piping (PVC) connecting this unit to the window panels, a timer, and controls including a solar thermostat. The motor-storage cylinder is 2 feet in diameter and contains the blower motors and necessary bead ducting, as well as a supply of the white beads. There are two

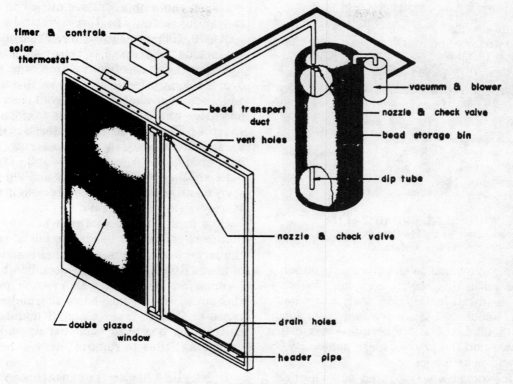

timer & controls
solar thermostat
bead transport duct
vent holes
vacumm & blower
nozzle & check valve
bead storage bin
dip tube
nozzle & check valve
double glazed window
drain holes
header pipe

FIGURE 7-2. Zomeworks' (Albuquerque, New Mexico) BEADWALL. In this Insulating Window, Styrofoam Beads are Blown Between 2 Panes of Glass to Prevent Heat Loss During Winter Nights and Heat Gain During Summer Days

115 volt AC 7.8 ampere vacuum motors mounted in the galvanized steel cylinder. Each motor has a 1-1/2-inch PVC extension at one end for easy connection to the PVC ducts leading to and from the Beadwall panels. The motors blow in opposite directions, blowing the styrofoam beads to fill the panels, or sucking them back into the motor-storage unit, depending upon the operation of the controls. There are 1-1/2 feet of 3-wire leads from each motor, making it easy to hook up the unit to your standard AC supply.

Three inches of styrofoam beads in one of these ingenious windows gives your wall the equivalent of 3 inches of fiberglass insulation. Zomeworks provides complete Beadwall panel frames sized to accept 3/16-inch tempered patio door glass. Standard widths are 34 inches and 46 inches (pane width) and

a height of 76 inches. Finished panels are 80 inches in height by either 37-1/4 inches or 49-1/4 inches wide for single panels, and 80-1/2 or 104-1/2 inches wide for double panels. Because one motor-storage unit will serve two panels, it is considerably more economical to use Beadwalls in the double-panel configuration if they will fit your window areas.

This device is patented, so you will need a license if you want to buy all Beadwall components except motor-storage units and panels. When you buy these components, the purchase price includes your license to install the entire system. Typically, Zomeworks furnishes the frames, glazing accessories, and panel ducting as well as the motor-storage units and controls. You buy panes of tempered glass locally and also suitable lengths of 1-1/2-inch PVC pipe to

FIGURE 7-3. BEADWALL
Installation at Pitkin County Airport,
Aspen, Colorado

connect your panel to the storage cylinder. Purchased in this way, a complete double-panel Beadwall installation with a window area of about 48-1/2 square feet costs just under $500 f.o.b. Albuquerque—to which you must add the price of glass panes, PVC pipe, and your labor.

An inexpensive way to find out whether you want to install Beadwall panels in place of conventional windows on the south side—or perhaps southeast or southwest sides—of your house is to buy a set of plans from Zomeworks. For $15 you will get seven pages of plans and specifications, including a detailed list of the tools and supplies you will need to install a Beadwall window system in either a conventional or a solar-heated house. These bead-filled panels have an insulation R factor of about 8.5 when full and 1.5 when empty.

Although Beadwall panels have been installed in many residences, one of the most impressive applications is in an airport terminal, the Pitkin County Airport in Aspen, Colorado. This building, shown in Figure 7-3, is the creation of Larry Yaw, AIA, of the architectural firm of Copland, Finholm, Hagman, and Yaw, with solar engineering supplied by Zomeworks.

The one-story complex of three connecting rectangular buildings has a total floor area of 16,800 square feet used for airline,

weather, and administrative offices as well as waiting rooms. The three vertical south walls, 70, 100, and 70 feet long, respectively, include 8, 12, and 8 Beadwall panels. Each panel has an effective area of slightly over 24 square feet (46 inches x 76 inches) and uses two sheets of Kalwall Sun-Lite polyester reinforced fiberglass transparent sheeting. This plastic pane material is lighter and more resistant to shattering than tempered glass. A space of about 2.7 inches between the two plastic panes is filled with styrofoam beads during winter nights, in stormy weather, or on hot days.

On a sunny day in winter, when the million-or-so styrofoam beads are out of sight, the large panels have a thermal resistance of about R-2. At night, with a million beads forming an insulating wall in each panel, this outer wall surface has a thermal resistance of R-9. It takes about 3 minutes to deliver the beads to each panel; and the same short time to remove them.

Skylids Make Automatically Insulated Skylights

Also in the Aspen airport building, where the solar engineering was performed by Zomeworks, there are two long monitors on the flat roof of each of the three structures in the complex. The south face of each monitor consists largely of skylights. There is a fixed outer glazing of two sheets of Filon, a reinforced transparent plastic. Behind this glazing at a distance of about 1-1/2 feet is a set of Skylids, another ingenious passive system patented by Steve Baer.

A Skylid is an insulated louver. A set of Skylids may be placed inside a building in a variety of locations: behind or beneath skylights, glass roofs, clerestories, vertical windows, or french doors. They open automatically during sunny weather and close by themselves during very cloudy periods or at night. When the Skylids are closed, they are an effective thermal barrier, greatly reducing heat losses through any glazed opening, including windows and skylights.

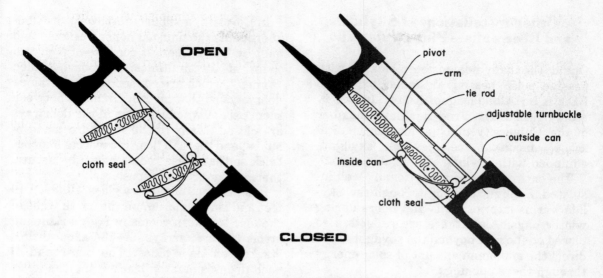

OPEN

pivot
arm
tie rod
adjustable turnbuckle
outside can

cloth seal

inside can

cloth seal

CLOSED

FIGURE 7-4.   Skylids Designed by Steve Baer

Shown in Figure 7-4 is a cross section of a skylight including two Skylids. These louvers are powered by a pair of cannisters connected by tubing and containing freon. When the outside cannister is warmed by the sun, its freon vaporizes and moves to the inner cannister. The weight of this freon in the inner cannister causes the Skylids to open as shown in the sketch. When the inside cannister is warmer, its freon goes to the outer cannister and this shift in weight swings the Skylids shut automatically.

Zomeworks constructs each Skylid by stretching an aluminum skin over wooden ribs. This insulated louver has an airfoil cross section: it is 2 inches thick at the edges, while the middle is 5 inches thick. Rotating on ball bearings, a Skylid is filled with fiberglass insulation and is light, weighing less than 2 pounds per square foot. The plastic tube connecting the two cannisters is carefully sealed with a polyester compound. Says Steve Baer: "Our first Skylids have now been in operation for nearly 5 years, opening and closing faithfully. We cannot see what will wear out in the mechanism."

If you are a reasonably handy do-it-yourselfer, you can install these automatic insulating louvers quite readily. Skylids are designed to fit inside the well of either a skylight or a window. They are supplied in assemblies consisting of either 2 or 3 panels, plus an adjustable linkage mechanism, freon driving device, edge-sealing strips and an override cord with tie-down, all mounted in a frame. Because the Skylid assembly is delivered preframed, you can install it in your rough opening like a prehung door. Braces keep the pair or trio of louvers in position until you've installed them.

Skylid units range in size from 52-1/2 inches long by 48 inches wide (2 louvers) to 124-1/2 inches long by 70 inches wide (3 louvers). In this context, the "long" dimension of a Skylid is the width of your window or skylight, while the "wide" dimension—48 inches (4 feet) for 2 louvers and 70 inches (5 feet 10 inches) for 3 louvers—refers to the height or vertical dimension of your skylight. Prices for these assemblies range from $241.50 to $425. While normally Skylids operate automatically, the override cord with tie-down permits you to adjust the position of these insulating louvers manually so that you can open or close them part way if you wish.

Other Installations of Skylids and Beadwalls — Plus Drumwalls

One of the many homeowners pleased with passive solar heating designed by Steve Baer is an Albuquerque doctor. In the 9-room house of Dr. Fred Herzon, a member of the University of New Mexico medical school faculty, are several skylights equipped with Skylids.

The entire house is exceptionally well insulated. Sunlight pouring through the Skylids warms interior walls and floors during winter days. Also, there are reflectors so placed on the roof beyond the skylights as to direct the maximum amount of solar energy through these openings.

Another very useful passive device incorporated in the Herzon home is what Baer calls a Drumwall. There are 300 square feet of glass on the south side of the doctor's house. Behind this large vertical area of glass are stacks of water-filled drums painted black to absorb solar heat. You might consider these 55-gallon drums to be passive liquid-type solar collectors. As previously mentioned in Chapter 2 in a discussion of Bob Marks's homemade solar hot water heater, such drums are quite inexpensive because they're made in great quantities for use in transporting oil and various chemicals.

The glass walls facing south are transparent during winter days so that the water in the black drums gets hot. Then at night, as you might imagine, millions of styrofoam beads are blown between the two layers of glass to form an insulating blanket. Thus, the combination of a Beadwall and a Drumwall, as well as the Skylids, brings a vast amount of solar heat into the house.

As backup, the Herzon home contains three woodburning stoves and some electric heaters. "We hardly ever use the electric heaters," reports the doctor, "and I've burned only two cords of wood all winter." He says that his large home stays around 70° to 75°F during the day without using anything but solar heating, while at night the temperature drops to about 65°F.

In Corrales, a suburb northwest of Albuquerque, is the unusual house designed and built by Steve Baer. It consists of a curved chain of 10 multifaceted rooms, called "zomes," which are connected by curtained doorways so that air can circulate between them except when curtains in the doorways are closed. Many of the walls are made of adobe, and the slab floor is concrete 5 inches thick so that these rooms have the natural thermal lag of heavy masonry.

Behind areas of window glass, 10 feet x 10 feet and single-glazed, on the south walls of the four southern rooms in Baer's rambling structure are arrays of 55-gallon drums stacked on their sides. The outer end of each drum is painted black while the inner portion is painted in a light shade to complement the decorating scheme of the room served by that specific array of drums. In a typical array there are 25 drums in a stack 5 feet by 5 feet.

During the day, the sun warms the water in these Drumwalls. At night, the window glazing beyond each wall is covered by a flat insulating cover hinged at the bottom of the wall and pulled into position by a nylon rope and handcrank operated from inside the room. A polished aluminum sheet forms the inner side of each insulating cover so that when it is lowered during the day, it acts as a reflector and directs added solar energy toward the black-painted ends of the drums.

Supplementary heating is provided by several skylights equipped with Skylids installed in 1972, about a year after Baer devised his Drumwalls. About 90% of this home's space heating is provided by these two passive solar systems, with a couple of wood-burning stoves as the only auxiliaries.

It is easy to see how you can operate both Drumwalls and Skylids in reverse in the summer. Insulating covers over the Drumwalls are closed during the day to keep out the heat, and lowered at night. Then cool night air flows past the drums and chills the water in them so that the cooled drums keep the rooms comfortable. On days when the ambient air is 100°F, the rooms or zomes in Baer's unusual structure can be kept at

80°F or cooler. As mentioned previously, Skylids automatically open to let in cool night air and close during hot days. Thus, the combination of these two passive solar systems, Drumwalls and Skylids, makes possible comfortable interior temperatures throughout the year while Steve Baer and his wife pay utility bills of $0 for space heating and cooling.

Although both Beadwall and Skylid are patented devices, many other users of solar energy have built structures with Drumwalls or a similar installation. One example is a mobile home in Escondido, California, where John Brand has contructed a solar space heater for $75. One large section of the south wall of his home is an insulated panel, hinged at the bottom, and lined on the inside with aluminum foil. On cold days, this reflector panel is lowered and exposes six "windows" made of Tedlar-coated sheets of reinforced transparent fiberglass. Behind these plastic sheets are ten 55-gallon drums, standing vertically, five on the floor and five above them in Brand's mobile home. The drums are filled with water and painted black, as you would expect. A small electric fan inside the mobile home is turned on when the water-filled drums are heated by the sun, and this fan sucks outside air into the structure past the drums. Brand says that this Drumwall system meets 90% of his heating requirements for a living space of 620 square feet.

More Skylids Installations

Another house, also having 10 zomes but somewhat more compact than the Baer home in Corrales, New Mexico, is the home of J. Kittle in Gaviota, California. Here, Steve Baer and his associates at Zomeworks designed the building with 300 square feet of skylights equipped with Skylids. There are also 150 square feet of south-facing windows.

Sunlight pouring through the Skylids and south windows is absorbed by massive interior walls insulated with 4 inches of fiberglass and also by the insulated slab floors.

With this passive solar heating and thick insulation throughout the Kittle house, about 75% of the space heating requirement comes from solar energy. Auxiliary heat, when needed, is provided by four wood stoves.

This type of structure, with heavily insulated walls, floors, and ceilings, points up the advantage of building with the maximum amount of thermal lag you can get. In the summer, the Skylids are opened automatically at night to let in cool air and closed during the day, while overhangs shade the south-facing windows. The house has the capacity to absorb enough cooling at night, and to retain it, so that no additional cooling is needed. You can imagine how pleased Kittle is as he saves on utility bills and uses about 1/4 as much processed energy as his neighbors.

At an altitude of 7,200 feet in Snowmass, Colorado, is a solar house built by R. Shore and described in this author's previous book. Combined in this home are useful and economical techniques for both active and passive solar heating. In an area so cold that it has 9,200 degree-days annually, this home is 100% heated by solar energy. The main heating system consists of Thomason-type trickling water collectors and a huge storage tank under the child's bedroom. However, considerable supplementary solar heat is provided by three sets of Skylids, each 2 feet x 8 feet for a total area of 48 square feet. Three reflectors, insulated panels faced on the inside with highly reflective aluminized mylar, are mounted on the roof and direct sunlight downward through the Skylids in cold weather. The reflectors are placed at a 62° angle above the Skylids during the winter and add an estimated 25% of solar radiation to the amount passing directly through these louvers. In the summer, the hinged reflectors are lowered from the ridge of the roof so that each reflector is horizontal and shades the Skylids from solar heat but admits diffuse light, helping to illuminate the house.

Another solar house utilizing both Skylids and flat-plate collectors is owned by J. Eddy in Little Compton, Rhode Island. As described by Dr. William Shurcliff of Harvard, the entire south face of this house slopes at an angle of 60° with Sunworks air-type collectors covering 360 square feet of the upper wall and below them a greenhouse wall covered by a single glazing over 4 tiers of Skylids. On winter nights, these automatic louvers close and provide the equivalent of 5 inches of fiberglass insulation. During the day the sun shines through a single pane of glass, and the Skylids are opened by solar heat. With a 240-square foot area with single glazing and Skylids, solar energy warms the earth of the greenhouse floor, which is about two feet below the main floor of the house. Then warm air from the greenhouse is circulated to rooms on the first and second stories of this unusual structure, designed by T. Price, one of the area's pioneer solar architects.

A building in White Rock, New Mexico, designed by solar architect David Wright, has a completely passive solar heating system. In the center of a large 4-bedroom house with thick adobe brick walls and good external insulation is an extensive greenhouse roof sloping at a 15° angle. There is a double glazing of plastic sheets over this 600-square foot roof and behind the glazing are many Skylid assemblies operated automatically by the sun. Additional passive solar heating is furnished by double-glazed (glass) windows at a 60° angle sloping down from the flat roof as well as some double-glazed vertical windows facing south. All the Skylids and windows admit solar energy effectively during the winter because they face south. The insulated adobe walls and floors absorb so much solar heat that this building at an altitude of 6,700 feet in a 6,000 degree-day location near Santa Fe is estimated to get about 90% of its space heating passively from the sun. Auxiliary heat is furnished when needed by wood-burning fireplaces and baseboard electric heaters.

It's not surprising that domestic hot water for this 3,350-square foot adobe brick house, owned by Charles Newton, is provided by a thermosiphoning hot water heater made by Zomeworks. This solar water heater includes 3 conventional flat-plate collectors, each with 20 square feet of collector area, an aluminum box containing a black-painted copper absorber plate on which is a serpentine of copper pipe, with fiberglass insulation under the absorber and a single glazing of glass. The 82-gallon glass-lined tank includes an outer-jacket heat exchanger and is mounted, for thermosiphoning, above the top of the collectors. Price of this solar heater, including three collectors, is under $900. In most of the Zomeworks installations of solar water heaters, one or two collectors do the job.

More Beadwall Installations

An interesting application of a Beadwall is on the sloping south face of the Hayes Regional Aboretum Solar Greenhouse in Richmond, Indiana. With the solar design by D. R. Hendricks, this 1,000-square foot building has a south wall 50 feet x 18 feet sloping 53° with two layers, separated by two inches of air space, of Tedlar-coated reinforced fiberglass. Styrofoam beads are blown into the space between these two plastic sheets on cold nights, and the beads are sucked back into cylinders during sunny days in a typical Beadwall operation. Sunshine going through this sloping south-facing Beadwall heats water trickling down a black plastic sheet hanging 1-1/2 feet away from the opposite (north) wall, and the sun-warmed water is collected in a large underground storage tank. Hot water from the tank heats the greenhouse potting benches as the water runs under them through finned tube radiators in a hydronic system.

Practically all the heating for this greenhouse is provided by a largely passive solar system. In the summer a variable-reflectance ThermoShade cover is placed over the south wall, the Beadwall. This type of cover is transparent when its temperature is be-

FIGURE 7-5.   House with Beadwall Panels on South Wall

low 90°F, but it becomes an opaque white and highly reflective at higher temperatures. During the summer, the sprayers used to wet the black plastic sheet hanging parallel with the north wall are operated only at night and serve to cool the water in the storage tank.

In a house in Bedford, New Hampshire, designed by Total Environmental Action, there are large Beadwall panels covering about 300 square feet of the south wall as shown in Figure 7-5. Each 9 foot x 4 foot panel consists of two sheets of Kalwall polyester reinforced fiberglass spaced about 3 inches apart, held in a virtually airtight frame with typical Beadwall ducts. At night the air space is filled with a million or so styrofoam beads. During the day, when these beads are sucked back into drums situated in the garage, the sun shines through the Beadwall and heats a rough concrete wall painted with dark paint, good for absorbing solar heat. There is a 3-1/2-inch air space between the Beadwall and this dark wall. Air heated in this space by the sun rises and flows through holes at the top of the dark concrete wall into the rooms beyond. Cooler return air flows into the sun-heated space through holes at the bottom of the dark wall. There are manual dampers which can be used to stop this air circulation when desired.

Additional solar heat is brought into this single-story house through 90 square feet of double-glazed windows on the south wall— the same side of the house that has 300 square feet of Beadwall and sun-absorbing dark concrete. A point worth noting is that the inner (north) side of this dark concrete wall is not insulated, so that it efficiently radiates solar heat to rooms inside the house. The south-facing windows are covered with styrofoam shutters at night.

There is thick fiberglass insulation on the ceiling and polyurethane foam insulation on exterior of the north, east, and west walls.

Earth berms cover the full height of the north wall and parts of the east and west walls as well.

Included in the foot-thick concrete wall which acts as the principal storage of solar heat are PVC pipes 3 inches in diameter which preheat domestic hot water before it goes into a conventional water heater. This passive solar system is estimated to provide more than 60% of the space heating and hot water for this New Hampshire house, owned by R. Tyrrell.

On summer nights, the space between the Beadwall and the thick concrete absorber wall is vented to the outside. Cool night air is drawn into the rooms by gravity convection through slots near the north eaves, to replace the warmer air escaping to the outside from the Beadwall space. As described earlier, in normal summer operation during hot days the Beadwall is opaque and provides R-9 insulation.

Another large addition to a farmhouse in the same area, in Concord, New Hampshire, also shows the imagination of a distinguished young solar engineer, Bruce Anderson of Total Environmental Action of Harrisville, New Hampshire. This house is owned by D. Freese and takes advantage of two notable solar techniques—Beadwall and Skytherm, the solar water bags discussed in Chapter 6.

Covering the south face of the roof, which slopes 60°, is a Beadwall made with sheets of Kalwall transparent plastic 4 inches apart. On sunny winter days, solar energy passes through the Beadwall and warms 13 black vinyl bags filled with water. These bags cover an attic space of about 300 square feet and are an example of what Harold Hay calls "Skytherm North."

Sun-heated air from the space above the water bags is sucked by a blower through a duct into an insulated crawl space below the first floor. From this space, the warm air rises through vents into the first-floor rooms, then up a stairwell to return to the attic. There is a duct feeding warm attic air directly to second-floor living areas.

This semipassive solar heating system is estimated to provide 50% of the space heating of the newly added 2-story wing of the Freese farmhouse—the existing house was left alone. There is an antifreeze mixture in the Skytherm water bags so that they won't freeze even if the house is left completely unheated during a prolonged spell of cloudy cold weather, although there is an auxiliary oil furnace.

In the summer, as you would expect, the operation of this solar system is reversed to provide cooling. The water bags are cooled at night by forced circulation of cool outside air. The Beadwall panels are closed during the day to keep solar heat out of the attic. Cool air surrounding the Skytherm bags is blown down into the crawl space, and circulates from there through the rest of the 2-story wing.

Other Passive Solar Heating Systems from Kalwall

In addition to providing transparent plastic sheets for use with Beadwall systems and as glazing for many types of flat-plate solar collectors, Kalwall Corporation of Manchester, New Hampshire, has designed several passive solar heating systems.

One of the systems works particularly well with Beadwall as the outer wall surface. A south-facing Beadwall, with Kalwall plastic sheets in an aluminum frame as the panels, permits sunlight to shine on large cylindrical plastic tubes. These vertical fiberglass-reinforced cylinders, typically either 12 or 18 inches in diameter and 8 feet high, are filled with water and placed in an insulated box. The manufacturer calls this entire assembly a "solar battery."

Air ducts are provided at each end of the insulated box. Air is blown into the box, past the plastic cylinders full of sun-heated water, and then the hot air is blown into the distributing ductwork of the building. See Figure 7-6.

Insulated Kalwall SUNWALL panels used as solar windows to provide sun-

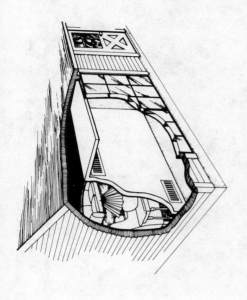

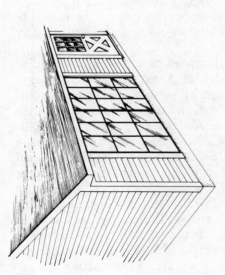

#1 Sunwall insulated panel system transmits 77% of the solar energy and insulates with a U equal to .40.

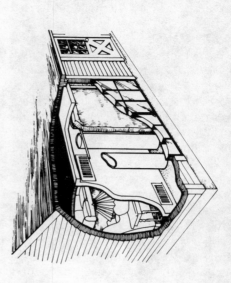

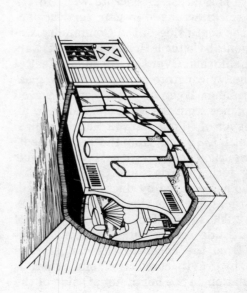

#2 Insulated "hot box" enclosure with air vents installed.

#3 Sun-lite collector/storage tubes, water filled, absorb and store heat.

#4 Moveable insulation provides control over sun's insolation and heat loss as required.

FIGURE 7-6. Passive Solar Heating System ("Solar Battery") Designed by Kalwall Corporation

FIGURE 7-7.   Kalwall Corporation's SUNWALL Panels Provide Sun-Heated
Air for the Wastewater Treatment Facility in Wilton, Maine

heated air for the Wastewater Treatment Facility in Wilton, Maine, won an energy conservation award. This passive solar system is credited with being a major factor in a reduction in heating costs estimated at 81.5% in this plant, shown in Figure 7-7.

There is a massive concrete wall, 16-1/2 inches thick, arranged in four vertical panels on the south side of the Community Environmental Council House in Santa Barbara, California. Over the 370 square feet of these heavy concrete panels is double glazing: an inner layer of 4 mil Tedlar placed 5-1/2 inches from the concrete wall, and an outer layer of 40 mil Kalwall Sun-Lite plastic sheet 1-1/2 inches from the Tedlar sheeting. The thick concrete panels absorb solar energy during the day, and this heat is distributed as required by ducts and a forced-air system to most of the 12 rooms in the 2-story, 2,200-square foot building. Some of the southside rooms obtain heat more directly from the concrete thermal storage panels, by gravity convection, since there is no insulation on the north (inner) side of the double-glazed concrete.

In the summer, cooling is provided by gravity convection, or the chimney effect, with hot air rising between the thick concrete panels and the glazing. Since these south-facing concrete panels weigh 30 tons, their thermal mass is great and the inside of the house remains comfortably cool on hot days, with roll-down redwood lath awnings covering the upper portion of the concrete panels and shades over upper south-facing windows.

In East Hampton near the eastern end of Long Island, New York, a passive solar system designed by solar engineer and architect J. Evans, with consulting assistance from Bruce Anderson, provides an estimated 50% of the heat for a 2,100-square foot house. Solar energy enters through two layers of Kalwall plastic sheeting providing a total of 750 square feet of double glazing for 10 windows on the 60° sloping south wall. Floors and walls absorb solar heat and the inside air is blown by a fan to a storage system consisting of 1,000 one-gallon plastic bottles full of water. These bottles are arranged in a rectangular concrete bin insu-

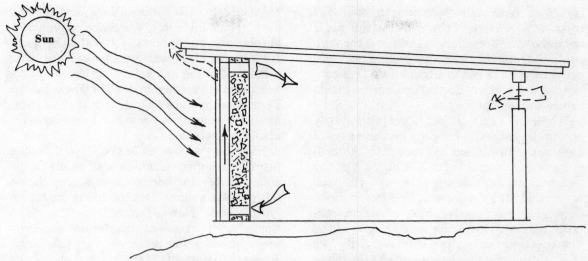

FIGURE 7-8. Simplified Cross Section of Trombe House

lated on the inside with 6 inches of Rapco-foam, a urea formaldehyde insulating foam which is also used to insulate the house.

When the sun isn't shining, the bin full of warm water bottles provides heat to a forced-air system. If the bin becomes too cool to provide room heat directly, a thermostat control turns on a heat pump, which can extract useful energy from the bin at a lower temperature. The fan in this system is part of a Westinghouse 5-ton heat pump installed in this home. Additional solar heat is picked up in a small, attached 1-story structure with a vertical south face having double-glazed (glass) clerestory windows covering 150 square feet. Again, heated air, warmed by contact with floors and walls on which the sun shines, is blown—along with the warm air from the main building—into the bin full of water bottles. Domestic hot water is heated by Sunworks liquid collectors previously described in Chapter 3.

Trombe Houses in France Set a Style

One of the true solar pioneers is French architect Felix Trombe, who has established a technique for passive solar design widely imitated in the United States and other countries. We use the word "widely" here to describe geographical spread—not total number of buildings. It is surprising that this simple, inexpensive, and effective approach has not been adopted more extensively. But then the global energy crisis has only penetrated popular thinking very recently. Certain American politicians are continuing to emulate the ostrich by denying that there is an energy shortage. Presumably they kept warm during the winter of 1977.

The first two Trombe houses were built in 1967 in Odeillo, a small community in the French Pyrenees near Spain. The technique developed by Trombe and his associates of the Laboratoire de l'Energie Solaire, is shown in Figure 7-8.

Basic passive element of these houses is a massive concrete wall painted black and facing south. Covering the wall is a double glazing of glass. The space between the wall and the glass is 10 centimeters (cm) (about 4 inches) and serves as a duct for sun-heated air. The concrete wall, painted a flat black on its outer surface, is 60 cm (2 feet) thick.

Sunlight heats the black walls so that a convective flow of air occurs in the duct between the wall and the glazing. Cooler air is drawn from the floor length openings toward the bottom of the wall. As this air is heated by the sun, it rises and flows through similar openings near the ceiling as indicated by the arrows in Figure 7-8. This continuing convective circulation warms inside rooms during the day.

While the sun is shining, the wall slowly accumulates thermal energy because a small part of the insolation diffuses into the concrete and is stored there. At night, the top and bottom air passages through the wall are sealed off by dampers. You can imagine how well this massive bulk of warm concrete serves to keep the inner rooms of the house comfortable after sundown. It's like the old-fashioned technique of a hot brick to warm grandmother's bed.

One interesting technical point is that the concrete wall, Trombe's thermal storage reservoir, radiates infrared (IR) wave lengths of energy like a radiant heating panel in buildings so equipped. Because the exterior glass is opaque to this IR radiation, the glazing blocks off most of the radiant thermal loss at night.

Trombe's houses are so designed that there is a roof overhang above the south wall, shading the house from most of the solar heat during summer days. One improvement in the original design has been to provide a vent at the upper end of the glazing that may be opened to exhaust warm air on a hot day while cooler air is drawn into the house from near ground level on the north side of the building.

An estimate of the energy savings achieved in the first two Trombe houses is that about 60% of the space heating is provided by the sun, with the remainder furnished by electric heaters. These 4-room houses have a total area of about 80 square meters (800 square feet) each.

In 1974, three additional Trombe houses were built in Odeillo. One is a 3-story building owned and occupied by Trombe himself; the other two have two stories. Wall colors of the concrete thermal storage walls on the south face of each of these buildings are,

respectively, dark blue, dark green, and dark brown instead of the more conventional solar-absorbent black. Typically there is 1 cubic meter of thermal wall for each 10 cubic meters of living space in each house. Walls are 40 cm (16 inches) instead of 60 cm (about 24 inches) in thickness of concrete. Again, auxiliary heating is provided by electric resistance heaters.

Examples of houses in the United States incorporating the Trombe wall as a passive solar heater include a new 2-story home with 2,500 square feet of living space in Northwood, New Hampshire. This is a house with excellent insulation and two ways of collecting solar warmth passively. A central area of 144 square feet on the south wall has Kalwall plastic glazing and behind it a 4-inch air space and then 16 inches of wall. This wall consists of an 8-inch thick core of concrete blocks filled with sand, with 4 inches of brick facing on both south and north sides of this core. As in other Trombe designs, there are open passages near the top and bottom of the heat-absorbent wall to provide convective flow of sun-heated air. A second source of solar heating consists of large double-glazed windows facing south. To conserve heat gained by these windows during the day, they are covered at night with insulating shutters.

A house in Princeton, New Jersey, designed and owned by D. Kelbaugh, has double glazing over its entire south face, then a 6-inch air space and a concrete wall 15 inches thick and painted black on its outer surface facing the sun, plus typical Trombe air passages through slots at the top and bottom of the wall. Additional heat storage, beyond the black concrete wall, is obtained from the floor of a greenhouse attached to the lower eastern portion of the home's south wall. Passive solar heating by these techniques has achieved a saving of almost 70% in energy use, with auxiliary heat (for 30% of the load) supplied by a conventional forced-air furnace.

In Santa Fe, New Mexico, a modern single-story house has a large double-glazed greenhouse on the west end of its south wall. Solar radiation entering the greenhouse heats a Trombe wall. Interior walls and floors of the house proper are also warmed by south-facing windows and skylights. These skylights are glazed with an outer layer of tempered glass and an inner layer of Plexiglas. Covering each skylight on cold nights is an insulated cover on rollers, easily pulled into position with a pole and hook. Again the combination of Trombe wall and solar heat absorbed by floors and walls warmed by sunlight from the south-facing windows and skylights results in another triumph of passive solar heating: a major portion of the space heating is provided by the sun at no cost. The only supplementary heating in this house, which is at an altitude of 8,000 feet, is provided by fireplaces in the bedrooms and electric heaters in the bathrooms.

A novel architectural design, incorporating both active and passive solar heating, has been created by Habitec: Architecture and Planning of Santa Clara, California, in the new Oakmead Industrial Park in that city. On the south walls of two large factory buildings are 3,000 square feet of passive solar collection area, where the sunlight heats Trombe walls through vast expanses of windows.

In contrast to most buildings—where you expect to see solar collectors on a south-facing roof—these two new structures provide 11 tilted concrete fascia panels above the front (north) sides. These panels extend out and above the side of each building at a 45° angle. Thus there is space on the south-facing side of these concrete panels, looking over the flat roofs of the two buildings, for 6,000 square feet of solar collectors.

According to Renault & Handley, Inc., Palo Alto, the developer, this combination of active and passive solar heating will provide up to 95% of the energy needed for space heating and hot water in these new industrial buildings. This amounts to a saving in energy costs of about 2 cents per square foot, which will increase with rising utility charges. Two additional buildings, with a total of 115,000 square feet, are planned for early completion in this, the nation's first sun-heated industrial park. Pacific Sun of Menlo Park, is the designer of the passive system, while Western Energy, Inc., of Palo Alto, is responsible for the active solar heating system.

Passive Designs by David Wright Are Efficient

One of the most effective solar architects is David Wright, who began by designing houses with passive solar systems in New Mexico and now is busy in other states. One of his latest designs is a relatively small single-story house he owns about 100 miles north of San Francisco. Much of his insulation for this house is furnished by earth berms covering the east and north faces of the structure. These berms join the roof so that the house appears almost like a man-made cave. But this "cave" has a vast expanse of glass on its south face, a double-glazed area covering 375 square feet and slanting at an angle of 70° so that sunlight pours in and heats the stone-masonry walls as well as the floors of the house. This entire window area is covered with insulating curtains at night to conserve solar heat stored by the building. More than 90% of the heating for a living area of 1,150 square feet is provided by solar energy, with a fireplace and wood stoves used as occasional supplements.

As a complementary feature, Wright heats his domestic hot water with 64 square feet of solar collectors. The sun's heat lifts the water into an 80-gallon insulated storage tank placed above the collectors in an effective thermosiphoning, as described in previous chapters, with no need for a pump or controls.

A solar house designed and originally owned by Wright has achieved about 90% of its space heating passively from the sun since it was built in 1974. Like other designs by this architect, the south-facing wall is double-glazed and wide open to the sun, while only a few small windows are provided facing in other directions. Located in Santa Fe, New Mexico, the house is shaped like half a cylinder, with the south wall of windows providing 400 square feet of two thicknesses of glass through which solar radiation heats massive adobe walls and adobe floors, as well as several water-filled drums next to the windows for a partial Drumwall. Walls, floors, and drums store sufficient heat so that the house is comfortable even after several midwinter days without sun. The thick adobe walls and floors are insulated on the *outside* with 2 inches of polyurethane foam—a feature added by modern science to improve on the thermal techniques of the southwestern Indian tribes.

During winter nights, the south-facing windows are covered with shutters made of canvas and 2-inch thick plastic insulation. When the sun is shining, a hand crank folds up each shutter like an accordion-type partition. Solar efficiency is so good that auxiliary heating for this 1,100-square foot house is provided by a single wood-burning stove, which used only 1/4 cord of wood during an entire Rocky Mountain winter. Two Zomeworks solar collectors filled with antifreeze solution heat the domestic water for the house through a heat exchanger.

In the summer, because Wright designed eaves which project 4 feet over the expanse of south-facing windows, the windows are shaded from the sun during most of the day. The architect also provided vents, opened during warm days to permit any accumulation of hot air to flow out through the roof.

One noteworthy feature of this type of construction is that thick, heavily insulated walls and floors retain solar heat for a long time. This is the reason such a house stays warm for three or four days during a winter storm. It also explains why David Wright and the present owner of the house, C. Kimball, have found it quite comfortable when a thermometer inside the house reads only 60°F. This is the temperature of the air in the room, but the walls and floor are warm, retaining their solar heat. Also worth noting is the fact that, during a sunny day in winter, the room air in this house may heat up from 60°F to 80°F. As you would expect, the adobe walls and floors absorb solar heat slowly and release it equally gradually. This explains why such a house can remain warm enough to be comfortable for prolonged periods in the winter with nothing but passive solar heating.

There are at least 10 other solar homes in the Santa Fe area, most of them designed by David Wright and all deriving a very large percentage of their space heating from passive solar systems. In every case, the basic construction of the house includes massive adobe walls and floors of adobe, brick, or cement laid on sand a foot thick over an insulating pad. South walls, whether vertical or at an obtuse angle from the horizontal, consist largely of double-glazed windows to admit a maximum amount of the warming winter sunlight. These window areas are covered by internal insulated shutters on cold nights. On summer days, overhangs provide shading from the sun's midday heat and there are ceiling vents which may be opened so that hot air escapes while cooler air at ground level is brought into the house by natural convection.

One additional point about such houses in the area of Sante Fe, Los Alamos, and Albuquerque is that they are designed with so much thermal mass that they not only absorb solar heat effectively—with a long slow warm-up and without, in general, special storage such as rock bins or large water tanks—but also these buildings would provide good thermal shielding in case of a nuclear explosion. This is particularly apropos in view of the fact that the first A-bomb was developed at Los Alamos, and generations of nuclear weapons have been designed by the Sandia Laboratories in Albuquerque.

Retrofitting for Passive Solar Heating

Although plastic bottles or drums filled with water and heated by the sun, as well as

Beadwall and Skylids, may be used in many existing structures—apartment houses, condominiums, industrial and commercial buildings, in addition to single-family homes —it's apparent that such passive solar systems as Trombe walls and David Wright's designs are most suitable when you're planning a new building. Or you may be able to use such a system if you're remodeling and are able to build a south wall consisting mostly of glass or transparent plastic sheet on the exterior.

However there are some interesting examples of retrofits, or dwellings where a relatively small and inexpensive addition has made possible a passive solar heating system with good performance. For instance on the outside of a small one-story adobe house in Taos, New Mexico, a special solar heat collector added at the center of the south-by-southwest wall (facing about 18° west of south) provides about 80% of the space heating required for the two heated rooms. This exterior structure has a frame of curved steel pipes. Over this framework are stretched two layers of Monsanto plastic sheet 6 mils thick and separated by a 2-inch air space. The area of this cylindrical section exposed to the sunlight is about 160 square feet. Solar radiation heats the earth floor inside this solar annex and also heats the brown-painted adobe wall of the house, as well as 16 vertical tanks against the outer (brown) side of this wall. Each tank, a vertical plastic cylinder, contains 20 gallons of water.

Heated air from inside this solar annex with the curved double-glazed plastic cover rises and flows by convection through two 15-square foot openings at shoulder height in the brown adobe wall. This sun-warmed air heats the two rooms of the house, and return air flows through two smaller vents at the bottom of the adobe wall into the solar annex for reheating. These four vents —two for each room—can be closed if the rooms get too hot. The sole auxiliary heating is a propane gas heater used only after prolonged bad weather.

In the summer, the glazing of this solar annex is removed and stored. At other times if the passive solar enclosure becomes too hot, a thermostat turns on a small fan and exhausts sun-heated air from this enclosure to the outside of the building. It is estimated by Dr. William Shurcliff that materials for this retrofitted solar heater cost about $1,500. Occasionally, plants have been grown in the enclosure so that it serves to some extent as a greenhouse as well as a passive system keeping this home's living areas warm.

A similar greenhouse structure, except that its cross section is triangular, has been added to a 2-1/2-story farmhouse in Elysburg, Pennsylvania, by its owner, C. Fried. The sloping cover, slanted against the house at an angle of 56°, is made of Kalwall transparent plastic sheets 25 mils thick and spaced 3/4 inch apart. These sheets are mounted on 1 inch x 6 inch joists placed 2 feet apart—the rafters of the transparent "roof" of this triangular lean-to. Total area of the solar collector is about 380 square feet and it is attached to the south wall of the wood-framed farmhouse.

Solar radiation passing through the lower one-third of the plastic glazing heats a vegetable bed in which Fried grows the makings for his family's salads throughout the year. Sunshine passing through the upper two-thirds of the glazing heats black-coated aluminum sheets formed by bending and joining 96 discarded printing-press plates. These plates, 9 mils thick, cost the ingenious solar designer about 12 cents each. A blower controlled by a thermostat circulates sun-heated air from behind the fins Fried formed on the back side of his blackened printing plates. This hot air is blown into wooden ducts leading to registers in the 9-room house or to a storage bin containing 40 tons of stones in the basement.

This might be considered a semipassive solar system which includes homemade air-type solar collectors and a storage system similar to those marketed by Solaron and other manufacturers, as described in a previous chapter. Fried estimates that the cost of materials for his solar annex or lean-to amounted to $650, while the rock storage bin cost $750. About 50% of the heating load of the house is provided by this solar system, with the remainder furnished by a homemade wood-burning furnace tied into the owner's wood ducts and forced-air heating system.

During a solar show in October 1976 in Albuquerque, a plastic solar collector-greenhouse caught the eye of Janice Jacobs and her husband. This tent, stretched over a curved frame like the one in Taos described above, was 15 feet long, 8 feet high and 7 feet wide and cost $550. The couple installed it themselves over a concrete slab on the south side of their house. The slab was formerly a patio.

The next step was to remove one window pane from the south wall now covered by the plastic greenhouse. They then installed a small fan to draw air heated by the sun from the greenhouse through the vent they created into the other rooms of the house. "I turn the gas off at 8:30 every morning," Janice Jacobs told a reporter for the Albuquerque *News* in late February 1977, "and I don't turn it back on until 8 p.m. or later. It gives us a greenhouse where we're growing lettuce, spinach, and parsley in midwinter. Our 3-year-old daughter enjoys playing in the greenhouse. Anyone who can handle a screwdriver can put one up."

A much more extensive and elaborate greenhouse, with 360 square feet of glass on its roof and south wall, is attached to a house in Jackson, Tennessee, designed by architect Lee Porter Butler and described in *The Solar Home Book* by Bruce Anderson with Michael Riordan. This greenhouse collects more than 500 therms (500,000 BTU) on a sunny day in winter. Solar heat from the greenhouse goes into the home through a glass dividing wall or through glass doors which can be opened for passage of heated air. Walls and roof have thick fiberglass insulation. There are no windows except on the south side of the house, which is largely covered by the built-on greenhouse. The 4-inch concrete slab floor, insulated with 2 inches of polyurethane foam below the slab, stores solar heat as do the insulated walls

and ceilings. Vents at floor level and sheet-metal ducts are provided for circulation of the sun-heated air. Total costs for this 1,440-square foot house, with its greenhouse providing most of the space heating, amounted to $38,000, including the price of the lot.

More about Greenhouses

If you have enough space to add a greenhouse on the south side of your house, this addition may pay for itself very quickly. It can provide you with passive solar heating and also give you vegetables, fruits, and flowers in midwinter—converting Siberia into Florida.

For those who don't want to design and build their own greenhouses, there is an inexpensive intermediate method. This is a do-it-yourself kit called a Solar Room, useful for both houses and mobile homes. The room consists of a curved metal framework, easily assembled, over which you stretch two layers of translucent plastic sheets. Included in the kit, along with the framing and plastic covers, is a small blower which inflates the space between the two plastic sheets to form an insulating layer.

During ambient air conditions as low as 10°F, the temperature inside this greenhouse will reach 75°F and possibly 85°F on a bright day with little wind. This solar heat can be circulated inside your house or mobile home using inlet and outlet pipes with suitable dampers to cut off air circulation when you don't want it, and with a single small blower to pull in the heated air.

The Solar Room can be used as a greenhouse, workshop, storage space, play area for children, or a combination of these. The DIY kit costs $499 for a room 12 feet long and $949 for an annex 39 feet long. These prices include framing, the two plastic sheets, blower, and instructions f.o.b. Solar Room Company, Box 1377, Taos, New Mexico 97571.

A far more elaborate greenhouse in Laramie, Wyoming, has converted "a cold, dead, grey-white Siberian wasteland" into a wonderful "warm world of greenness and life," according to Joseph B. Orr in a paper read by the author and builder at the Aspen Energy Forum, May 27-29, 1977. The description is reprinted in the July 1977 issue of *Solar Energy Digest*, only partially because Bill Edmondson, solar pioneer and publisher of the *Digest*, suggested this greenhouse and also served as a consultant during its construction.

The greenhouse is built over an unusual thermal storage bin consisting of wet dirt warmed by ABS plastic pipes (see Glossary) through which is blown air heated by solar collector panels on the roof of the adjoining structure. It turns out that wet-dirt storage is both efficient and cheap. As Orr points out, this dirt is readily available on the building site. It has high heat capacity, greater than rocks, although lower than water. The following simple table gives a reasonable comparison:

Heat Capacity of Thermal Storage Media in BTU per Cubic Foot per Degree F

Rocks	20
Wet Dirt	30 to 44
Water	62.4

Orr points out in his paper, which appears in *Solar Architecture 1977, Proceedings of the Aspen Energy Forum*, that the plastic-lined storage bin for wet dirt 15 feet x 6-1/2 feet x 9 feet or 878 cubic feet, including 456 feet of ABS pipe 3 inches in diameter and pipe fittings, cost a total of $231 for materials. Even the cheapest water storage system with equivalent heat capacity would have cost more than 2-1/2 times as much for materials. Also owner-built air-type solar collectors and associated piping, blowers, and dampers are less expensive than a liquid-type solar collector system, particularly for service in an area like Laramie, notable for long dreary winters.

The black ABS pipes are spaced 18 inches apart in horizontal runs, and 9 inches apart as vertical heat exchangers. These pipes conduct heat into the wet dirt slowly, but then Orr and his advisers are well aware that wet dirt receives this solar heat only 1/5 as fast as if conduction took place through the pipes. The plastic pipes are cheap and durable—higher heat conduction through far more expensive metal pipes wouldn't make sense. Two storage fans drive air through the storage pipes. One fan flows the air into the bin from the solar collectors in a clockwise direction when the sun is shining. The other fan operates during the night or bad weather cycle in the opposite direction to draw stored solar heat from the wet dirt bin to warm the greenhouse and an adjacent workshop area.

One reason for building this greenhouse in what Orr calls "America's own Outer Mongolia" is that for 30 years his family's previous attempts at gardening were a resounding failure. Snowfalls during every month of the year—not every year, but predictably in June, July, August, and/or September—give you a clue. But with his solar greenhouse on a wet-dirt thermal storage bin the owner reports gardening success in midwinter, growing tomatoes, cabbages, beans, squash, broccoli, lettuce, spinach, turnips, beets, cucumbers, peas, potatoes, and corn. Heating of this greenhouse is 100% solar and has been successful for two winters. One additional benefit is that living even part-time in this warm, humid area has cut down on the family's colds.

The conclusion of Orr's paper, in which he notes that he's now trying dry dirt with considerable success for his thermal storage bin, is a lyric gem:

"The sight of green beans growing a few feet from a snowbank, separated by a miraculous Tedlar-bonded membrane about 1/32 inch thick—it finally gives rhyme and reason to Man's long evolutionary haul up from the slime, down from the tree, and along the halls of Du Pont. For this alone we acquit Science completely for its blunderings. All is forgiven for giving us Tedlar-laminated Filon."

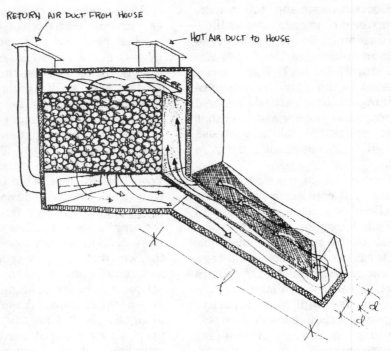

RETURN AIR DUCT FROM HOUSE

HOT AIR DUCT TO HOUSE

FIGURE 7-9. A Solar Chimney, Designed by Steve Baer of Albuquerque, for Passive Heating

Other Ingenious Ideas

In Steve Baer's lively book *Sunspots* he describes how to build a solar chimney for passive heating. This chimney is a long duct, open at the lower end as shown in Figure 7-9, and leading to a stone-filled storage bin. The cover of this duct is either a single or double (in a cold area) glazing of glass or a plastic sheet like GE Lexan or Kalwall Sun-Lite. The chimney collector should slant upward at an angle of at least 45°. Inside this collector is a diagonal piece or pieces of black metal lath, which slow down the air flow and help to absorb solar heat. This metal lath is placed in the upper section of the chimney, where the sun-heated air rises and flows past a 1-inch thick insulating board placed in the stone storage bin. Above the bin is an opening into a hot-air duct connected to the forced-air or gravity convection system of the house.

As shown in Baer's drawing, return air from the house flows past the underside of the rock bin and down the lower duct of the chimney into the outdoors. The inventor suggests placing the rock bin above the solar collector-chimney or else using a damper. The storage bin should be below the house—otherwise you will need a fan system. Make the collector or solar chimney at least 6 feet long. Build a vent flap into the top of the chimney's heated duct so that you can open it on hot summer days, when you don't want to heat your house.

Another bright idea from the founder of Zomeworks is what Baer calls a Nightwall. This is an easily attached, or removed, insulating board which you place over windows, french doors, or skylights at night during cold weather so as to keep heat in your house. You buy 1-inch thick beadboard, styrofoam, or pressed fiberboard at your building supply store. Don't use urethane foam, advises Baer, because it goes to pieces in the sun and gives off poison gas when it burns. But your insulating board should be a fire-retardant material, which is usually available in 2 x 8-foot or 4 x 8-foot sheets.

Measure your window, and cut a suitable piece of insulating board, leaving about 1/8 inch around the edges so that it's slightly bigger than your window. Mark places around the outside edges of your board where you will attach small metallic Nightwall magnets, available from Zomeworks, and apply a good adhesive such as Goodrich PL200 over each area where you will fasten a magnet. These 1/2 inch wide magnets are made of rubber mixed with a magnetic material, barium ferrite, oriented to form north and south poles. These are strong permanent magnets, which get somewhat stronger at temperatures below 70°F and weaker at higher temperatures.

With a good adhesive, all you need is a bead of glue along the outlines of each magnet you've marked on the edges of the Nightwall. Then you press the magnets, metal side down, on the adhesive. This leaves the paper side of each magnet up. Now peel off the paper strips, and press your completed Nightwall against your metal-framed window. Of course, this kind of insulating cover will work only if you have windows framed in a material to which magnets will cling.

The glass in your windows should be thoroughly cleaned and dried before you apply the Nightwalls, and the glass temperature should be above 50°F.

Don't paint the outside of this insulating panel a dark color. If the beadboard or other board you use is a light color, leave it the original color or paint it white. Don't use Nightwalls against tinted windows exposed to sunlight because the added heat can crack the glass. Observe the glass manufacturer's warnings about blinds and drapes: this information is also available at your hardware or building supply store. Don't cover only part of a window because this can cause thermal stresses which might crack the glass.

If you need to look through a window covered with Nightwall, you can melt a peephole with a soldering iron.

Pivotable Solar Heat Exchanger Window Wall

Walter S. White, an architect, and Dr. Robert A. Golobic, senior systems analyst of Research, Analysis and Development, Inc., are inventors living in Colorado Springs who have developed a patented triple glazing which can be pivoted from a winter position to a summer position. This results in windows with improved year-round performance, according to a paper presented by the two inventors at the International Solar Energy Society meeting in Orlando, Florida, in June 1977.

The basic modes of operation of this "Window Wall" are shown in Figure 7-10. During a winter day, when the clear glass double glazing is on the outside, air is forced between this pair of panes and the single layer of energy-absorbing glass. This latter glass sheet might be PPG Solarcool bronze thermopane, with the reflective side on the inside of the room in this winter mode (Mode A). The window wall, according to tests, adds nearly 1,000 BTU per square foot during a sunny day and loses less than 200 BTU per square foot at night, outperforming ordinary windows with and without shades.

In the summer, the window wall is pivoted so that the energy absorbing reflective glass is on the outside, and the double-glazed inner section is on the inside of the building. This makes the interior of the building notably cooler than conventional windows. Cost of window walls, the patented Solarsync, is estimated at $15.56 per square foot in one application. White says these Solarsync windows add about 5% to the average building cost: "It runs anywhere from $9.50 to $16.50 per square foot of the exterior wall surface."

Thermic Diode Panels for Passive Solar Heating and Cooling

A new kind of wall panel, designed for passive solar heating in winter and, with a

183

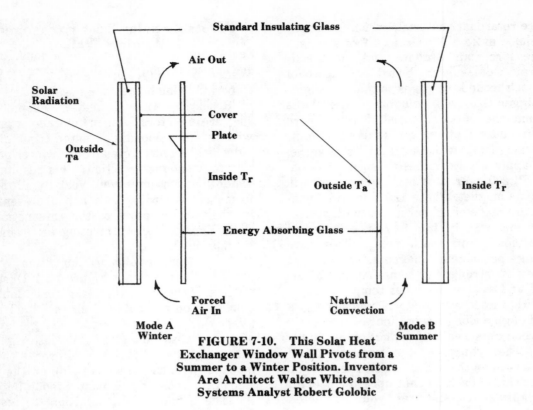

Standard Insulating Glass

Solar Radiation

Outside Ta

Air Out

Cover

Plate

Inside T_r

Outside T_a

Inside T_r

Energy Absorbing Glass

Forced Air In

Natural Convection

Mode A Winter

Mode B Summer

FIGURE 7-10. This Solar Heat Exchanger Window Wall Pivots from a Summer to a Winter Position. Inventors Are Architect Walter White and Systems Analyst Robert Golobic

minor change, for cooling during the summer, has been patented and is called a "thermic diode" by principal inventor, Dr. B. Shawn Buckley, associate professor of mechanical engineering at the Massachusetts Institute of Technology. A diode is an electronic component which permits flow of electrical current in only one direction. Similarly, thermic diode panels, first built at M.I.T. in 1974, permit heat transfer in a single direction.

The basic concept of this wall panel is simple. An exterior solar collector, a vertical version of flat-plate collectors described in earlier chapters, forms the outer surface heated by the sun. Water from this heated collector travels by convection—our old friend, thermosiphoning—upward through waterways, then through a one-way valve (the thermic diode), into a larger storage chamber filled with water. The coldest water in the system flows through an inlet to the bottom of the outer collector, and the

heating action repeats itself as the water continues to flow in this convective loop.

Operation of the system is shown in Figure 7-11. The thermic diode is the oil valve shown at the top. When warm water from the front solar collector panel flows up and into this valve, the minute convective force exerted by this sun-heated water is sufficient to push the oil up in the plastic cylinder (the valve housing) so that the warm water will flow down into the plastic storage fins at the back of the panel. This action is shown in Figure 7-11. At night, when the water in the small plastic channels or waterways below the black aluminum sheet of the collector is cooler than the heated water in the storage section, there is not enough convective force to open the oil valve. The light oil layer prevents reverse flow, and thus the heated storage water keeps warm throughout a winter night—or in fact for several days of bad weather.

Original designs of the thermic diode pan-

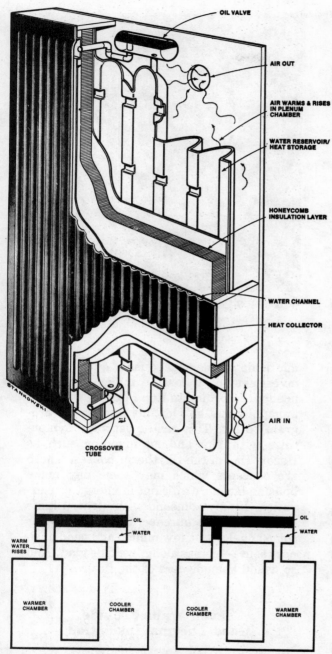

OIL VALVE

AIR OUT

AIR WARMS & RISES
IN PLENUM
CHAMBER

WATER RESERVOIR/
HEAT STORAGE

HONEYCOMB
INSULATION LAYER

WATER CHANNEL

HEAT COLLECTOR

AIR IN

STANKOWSKI

CROSSOVER
TUBE

OIL
WATER

OIL
WATER

WARM
WATER
RISES

WARMER
CHAMBER

COOLER
CHAMBER

COOLER
CHAMBER

WARMER
CHAMBER

DAYTIME: Sun-heated water rises from
warm chamber through valve to cool
chamber, which supplies cool water.

NIGHTTIME: As temperature in chambers
reverses, water wants to flow backwards
but is unable to push light oil in valve.

**FIGURE 7-11. "Thermic Diode" Wall Panel,
Invented by M.I.T. Professor B. Shawn
Buckley, Permits Heat Transfer in Single
Direction. (Drawing Courtesy** *Mechanix
Illustrated,* **December 1976.)**

el were inefficient until some drastic changes were made by Ron Petrich & Associates of Seal Beach, California, a firm of consulting mechanical engineers with considerable expertise in making a variety of plastic structural panels suitably insulated for mobile homes.

The present production prototype design consists of a black-painted aluminum sheet behind which are waterways in an expandable unicellular plastic compound. This material permits sufficient expansion, Petrich explained to this author, so that water can be used in it instead of antifreeze. Temporary freezing will not damage the panel. Behind this solar collector is a plastic-impregnated paper honeycomb 3 inches thick and faced on each side with aluminum foil. This is an insulating layer, just like that below the liquid-type solar collector on your roof. Behind this honeycomb insulation are white plastic reinforced fiberglass fins containing about 56 gallons (450 pounds) of water as the thermal storage. The entire structure, except for the outer black aluminum face, is enclosed in a box of insulating board. As shown in Figure 7-11, room air enters a hole in the back of this box, is warmed by contact with the storage water, and travels upward and out through a hole at the top of the panel to warm the room.

Weight of the completed wall panel, 4 feet x 8 feet in area and 9 inches thick, is 150 pounds dry, and 600 pounds in place and filled with water. As pointed out by such writers as Robert G. Beason in *Mechanix Illustrated* (December 1976) and Terence M. Green in the *Los Angeles Times* (January 16, 1977), these thermic diode panels are not the kind you would build into an existing house unless you were adding a large wing or remodeling from the ground up. It's estimated by Buckley that 16 panels with water warmed to 100°F will store about 200,000 BTU and therefore will provide adequate passive solar heating, with some backup, for a house with 1,600 square feet of floor area if you design your house to place these panels on the south-facing wall. They could also be used as roof panels, says Petrich.

At present the thermic diode panels have been shipped from the Petrich assembly plant in California for testing at state universities in Arizona, Georgia, and Louisiana as well as at M.I.T. Additional panels will be used by Pacific Gas & Electric Company in some test homes and storehouses in San Ramon, California. Part of this program is federally funded by ERDA.

According to estimated costs for thermic diode panels—when a substantial investment has been made in tooling—it should be possible to build them into a 1,500-square foot house for $3,500, for 16 diode panels. It's also possible by substituting an oil valve turned around for summer use, so that water in the outer collector cooled by night breezes cools the storage water, to make these panels useful during the hot months. This would probably work best in an area where you're sure of having cool night air so that the water in the outer collector is cooled by radiation to the night sky and also by convection currents of cool outside air. In this case the water density in the cool outer layer becomes greater than the density of the water in the storage fins inside the house. Cooled water from the collector waterways flows through the return port at the bottom of the panel, and storage water is forced upward to open the oil valve and permit convective flow. During the day, the action of this "summer diode" is to stop convective action by the oil valve. The net effect is that the panel loses more heat at night than it gains during the day, and thus the thermic diode panel tends to cool the building.

It is hard to predict what is going to happen with this new thermic panel, shown assembled in Figure 7-12, which could be useful in many types of new construction. If some major company in the building materials field, or a group of developers constructing homes, apartments, industrial buildings, or shopping centers, gets sufficiently interested in this passive solar system to make a large investment in tooling for mass production, then we can expect to see ther-

FIGURE 7-12.   Ron Petrich with an Assembled Thermic Diode Panel (Foreground)

mic diode panels widely used. An estimated investment of at least a million dollars is needed, according to Ron Petrich, who says unhappily that he's lost his shirt on the program so far. This writer can only sympathize with him and an inventor such as Harold Hay of the Skytherm houses. These are concepts which may some day make housing far more efficient in energy conservation. If only someone with a sharp knife designed to cut bureaucratic red tape—or some angel with a few million and good business sense—comes along, we'd be glad. And so would homeowners of the future.

Savell Walls Provide Good Thermal Insulation

Jesse J. Savell, Jr., a builder from Colton, California, about 40 miles east of Los Angeles, has patented a building system that has a high thermal lag and yet is quite easy to construct. His walls are precast concrete on which a layer of foamed insulation is applied when each wall is cast in a horizontal position. Completing the sandwich is another layer of lightweight concrete over the foam insulation.

According to William Edmondson, practical solar engineer and designer as well as the publisher of *Solar Energy Digest:*

> Savell has also solved such problems as expansion and contraction formerly associated with concrete building construction and has devised a flexible system which permits a home to be built in almost any configuration. . . . Because of the thermal capacity of the home's walls and floor, the walls and floor can be used as the heat storage medium, virtually eliminating the need for such storage systems as rock bins, tanks of water, bins of eutectic salts, and the like except in the more extreme climates.

In the mild climate of Southern California, houses built by the Savell system have proved capable of keeping inner temperatures remarkably stable. One typical house warms up in winter to an inside temperature of 74°F during the day and then cools to about 72°F at night. Walls built with this technique are reported to have no problem with sweating, and to have numerous other advantages over conventional precast concrete construction, including improved resistance to fires and earthquakes as well as adaptability for mass production.

This last feature indicates that walls and floors made by the Savell system may become popular for energy-saving construction in many areas. We know how massive walls of concrete or adobe—south-facing, glazed, and suitably ducted—serve to provide useful solar heating in mountainous regions where winters are far more severe than in Colton. Houses using such walls designed by Trombe and David Wright were described earlier in this chapter. Even where winters are bitter and summers are hot, the high thermal lag built into walls and floors by Savell will mean that if active solar systems are provided, they can be smaller than for less well-insulated houses and therefore less costly. Also, auxiliary heating and cooling can be minimal.

Efficient Solar House Design from Israel

Such fuel-poor nations with high technology as Israel and Japan are far ahead of the United States in per capita utilization of solar energy. In both countries, it is now commonplace rather than unusual to use the sun's heat for warming domestic hot water. Many ingenious building designs use solar energy largely in a passive manner. One simple design has been developed by Professor B. Givoni of Technion Israel Institute of Technology, Haifa, and is shown in Figure 7-13. A single-family home following this Givoni design has just been completed in the Negev Desert. Its solar system has added about 15% to the cost of the house, but savings in fuel and power costs will pay for these added costs in less than 5 years, it is estimated.

In this design, a double-glazed (glass or plastic) transparent surface on the south side of the house at A permits solar radiation to warm the black absorbent roof surface C. There is a hinged door below window area A with reflective aluminum foil on an insulated panel. This reflector is open on winter days to add solar radiation for heating absorber C. It is closed on winter nights to keep heat in the house and on summer days to keep out heat but it is open on summer nights, as you would expect, to exhaust heat.

On winter days, solar energy warms absorber C, which is a black-painted thick material capable of storing a large amount of heat. This storage of solar energy could be increased by arranging an array of plastic bottles filled with water above C, so that they also store heat. The air in the space enclosed by double-glazed window or skylight A and the thick roof and attic wall insulation B is blown from this attic-heated

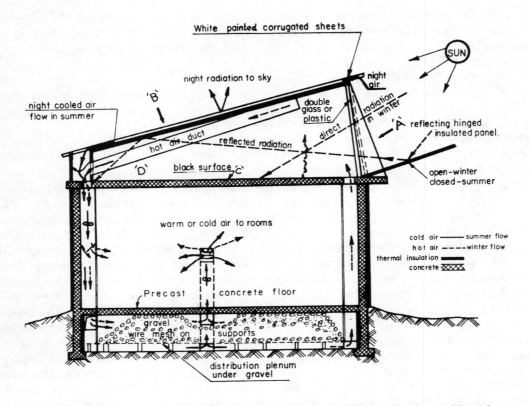

FIGURE 7-13. Passive Solar Heating and Cooling System Using Hinged Insulated Reflector Panel. Design is by Professor B. Givoni of Technion Institute in Haifa, Israel

space through a duct to a large gravel bin under the precast concrete floor.

Warm air enters the rooms in the house from the duct carrying hot air down to the gravel bin, and also by convection from this bin upward through floor registers. Additional solar heat is provided by the warmth radiating from the solar absorber and the ceiling C.

During the summer, the white-painted galvanized steel roofing sheets above insulation B on the roof act to reflect solar radiation during the day. Then at night the air under this corrugated roofing, separated from the insulation by about 2 inches, cools rapidly as daytime heat is radiated into the night sky. This cool air is pumped into the space D, once the day's warm air has been exhausted from this space by opening the lid at A, and after this lid is closed, most of

the cool air goes into the gravel bin, where the stones are cooled.

To circulate this cool air during the day will also take the energy from a fan, since the heavier chilled air must be blown upward. However, more than enough electric power for the fans required in such a semi-passive system could be obtained from batteries charged by a panel of solar cells exposed to desert sunlight. See Chapter 11 for a discussion of the wide variety of ways in which solar cells are being used.

Solar Illumination to Save Energy

One passive application of solar energy which should receive more attention than it's now getting is the use of sunlight to illuminate buildings—and thus save on the power required for electric lighting. By putting a sun-tracking mirror on the roof of a building, then reflecting this light onto a fixed spherical mirror and beaming the sunlight into the building through a porthole or skylight, it is possible with suitable mirrors in several rooms to provide solar illumination for inside rooms.

One such installation is at the Hyatt Regency Hotel in Chicago, where during daylight hours on sunny days, beams of sunlight are used for illumination through the glassed roof of the hotel lobby.

Another experimental system was set up by two physicists at Sandia Laboratories, Albuquerque. Michel Duguay, who was on loan from the parent Bell Laboratories in New Jersey, and Robert Edgar decided to improve the illumination of their windowless offices. A small flat mirror with an area of about 3 square feet (0.3 square meter) was placed on the roof and its position changed by a photoelectrically triggered tracking system so that it always followed the sun to direct maximum sunlight into the building. Inside the structure, a system of mirrors and lenses distributed this sunlight into a couple of offices. In one room about 10 feet x 16 feet in area, a solar beam diffused by a sheet of white plastic gave better illumination than fluorescent lamps. And since filters were inserted in the focused solar beams to filter out infrared (IR) energy, the solar illumination produced only one-fourth the heat of fluorescent lighting.

It's been suggested that a solar illumination system could provide not only lighting but also give indoor workers an indication of the weather outside. "In the few instances in which it (solar lighting) has been tried, the effect is reportedly quite pleasing esthetically, and when clouds pass overhead they can be seen running across the image of the sun projected into the solar-lit room," reports *Science* magazine, volume 194. "Such a system could serve as a local weather indicator, providing a measure of psychological relief in office buildings, and could also have other benefits. If one system were used to illuminate many rooms on different floors, it could create new possibilities for interoffice communication as light beams destined for lower floors pass through the offices above."

Here is another area where architects designing new buildings will be able to use sunlight effectively—to save energy in illumination as well as in heating and cooling future structures.

Many Ways to Use Solar Energy

In Weston, Massachusetts, a suburb of Boston, N. B. Saunders, a solar engineer, has created a number of ingenious passive solar systems. His own 2-story house uses the entire south wall for solar heating in a modified Trombe wall, and sunlight provides a considerable amount of illumination.

The Saunders solar design for the Cambridge School Solar Building in Weston is particularly interesting. This building faces 26° west of south and contains a floor area of 14,400 square feet, with the upper story including a large kitchen and dining room, while the lower story contains classrooms and utility rooms. Some transverse walls and all north walls are a foot thick and made of concrete blocks which are 75% solid. The massive exterior walls are insulated on the outside with 4 inches of fiberglass covered by a layer of stucco, so that they are not only highly fire-resistant but also store a large amount of thermal energy. A major portion of the vertical south-southwest wall consists of windows, providing both a view and collection of solar heat. About 40% of this window area is double glazed, the remaining 60% single glazed.

An unusual additional collector of solar heating and lighting is the 1,700 square feet of skylight on the south-southwest roof with 25° slope on the two western sections of this school building. There is a top glazing on the skylight of corrugated Filon, a polyester-reinforced fiberglass. This transparent plastic sheet rests on a unique "staircase" made of reflective aluminum treads or horizontal

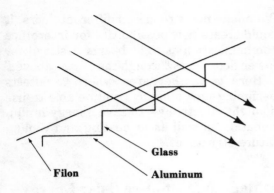

Filon   Glass

Aluminum

FIGURE 7-14.   **Cross-section of Skylight System Designed by N. B. Saunders**

sections 18 inches wide, and vertical risers of glass 8-1/2 inches high as shown in Figure 7-14. Sunlight goes through the glazing and the risers, with additional energy reflected through the risers from the aluminum treads. This solar heat is absorbed by the masonry walls and floors of the building—the New England equivalent of adobe.

The skylight, including its ingenious solar staircase (patent pending), provides solar illumination to rooms on the second floor, reducing the need for electric lighting. By adding mirrors and transparent sections of floors when such a building is constructed, you could extend this solar lighting to the classrooms on the first floor, which do get both light and heat from the south-facing windows.

Solar heating and lighting, entirely passive, save considerably energy in this school. Data on specific savings are being collected and analyzed under a grant from ERDA. On summer nights, windows as well as upper vents are opened so that hot air escapes and the massive walls and floors are cooled by outdoor air.

In Southern California, an inventor named Carl E. Derry has developed a new, thermally insulated roofing tile consisting of an upper aluminum sheet, rippled to make it resemble a piece of cedar used on a typical

shake roof and bonded to a 2-inch thick layer of closed-cell polyurethane foam insulation. Coated with fire-resistant paint, this new roofing is said to be economical to produce on a large scale, lighter in weight than most roofing materials, and useful in keeping attics much cooler than with conventional shakes, tile, or composition roofing.

In addition to Jesse Savell, other builders are developing processes using urethane insulation and spray-on concrete techniques. The Southern California Edison model home in the desert described in a previous chapter uses a plastic sheet formed into arches over steel framework as the shell over which a thick layer of concrete is sprayed by the gunite process, resulting in a structure with high thermal lag—storing solar heat in winter, easy to keep at a comfortable temperature in summer.

Throughout the world, with the public eager to save energy because utility bills are soaring and will continue to climb, architects and builders are being aided by solar engineers in creating designs that let sunlight do a large part of the heating and, in some cases, illuminating of new buildings.

Even with existing buildings, as pointed out earlier in this chapter, there are all kinds of useful things you can do. Such devices as Beadwalls, Drumwalls, Nightwalls, Skylids, and solar chimneys have potential applications in millions of existing structures, as economics permit. You can store some solar heat very inexpensively with plastic water bottles and a partially transparent sheet of gray plastic hung a few inches away from a south-facing window. You can do still better by attaching a greenhouse to the south wall of your house, and providing openings so that the sun-heated air from the plants you're growing and the greenhouse earth circulates through your house.

Future solar homes will use a combination of passive techniques as well as providing their own electricity and heat from panels of solar cells as described in Chapter 11.

190

8
Solar Heating for Swimming Pools and Spas

Who wants to swim in a cold pool? Yet if you have a swimming pool, it makes good sense to take advantage of that sizable investment in pleasure and good health—which means heating your pool during several months of the year.

Until the energy crisis became both chronic and apparent, thousands of pool heaters using gas or, more rarely, electricity were installed. As early as 1975 many state laws or local regulations were passed to outlaw or curtail installations of heaters for new pool construction. In the winter of 1977, the use of natural gas was widely banned for heating any pools except where the owner could prove he or she needed a warm pool for therapeutic reasons.

It seems likely that such regulations will continue and be extended. But the alternative, if you own a swimming pool or spa, is both easy and relatively inexpensive. A solar heating system for your pool will pay for itself, usually in three years or less. Because adding solar collectors to your present pumping and filtration system is readily accomplished if you are a handy do-it-yourselfer, you can install a solar heating system quickly and with very little additional cost beyond the materials required.

Consider Passive Savings First

Just as it was pointed out in the previous chapter that you can gain solar heat economically by various passive techniques, so it's worthwhile to make your first step a consideration of several kinds of pool coverings which will help in both gaining and retaining heat.

For example, a number of manufacturers make blue plastic circles, typically 5 feet in diameter, designed to float on the surface of your pool like lily pads. CaTel Solar Circles made in Monrovia, California, are formed from polyethylene plastic, said by the manufacturer to resist ultraviolet deterioration, and retail for $11.95 each. You can easily calculate how many of these circles will cover the surface of your pool. When you're ready to swim, you simply remove the plastic pads and stack them at poolside.

A similar device that provides even greater coverage is made as Solar Squares by The Pool Cover Company in Huntington Beach, California, which also makes the Porta-Flate, an inflatable plastic cover for backyard pools.

Such devices reduce loss of water and heat by evaporation, and they help the water in your pool to collect solar energy during the day and to retain part of this heat at night. In several states, these energy-saving devices qualify as part of a tax credit program.

CaTel Manufacturing and others also furnish closed-cell foam plastic covers to retain heat in various sizes of spas. Sizes range from 6 foot x 6 foot to 8 foot x 8 foot sheets which can be easily cut with scissors or a sharp knife to fit your Jacuzzi or spa.

There is a similar solar blanket, available in a considerable range of rectangular and round sizes (up to 24 feet x 40 feet or 28 feet in diameter) for pools as well as for spas, made of cellular foam plastic by Sealed Air Corporation. The company has plants in New Jersey, Massachusetts, Illinois, Texas, and California as well as in several European countries and Canada. The maker claims that such a plastic blanket absorbs enough solar heat to raise the temperature of a pool by 10°F. The plastic sheet is light and readily rolled into a bundle when not covering your pool. Again, this material is easily trimmed to the necessary size and shape.

Another cover of cellular foam plastic is available in still larger blankets, which are supplied rolled on a reel with a stand, if you wish, so that you can unroll this SolarCap modular blanket from the edge of your pool and let it float out over the surface as a cover. Then when you're ready to swim again, you simply turn the reel crank and wind the plastic cover up on its reel. Made by L. M. Dearing Associates, Inc., of Studio City, California, these plastic blankets are made in sections from 16 to 20 feet wide and 75 to 100 feet long, each on its own reel core. Although such larger covers are made for public swimming pools, the same design could be used in smaller pools. Dearing also supplies positioning devices to keep adjacent sections of plastic blanket fastened together, or to keep the cover in place at the edges of the pool. When off the pool, the reeled-up sections are usually stored in cabinets which double as benches.

Expert Testimony on Passive Solar Heating Devices

A recent bulletin by the Southern California Solar Energy Association declares:

With the addition of pool blankets alone with conventional fuels, one can save about 75% on his fuel bills. Pool blankets reduce evaporation, night sky radiation, and convection losses.

During the summer, about an inch of water evaporates from the swimming pool each week. (Author's note: Because of the drought in the western United States, we are particularly conscious of ways to save water.) This corresponds to a heat loss of 1,047 BTU per pound of water at temperatures of 80 degrees. Thus the yearly loss for a 600-square foot pool is about 3,000 pounds or 33 million BTU.

Night sky radiation accounts for a major heat loss to pools. On clear nights, the warmth of the pool is absorbed by the black sky. The loss can be as much as 100 BTU per square foot per hour. Convection losses caused by wind and lower air temperatures are also minimized by the use of an insulating blanket.

Dr. Farber of the University of Florida has found that a single sheet of transparent plastic floating on the pool when not in use will raise the average temperature of the water 10°F, extending the swimming season by about 2-1/2 months. However it is important to avoid air bubbles when placing the cover on the water surface, since the droplets formed will act as reflectors of the sun's heat. . . . We also suggest painting the pool a dark blue color to increase absorption of the sun's energy.

It is suggested that if one installs solar collectors, the system include automatic controls and a pool blanket.

Among the more elaborate kinds of pool covers available are motorized automatic units—some operated by timers, others by solar cells—with manual override so that the pool is covered or uncovered with a minimum of labor. Such an automatic unit is considerably more costly than a plastic cover you put on from a reel or by spreading it over the pool. And you need a solar heating system in addition, to bring your pool temperature up to a comfortable level and keep it there when the local air temperature, or ambient air, is cool.

Basic Design of a Solar Pool Heater

The basic elements of a solar system for heating your pool are shown in Figure 8-1. This is the simplest possible system and will work, although it's desirable to include the refinements discussed in subsequent paragraphs. Water coming through the filter, having been pumped out of your pool, is bypassed through solar collector panels and then returned to the pool. So that you can include or exclude the solar heating loop, you have a control valve. If the valve is closed, water flows up to your solar collectors and back into your pool. When the valve is open, your solar heating is not being used.

One of the simplest techniques, a popular and very economical method of providing solar heating for a small pool, is to use a long serpentine of black-painted garden hose—several hoses connected together—as the collector of the sun's heat. For example, one pool owner interrupted his return water pipe to the pool and inserted 300 feet of large-diameter plastic hose, painted black, which is arranged in a serpentine on his south-facing garage roof. He also has a manual control valve so that he can insert his solar hose collector, consisting of six 50-foot hoses connected in a loop with no leaks, as a heater or cut it out when desired.

There are commercial versions of this hose-type collector available, some with plastic hose painted green—a good color for

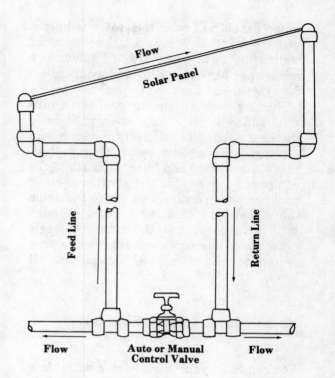

FIGURE 8-1. Basic Elements of a Solar Heating System for a Swimming Pool

absorbing the sun's infrared heat energy. Such hoses coiled in a helix are mounted in a frame that you can attach to your roof.

Your objective in building a solar heater for your pool is quite different from heating domestic hot water for your home. The water you need for baths, showers, and washing dishes and clothes is at a much higher temperature, typically from 120°F to 160°F, depending on personal preference. By contrast, your pool water is generally no hotter than 80°F because higher temperatures in most areas foster the formation of algae. As any experienced pool owner knows, you want to avoid algae because these minute organisms, once present, are difficult to get rid of.

Furthermore, even a small home pool contains several thousand gallons of water. The job of your solar heater is to raise the temperature of this water by a few degrees. Typically, the loop through your solar collector panels will raise the water temperature from 2°F to 5°F as a large volume of water, flowing at a rate of 4 to 5 gallons per minute per panel, goes through your collector system and back to the pool.

Heating your swimming pool is an efficient and ideal use of solar energy. Because the heat needed is relatively low, you can use simple collector designs. Your pool already has a pump and filter, so much of the equipment you need is already there—most pool pumps are entirely adequate to handle the added load of driving water through your solar loop, and the filter (properly maintained) and pool chemicals assure your system of clean water with a consistent pH level.

Recommendations on Solar Collectors

You can build your solar heater with black garden hose. Or you can use flat-plate collectors made of plastic materials available from several manufacturers. You may decide to step up to more durable and efficient metal collectors with copper waterways. As the most elaborate kind of system, your choice may be concentrating collectors with automatic sun-tracking. A still more sophisticated approach which may prove increasingly useful to homeowners with pools, is to heat your swimming pool with solar energy and then to use this heated water for year-round thermal storage, in conjunction with a heat pump, for efficient space heating and cooling of your home. Advantages and disadvantages of all these alternatives are discussed in subsequent pages.

But first some of the basic facts about placement of your solar collectors will be useful.

- Mount your solar collector panels on a structure facing south in the Northern Hemisphere. An angle of 10° west of south is ideal. Tests show that 90% of the sun's radiation is received during the middle two-thirds of each day. If you can't mount your collectors on a south-facing roof, perhaps you can find space for a rack within 100 feet or so of your pool. Be sure that whatever area you choose is not shaded by trees or another building during any part of the day.

- The angle at which you mount your collectors has some significance. For best results in getting solar heat during the winter, an angle of about 10° greater than your latitude is desirable for flat-plate collectors because this means that the sun's rays will be striking your collectors at an approximately perpendicular angle during the winter months. If you plan to use your pool only during the six warmest months of the year, an angle corresponding to your latitude is satisfactory.

- If you want to mount your solar collector panels on your roof without a rack, or even use your collectors as a roofing material, as has been done particularly with copper panels in some installations, you will lose only a few percentage points in efficiency of your collectors if they are not tilted at the most desirable angle.

- If you decide to use concentrating collectors, either with a tracking system or with Fresnel lenses, you can mount them on a flat or tilted roof with negligible difference in performance.

Cost versus Lifetime Service of Solar Collectors

Since you don't need to heat your swimming pool water more than 15° above the ambient air generally, and usually you don't want a pool temperature higher than 80°F, it is quite feasible to use plastic solar collectors. They are often considerably cheaper than metal ones. A disadvantage is that plastic collectors are more apt to leak, and their

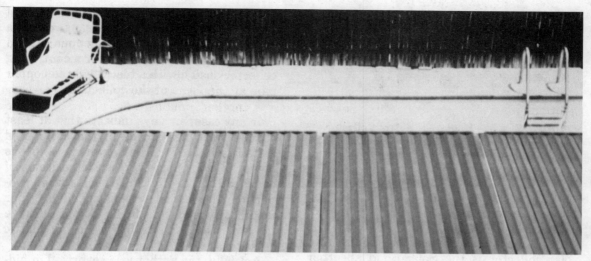

FIGURE 8-2.   Unglazed Collectors by Energy Systems, Inc., Heat a Swimming Pool Efficiently

service lifetime is much shorter. An estimate by Southern California Solar Energy Association places the life of plastic solar collectors at 4 to 5 years.

By contrast, a durable metal collector—either homemade or bought from a reputable manufacturer—should last for at least 20 years or longer. Because you are not trying to heat water to a high temperature, your metal solar collector needs no glazing. In fact it is more efficient to use a bare, unglazed collector as shown in Figure 8-2. The point of this graph is that, when the temperature difference between the water in the solar collector and the ambient air is less than 20°, the efficiency of the unglazed collector is higher than that of an identical unit with single glazing.

This means that maintenance of metal solar collectors for your pool is minimized, with no glazing to replace. Repainting the collectors with a good flat black commercial paint perhaps once every three years should be sufficient.

There are several manufacturers of plastic solar panels designed for heating swimming pools, including three California firms: Fafco, Inc., of Menlo Park, Burke Industries in San Jose; and Sundu Company of Anaheim.

The author would like to make the following recommendations.

If you are going to make your own installation and your budget is very limited, look over the various kinds of plastic solar collectors. There are installations of plastic panels which have been in service for heating pools for as long as 8 years. In considering the amount of labor required to install these plastic collectors, remember that you will have to provide a secure method for attaching them to your roof, frame, or rack. Details on this were provided in the author's first book and are outlined briefly here on a subsequent page.

If you want an installation with maximum life and minimum maintenance, select metal collector panels of good quality. Because you are running large volumes of water through your collectors without a heat exchanger, use copper pipe for your waterways. Many manufacturers of metal collectors use copper pipe mounted either in aluminum fins or on a copper absorber sheet. If you want to make your own metal solar collectors for your pool heating system, there are detailed instructions on a copper model in the excellent booklet, *How to De-*

195

FIGURE 8-3. Unglazed Solar Collector, Solar-Bond, Suitable for Heating Swimming Pools

sign and Build a Solar Swimming Pool Heater, by Francis de Winter, available from the Copper Development Association, Inc., of New York City.

One of the best values in an unglazed solar collector is the Solar-Bond absorber panel made by Olin Brass of East Alton, Illinois. These panels provide integral tubes and headers within a copper plate. They are made by metallurgically bonding two sheets of copper together and then expanding them in selected unbonded areas to form integral flow passages through which the water flows. A panel 34 inches x 96 inches (2 feet 10 inches x 8 feet = 22.66 square feet) is priced as of May 1977 at about $95 each including a packing charge but not shipping costs. Other standard sizes include 22 inches x 96 inches and 34 inches x 76 inches. An illustration of the Olin Solar-Bond panels appears in Figure 8-3. This price is slightly more than $4 per square foot.

As a comparison, this author and his associate, who are making installations of solar heating systems for large community pools in Southern California, recently purchased some 4 foot x 10 foot unglazed collectors with copper waterways clamped in aluminum fins from Energy Systems, Inc., of San Diego. At the installer price, these collectors cost us about $3.50 per square foot.

If you are not making your own installation, our recommendation would be to get bids from at least three reputable installers. If possible, get them to show you typical swimming pool installations they have done in your area, and talk to the owners. Then plan to get an installation using the best materials available. This means using a metal collector plate with copper waterways. Or you may decide on a concentrating collector design with a black-painted copper pipe at the focus of the collector.

In any case, surveys indicate that at least 45%—sometimes more—of the cost of an installation of a solar heater to a pool's owner is labor plus the associated items of overhead and profit. Since such a large proportion of the dollars you spend on your installation is essentially fixed, you will save no more than about 15% by using plastic collectors.

Actually, the author was surprised in bidding on a recent installation of a fairly large public swimming pool system that our winning, and lowest, bid was considerably lower than that of a major maker and installer of plastic solar collectors. And we chose to furnish metal collector plates with copper waterways.

Mounting Positions for Collectors

How many solar collectors will you need for heating your pool? If you have the time and desire to go through calculations involving a large number of physical factors such as the volume of water in your pool, the average temperature in your locale for each month, the number of therms (hundreds of thousands of BTU) gathered by the collectors you have chosen, and the chill factor caused by winds at various seasons you may arrive at an extremely precise number of collectors for your installation. The book by de Winter as well as some other references in the bibliography provide those mathematically inclined with all sorts of interesting exercises for long winter evenings.

For a practical rule-of-thumb, most experienced installers of solar heating systems use a very simple formula:

Area of solar collectors =
1/2 surface area of your pool.

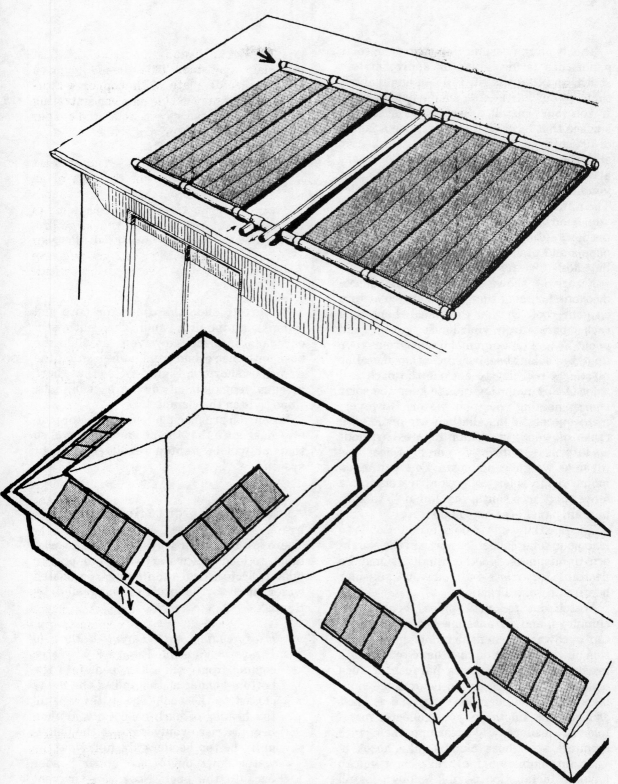

FIGURE 8-4. Alternate Methods for Mounting Solar Collectors to Heat a
Swimming Pool

197

This is on the assumption that your solar panels are facing south or approximately south, and that the tilt is at an angle about that of your latitude or somewhat greater. If you must install collectors on a sloping surface that faces east or west, use a factor of 70% of your pool area to get the collector area required. If you're installing your panels on a flat roof, put them on a rack so that you have them inclined at a suitable angle. The minimum angle for a rack is a 5° slope: you need that much inclination to ensure proper venting of the air trapped inside the panels and piping. When panels are almost flat, add 10% to your collector area.

Figure 8-4 shows a variety of alternative methods for mounting your solar collectors on your roof. Or you can place them on a rack separate from your house, garage, and pool. To get maximum benefit from your unglazed solar absorbers, whether metal or plastic, it will pay to enclose the back and sides of this mounting rack to keep the solar energy heating your pool water. However, many successful installations are made with racks of wood, aluminum or steel without enclosures, sacrificing 5% or so of heat loss to save weight and cost. You can even mount your solar collection system on a fence that faces south, but add 10% to 15% to your panel area to compensate.

The one thing *not* to do in orientation is to face your solar collectors north in the Northern Hemisphere. Northern lighting may be desirable for artists, but you won't get solar heating in that direction.

Watch out for vent pipes, ventilators, chimneys, and TV antennas—or other roof-top hardware—when planning an installation on your roof. You may have to separate groups of solar collectors because of such obstructions. Using neoprene or some similar synthetic rubber hose material at least as large in diameter as your collector manifolds or headers, and attaching them with stainless steel hose clamps (like hoses in your automobile engine) will permit you to have an installation flexible enough for all kinds of roof configurations.

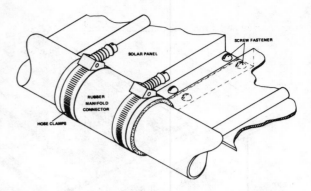

FIGURE 8-5.   Feeding Water to Solar Panels

Be sure to slide the connector hose and clamps onto the first panel. Then put a second panel in place. Now you can slide the hose onto the second panel and position the clamps as shown in Figure 8-5 so that there is equal engagement on both manifolds. Then tighten the clamps.

When you are placing your connector panels, make sure that the headers are level so that air will be vented readily from your system.

Feeding Water to Solar Panels

There are four basic ways, plus some variations, to feed cool water from your pool to your collectors and then bring sun-heated water back to the pool, as suggested by Raypak.

- *End Feeding with Direct Return (6 Panels or Fewer)*, Figure 8-6. Water coming from your filter feeds into the bottom header at the end of the array closest to the pool. The water will fill the header of each collector and then begin to rise evenly through the panels until the top headers are full. Now the water flows out of the upper header back to the pool. Note the air vent mounted near the upper header at the

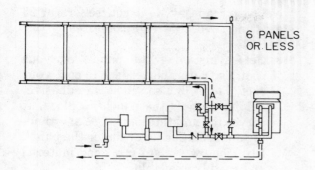

FIGURE 8-6. End Feeding with Direct Return

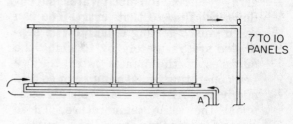

FIGURE 8-7. End Feeding with Reverse Return

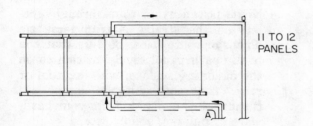

FIGURE 8-8. Center of T Feeding with Direct Return

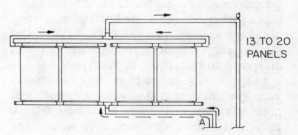

FIGURE 8-9. Center of T Feeding with Reverse Return

end of the array nearest the pool. There must be a tightly fitted cap at the final end of each header.

- *End Feeding with Reverse Return (7 to 10 Panels)*, Figure 8-7. Water is brought into the bottom header at the end furthest from the feed line, and the opposite end of this bottom header is capped.

- *Center of T Feeding with Direct Return (11 or 12 Panels)*, Figure 8-8. Water is fed into your panels through a T which divides and sends it to arrays remote from each other. You may wish to use this technique with more or fewer than 11 or 12 collectors, separated or

mounted at different levels as shown in Figure 8-4.

- *Center of T Feeding with Reverse Return (13 to 20 Panels)*, Figure 8-9. The diagram shows how separate streams of sun-heated water come together at the T from reverse loops from the upper headers of two arrays of panels.

You may find it necessary to place collectors in more than two locations. Merely by using Ts and keeping the flow consistent with previous diagrams, you can make such a multiple installation. If your water distribution system produces uneven flow between collector arrays, you can easily fix this.

199

Put a gate valve in the line feeding the array receiving too much water and cut down the flow to that array. You can tell if you're getting equal flow in separated arrays merely by touching the surfaces of the panels after they've been operating for 30 minutes or so on a sunny day. All the surfaces should be at about the same temperature. Those getting hotter than about 85°F for plastic and possibly as high as 100°F with copper (waterways) are not receiving enough water.

Efficiency of your solar pool heating system depends on a high flow rate and a relatively low surface temperature. When your collectors are no hotter than the temperatures just cited, the solar heating efficiency is as high as 75%, or even 80%. Most of the solar energy warming your panels is being delivered to the water in your pool.

Suspect an obstruction somewhere in your system flow if the water coming from your solar heater is more than from 6°F to 10°F hotter than your pool. It is much more likely, after the system has been operating for some time on a sunny day, that this temperature difference will be about 3°F.

Installing Plastic Collectors

Each panel must be properly tied down to the roof or mounting rack. There are times when you will want to drain your collectors, and plastic units are so light the wind can lift them and damage either the collectors or piping, or both. Even when collectors are filled, a strong wind can shift them if they are not securely fastened to the support structure.

Shown in Figure 8-10 is the technique recommended and used by Fafco, largest maker of plastic panels. Incidentally, this manufacturer moved into a larger plant early in 1977 and announced that 100,000 of its collectors had been installed for swimming pool heaters. Many of these installations have been made by do-it-yourselfers in 26 states and several foreign countries.

- Before installing the panels on your roof, use a durable sealant to coat your roof. This will also act as an adhesive, helping to hold the panels in place. It serves the additional purpose of providing an insulation layer under the panel. Black epoxy sealant is a good material and readily available.

- Use nylon straps on the upper side of each array of solar panels. Then secure the bottom side of each panel with vinyl straps. The more elastic vinyl allows for expansion and contraction of the panels with changes in temperature.

- Next, fasten nylon rope through eyelets on the straps as transverse tie downs or center ties. Be sure that you fasten each panel firmly to clamps on the mounting surface, whether roof or rack. The most suitable clamps are turnbuckles, available from your hardware or building supply store.

- When first installing an array of panels, tighten the turnbuckles holding the straps and the center ties only about 1/2 of the thread. After all your panels are in place, tighten your clamps further, to at least 3/4 of the thread. Tighten the clamps cautiously at the end panels, where you are clamping against PVC or ABS plastic pipe. Be sure to place turnbuckles carefully so that there is no skewing of either panels or the hose couplers between panels. Use an extra long set of couplers at the end points where the array of panels connects with the feed line from the pool and the return line to the pool.

- Makers of plastic panels check these units for leaks before shipment. If you receive a collector that leaks, return it to the factory for replacement. If one of your panels develops a leak some time after installation, use the patching kit

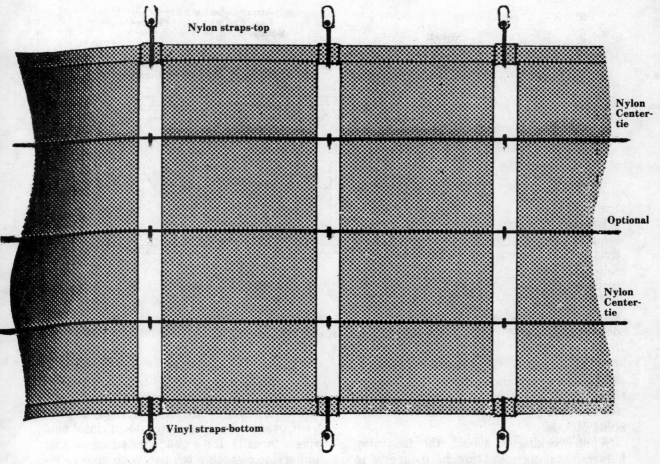

Nylon straps-top

Nylon Center-tie

Optional

Nylon Center-tie

Vinyl straps-bottom

FIGURE 8-10. Technique Recommended for Securing Solar Collectors to Mounting Rack or Roof

and instructions provided by the manufacturer. Should any panel be too badly damaged for repair as installed, remove it and fill the space top and bottom with suitable lengths of plastic pipe until you can replace the panel.

Installing Metal Collectors

One method of installing unglazed metal collectors on a roof is to use wood runners attached to the roof with screws. Of course at each place you put in a screw or other attachment to the roof, you must put epoxy sealant around it to prevent leaks. If your roof has a suitable tilt, you attach a wood runner at the top and bottom positions for mounting each collector, so that the top and bottom manifolds are each placed on a runner. Then you attach each manifold or header at two points to the runner. Wrap pipe straps or steel plumber's tape around the header, and screw the tape securely into the runner.

Construction of a wooden rack is shown in Figure 8-11. Note in the elevation view that the manifolds are attached to the rack with steel tape at two points on each manifold, top and bottom. There are also available from many sources racks made of aluminum or steel, painted for protection against the

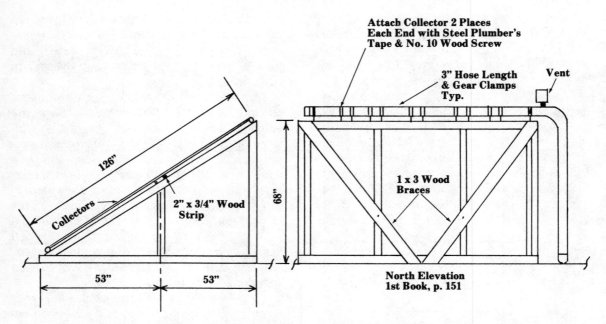

Attach Collector 2 Places
Each End with Steel Plumber's
Tape & No. 10 Wood Screw

3" Hose Length
& Gear Clamps
Typ.

Vent

126"

Collectors

2" x 3/4" Wood
Strip

68"

1 x 3 Wood
Braces

53"   53"

North Elevation
1st Book, p. 151

**FIGURE 8-11.   Design of Wood Support Frame for Swimming Pool Solar
Collectors. By Sennergetics Solar Systems**

weather. For instance, this author has obtained racks of the correct size and inclination made of painted aluminum from Reynolds Metals.

When working on a roof, the first step before installing mounting hardware is to prepare the roof area. For asphalt-shingle roofs, mount each hardware item on a flat spot. If this is not possible, cut off part of one shingle. When you're working with concrete tile, remove part of the tile to expose the subsurface. On a tar and gravel roof, remove as much gravel as possible and soften the roof tar with paint thinner.

A favorite technique is to use a pitch pan made of copper. The roof fasteners go through the brackets (attached to the collector), then through the pitch pan into the roof rafter. Before you place each pitch pan, drill a pilot hole into the rafter. Then you put the pitch pan on the rafter and screw it in with wood screws. A small piece of plywood in each pitch pan will distribute the load more evenly.

After you have fastened the pitch pan in

place with lag screws, fill it with pitch or plastic (epoxy) roofing cement. Thus, you cover fastening hardware completely to prevent water from getting down into the screw threads. It's a good idea to smear the underside of each pitch pan with epoxy.

An alternative to using pitch pans is to put tar tape under your mounting brackets, and then cover the screw heads fastening bracket to roof with a silicone or epoxy sealing compound. Both of these methods assume you're using racks or some mounting method other than the wood runners first mentioned.

Because metal collectors are self-supporting, you can lean them against posts in a rack structure on the ground similar to that shown in Figure 8-11. Or they can be mounted on garages, sundecks, cabanas, or any suitable structure. Just be sure your collector array, if it is near ground level, is protected from vandalism. If you use unglazed metal collectors as recommended, however, ordinary mischief won't harm them.

Maintenance of metal collectors is very simple indeed. Repainting your collectors with a good quality flat black enamel about once every three years should be adequate in most climates.

When you use an unglazed metal collector, your panel will collect diffused or sky radiation from the sun as well as direct sunlight without the reflective loss inherent in glazing. Therefore, tilting your collectors to the most favorable angle is useful but not imperative. As previously indicated, you can mount your collectors in an almost flat position, but allow a 5° tilt to elevate the header delivering sun-heated water so that your air vent will work.

Piping for Your Solar Heater

Whether using metal or plastic solar collectors, it is most economical to use pipe of one of the accepted plastic types, such as PVC or ABS, readily available from your building supply or hardware store. Copper pipe is ideal material but at mid-1977 prices is several times as expensive as the plastic.

However, if you are installing metal collectors, it is desirable to run a few feet of copper pipe beyond the outlet (sun-heated) side of your collector array. This is a precaution for the occasional times when the outlet water temperature is hot enough to soften plastic pipe at this point of maximum heat.

Because you want to maintain high flow rates through your solar heater and to present a workable load to your pool pump, use 1-1/2-inch diameter pipe for runs to and from your panels. If your solar array is more than 60 feet from your pool, use 2-inch pipe.

The very simplest manually controlled system appears in Figure 8-1. In this case you open the bypass valve when you want to shut off the solar system, and close the valve during sunny days when you want your solar collectors to heat your pool. Even with this simple system, you should have an air vent valve at the highest point of the outlet—beyond the end of the top header in

your final collector in your array. This valve is necessary to purge the air from your system when you're filling it with water, and also to permit air to enter your system to help drain it.

A more efficient system, with automatic control, is shown in Figure 8-12. Now the solenoid bypass, or pinch valve, is controlled automatically by the differential controller. A temperature sensor—the sun sensor—which may be mounted on a miniature simulated collector, senses the temperature available at your collector array. This temperature signal, an electrical voltage level, is transmitted to the controller, which also receives a signal from a pool sensor checking the temperature of water coming from your pool filter.

When the collector temperature is higher than the water temperature by a predetermined amount—a few degrees, adjustable by you—the controller closes the solenoid pinch valve. (You can also set up your system so that the same temperature signal will turn on the pool pump.) With the solenoid valve closed, water flows through your warm solar collectors and adds heat to your pool.

When the difference between collector and water temperatures falls below the preset amount, the control unit opens the solenoid valve so that your collectors are bypassed. In areas where there is a possibility of freezing, the differential control unit has a circuit which automatically causes the collectors to drain into the pool when the collector temperature reaches a danger level, say 36°F.

The check valve shown in this system is a one-way valve to protect the system from direct drain-down of the collectors by gravity back through the filter. Most pool systems have such a check valve in the main line, so you may not need to add one. But you must be sure your collectors will drain through an auxiliary heater—if you have one. Or you must provide a bypass around the heater, or direct drainage if you don't have a heater.

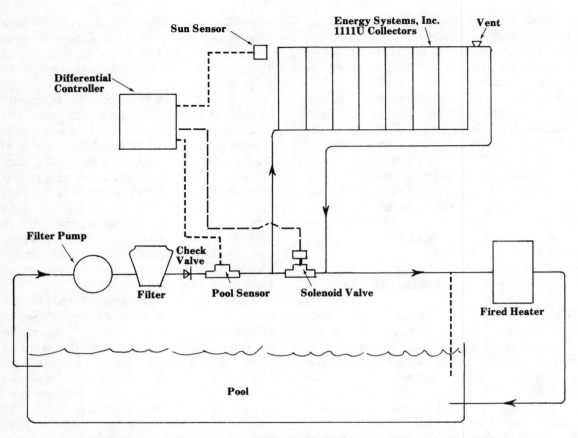

**FIGURE 8-12.   An Efficient Solar Pool Heating System with Automatic Control.
By Sennergetics Solar Systems**

Unusual Retrofit Solar System for Large Indoor Pool

The diagram in Figure 8-13 shows how a large indoor pool in Black Lake, Michigan, has been equipped with a solar heater as a retrofit which supplies about 1/3 the energy required to keep the water at 78°F. Designed by the Research and Design Institute of Providence, Rhode Island, this solar heater takes advantage of the original design of the building, owned by the United Auto Workers.

On the entire south-facing roof is a copper sheathing with vertical risers forming channels running from the peak down to a gutter. A cover of Kalwall Sun-Lite plastic sheet is fastened to the tops of these risers. Water is pumped through pipes feeding a

trickle into each of the channels on the copper roof absorber. Collected in the gutter, the sun-warmed water flows to a heat exchanger in the basement of the building. This exchanger warms water in a tank, from which a pump takes the water through a gas-fired boiler to the indoor Olympic-size pool. The pool return goes back into the tank containing the heat exchanger as shown in Figure 8-13.

In a typical week, the pool is heated for 75 hours, with 50 hours of water heating provided by the gas boiler and 25 hours by the sun. An automatic control system keeps the water temperature at 78°F.

Solar Heater for a Spa

A typical spa or Jacuzzi is heated to a temperature of about 105°F or slightly hotter.

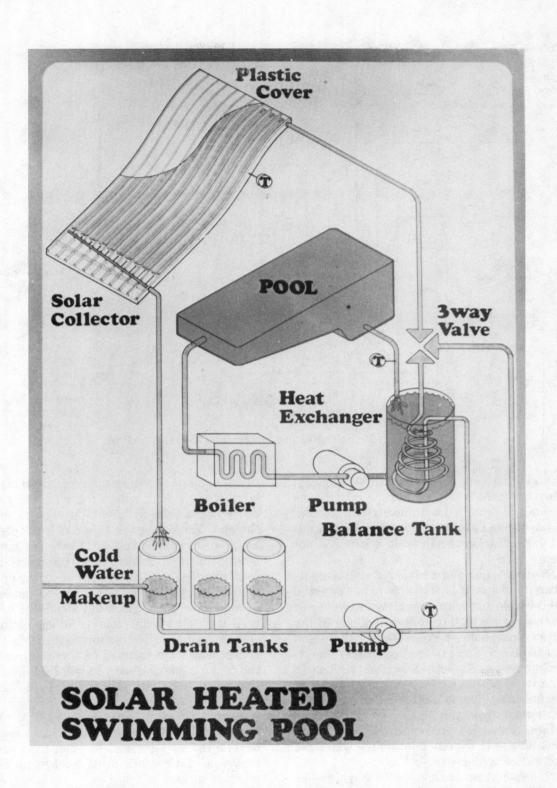

SOLAR HEATED SWIMMING POOL

13. Retrofitting of Large Indoor Swimming Pool in Black Lake, Michigan, with Solar Heater

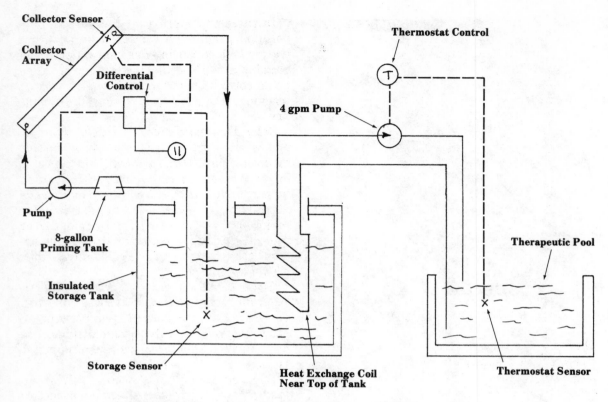

FIGURE 8-14. Solar Heating System for a Therapeutic Pool

It will have a capacity of 800 to 900 gallons. Most therapeutic pools are sunk in the ground or provided with insulation. To conserve the heat in your spa, you should put an insulating cover over it when it's not being used.

Because you need a higher water temperature for a spa, it is desirable to use a glazed metal collector with copper waterways, or even a concentrating collector of one of the types—parabolic or Fresnel lens—discussed in Chapter 6. You can feed the water directly into your spa with a system similar to that used with a swimming pool, but it is desirable to include a mixing valve ahead of your inlet from the solar heater. Set this mixing valve for your desired water temperature so that your inlet water won't get too hot on a sunny day.

Another variation on a heating system for a spa is shown in Figure 8-14. This simpli-fied schematic shows an unpressurized insulated storage tank where the water is preheated by a solar system before going into the spa. The heat exchange coil is simply a helix of soft copper tubing. There are large plastic storage tanks now commercially available for use in such a preheating application. This tank may be placed underground or on the surface but should be covered with an adequate layer of insulation. One of the most effective forms of insulation is urethane foam sprayed on the exterior of the tank. In most areas you will find insulation specialists with equipment to do this job.

Again you must have an air vent at the highest point of your solar collector array, beyond the outlet manifold pipe, to ensure that your panels will drain each time the pump is turned off.

FIGURE 8-15. Novel Circular Solar Collector Manufactured by Solar-Eye Products of Ft. Lauderdale, Florida

Buy Collector Panels Locally

Unless you intend to make your own solar collectors, it makes good sense to purchase them from a reputable manufacturer somewhere within 200 miles or less of your installation. In Appendix 1, at the back of this book, is a fairly extensive list of manufacturers of liquid-type solar collectors, the kind you need for swimming pool, spa, and domestic hot water systems.

Examples of a few manufacturers from various parts of the country making suitable liquid-type solar collectors, in addition to those previously mentioned in this book, are:

Solar-Eye Products, Ft. Lauderdale, Florida, makes an unusual 5-foot diameter circular collector shown in Figure 8-15. The housing is spun aluminum and the glazing is Kalwall Sun-Lite plastic sheet. There are two alternatives for the inner absorber. One consists of 120 feet of 3/4-inch coiled black-painted copper tubing on a black copper plate. The second, designed primarily for pool systems, has 200 feet of 1-inch coiled black polyethylene tubing. In each version the sides and bottom of this novel cylindrical collector are insulated with polyurethane foam.

In the same Florida city, *Solarcell Corporation* produces a 4 foot x 6 foot concentrating collector using focusing reflectors of aluminum with copper waterways. Each panel contains 6 reflecting troughs, is non-tracking, and weighs less than 70 pounds dry.

Solar Dynamics, Inc. of Dania, Florida, makes an unglazed collector designed for mounting on a flat surface. This collector includes hinged reflective shields that stand up perpendicularly around the panel on the north, east, and west sides to provide extra radiation. This shielding can be folded over the collector in the summer to prevent excess heat collection, or to avoid damage during high winds.

Solar Energy Products, Inc. of Gainesville, Florida, has metal flat plate collectors as well as heat exchangers, pumps, temperature controllers, valves, and fittings. The company has an impressive record of installations.

Southeastern Solar Systems, Inc. of Atlanta, Georgia, supplies all-copper collectors at the favorable price of $3.75 per square foot painted black, and $3.65 per square foot unpainted.

Sunray Solar Heat of Brooklyn, New York, provides an aluminum container lined with urethane insulation on the sides and both fiberglass and urethane on the bottom under a blackened copper absorber plate bonded to 1/4-inch copper waterways and 3/4-inch copper headers, with a single glass glazing.

Author's Note: Sunray advertises its glazed collector panels for swimming pool installations, and such glazed units are certainly desirable in coastal areas and northern locales where there is considerable fog and more solar heating is needed than you can get with unglazed collectors. Solarcoa, a leading Southern California manufacturer, has swimming pool installations along the Pacific Coast—including a solar heater for an indoor pool on the Balboa Peninsula, Newport Beach, with cold ocean water on both sides—where glazed collectors are needed to keep the pools comfortably warm.

Columbia Chase Solar Energy Division, in Holbrook, Massachusetts, has developed a new collector design with the copper absorber and waterways in a 1-piece fiberglass frame with transparent plastic (fiberglass with polyester resin) glazing. Each dry panel weighs only 45 pounds, and this new design is available in a choice of several colors.

Heilemann Electric of Warren, New Jersey, provides collectors with copper tubing and GE Lexan plastic glazing in a self-supporting design. The tubes of which the collector is made can be rotated to the angle most suitable for the surface on which the panels are mounted.

Halstead & Mitchell of Scottsboro, Alabama, makes a solar collector with copper tubes held in aluminum fins, available as a SunCeiver in an insulated and glazed frame. Using five SunCeiver panels in a Florida installation, the sun-heated water is from 2 to 10 degrees warmer than the pool, and the pool water is kept at 80°F even on cloudy and overcast days, according to this manufacturer.

Daystar Corporation in Burlington, Massachusetts, whose collector features copper absorber and waterways and efficient glazing, states that the higher efficiency of its design, proved by independent testing according to the National Bureau of Standards procedures, means that fewer collectors are needed for each installation. These panels have been widely used in large and small applications.

Sun-A-Matic, a division of Butler Ventamatic Corp. of Mineral Wells, Texas, has a collector with rectangular copper waterways said to give greater surface heating from absorber to water. Insulation is styrofoam, with double glazing of Tedlar, and a two-piece container of the tough Borg-Warner Cycolac plastic.

Original Power Equipment Company located in Garland, Texas, makes collectors with copper waterways and either plastic or glass glazing in two sizes: 2 feet x 4 feet and 2 feet x 8 feet.

Cole Solar Systems of Austin, Texas, supplies an unglazed collector with copper pipes and headers available with or without a mounting frame in a size approximately 4 feet x 10 feet. A similar collector with glazing and insulation in a frame is available.

Sun Power Systems in Sunnyvale, California, uses an Olin Roll-Bond copper absorber in an aluminum frame insulated with urethane foam and single-glazed. Its dimensions are 3 feet x 8-1/2 feet in area, 3-1/2 inches thick.

Kastek Corporation of Portland, Oregon, manufacturers a collector called a Solar Heatrap, designed for swimming pool installations, with a special aluminum extrusion to keep the panels above the roofing material. These panels may also be used as patio covers or roof extensions, according to the maker.

Swimming Pool and Heat Pump for Efficient Solar System

When you are planning to heat your swimming pool, it makes sense to consider solar heating and cooling for your house—and, of course, sun-heated domestic hot water. There is an increasing number of such installations. One of the pioneer examples, beautiful in design and architecture, is the solar house in Tucson, Arizona, sponsored by the Copper Development Association and described in a previous chapter.

There is an even more elegant approach, developed recently by Solartec Corporation of San Diego, which uses tracking solar collectors to heat a swimming pool and then uses the heated water from the pool, along with an efficient water-to-air heat pump, for both space heating and cooling of your house. As an added dividend, the hot gas from the heat pump's compressor heats water in a heat exchanger connected to a storage tank to supply your domestic hot water. Thus, the big volume of water in your swimming pool, heated by the sun,

FIGURE 8-16. Plumbing Industry Representative Paul H. NanKivell Building his own Solar Pool Heater with Copper Collectors. Now he saves $100 a Month on his Energy Bill

FIGURE 8-17. Pool Heated by Parabolic Concentrating Collectors made by Sunpower Systems Corporation, Tempe, Arizona

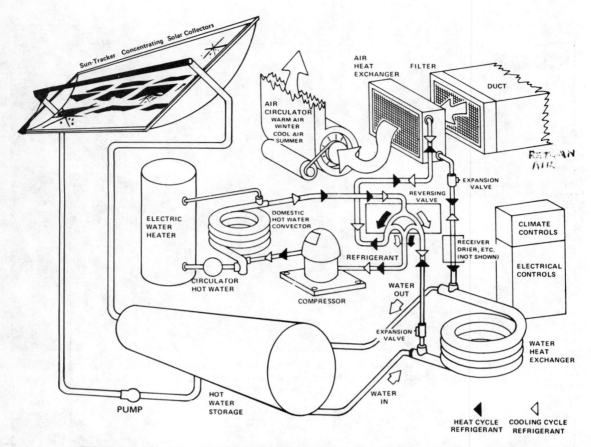

FIGURE 8-18.   Operation of Solartec Tracking Solar Collectors to Supply Space Heating and Cooling and Domestic Hot Water

serves instead of a large hot water tank as your thermal storage. And because a heat pump has a high COP (coefficient of performance), even with water supplied at a relatively low temperature, this system does an excellent job.

This author sees no reason why the Solartec system, designed primarily for use in areas with relatively mild climates and outdoor swimming pools used all year, should not also work in more severe climates for buildings having indoor swimming pools. This would make the system useful in many public buildings such as schools, colleges, YMCA and YWCA buildings, athletic clubs, hotels and motels, as well as residences with indoor pools.

The Solartec Sun-Tracker solar collector is a parabolic design similar to those made by Aerotherm of Mountain View, California; Sunpower Systems in Tempe, Arizona; Albuquerque Western Solar Industries; and others. The Solartec unit has a coated aluminum reflector 4 feet wide and 10 feet long, with a black-painted 1-inch copper pipe at the focus of the reflector. Framing is made of steel and aluminum tubing.

The collector tracks the sun automatically because each collector in a series is tilted by the action of a small electric motor. This motor works from a 115-volt AC supply and draws only 1 ampere of current—power consumption is 115 watts. A 1,780:1 gear reduction system makes it possible for this one motor to drive up to 50 collectors and keep them pointing at the sun. The motor's driving action is controlled by two sensitive photocells which compare the amount of

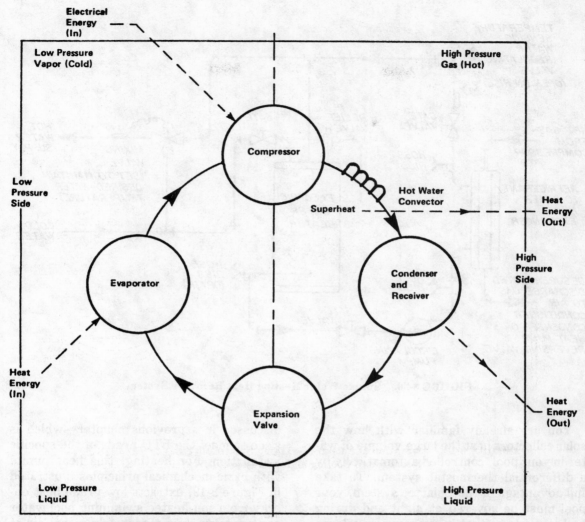

FIGURE 8-19. Simple Water Heating Heat Recovery System Designed by Solartec

Labels in figure:

Electrical Energy (In)

Low Pressure Vapor (Cold)

High Pressure Gas (Hot)

Low Pressure Side

Compressor

Hot Water Convector

Superheat

Heat Energy (Out)

High Pressure Side

Evaporator

Condenser and Receiver

Heat Energy (In)

Expansion Valve

Heat Energy (Out)

Low Pressure Liquid

High Pressure Liquid

sunlight coming to them from two angles. The resultant electrical signal keeps the parabolic reflectors pointing at the sun.

According to Solartec, this Sun-Tracker collector delivers solar energy to the user at a cost per BTU lower than that of solar heat from a flat-plate solar collector with double glazing and a selective black absorber surface.

How the Solartec System Works

In Figure 8-18 is a simplified diagram of how the Solartec system works to supply space

heating and cooling and domestic hot water from a heat pump connected to water warmed by tracking solar collectors. In this diagram, substitute your swimming pool for the cylinder labeled "hot water storage." The entire system consists of the following principal elements:

- Solar collectors used to heat your pool
- Water source components
- Refrigeration circuit components
- Air handling components
- Domestic hot water components
- Controls

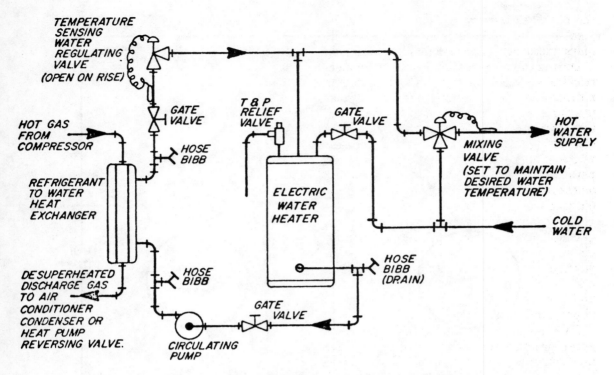

FIGURE 8-20. Simple Water Heating Heat Recovery System

You are already familiar with how the solar collectors heat the large volume of water in your pool, controlled automatically by a differential thermostat system. To take full advantage of the Solartec system, your pool must be covered at night and during bad weather so that it can serve as a large thermal storage tank—as well as a place where you and your family enjoy swimming.

Heated water from the pool goes through a heat exchanger made of cupro-nickel coils. Sun-warmed water circulating through these coils warms freon refrigerant in a contacting coil, and then returns to the pool. According to Solartec, the key to successful performance of the system is to have an adequate flow of water at temperatures of from 35°F to 100°F. This range is well within the expected temperature range of solar-heated pools, using a pool blanket when necessary to preserve heat.

The Solartec heat pump works in a cycle —the reverse cycle refrigeration principle

discussed in a previous chapter—which is sized to meet the BTU needs of the specific installation. For heating, this heat pump, with basic mechanical principles illustrated in Figure 8-19, extracts low-grade heat energy from sun-heated swimming pool water and converts it to moderately warm air to warm the building. When cooling is required, the water from the pool is used to cool the refrigerant by means of the heat pump, and air blown over chilled coils circulates through the house and keeps it comfortable in hot weather.

According to the manufacturer, this system uses a higher volume of air blown at lower speeds than other air systems, resulting in quieter operation. A squirrel cage blower, filter, air heat exchanger, and controls are mounted in a single frame. The integral blower motor's ball bearings are permanently lubricated with a direct drive to the evaporator, and the system includes a permanent type of air filter. Ducts to carry the circulating warm or cool air should be insulated and might be made of 1-inch fiberglass ductboard as a recommended material.

During the compression cycle, when electrical energy is used by the heat pump in both heating and cooling modes, superheat is available. This superheated hot gas from the compressor is directed through a special refrigerant-to-water heat exchanger which supplies domestic hot water at temperatures from 140°F to 160°F, depending on the setting. This water heating system is diagrammed in Figure 8-20. Solartec suggests that the simplest way to be sure of getting hot water from this system throughout the year is to incorporate a standard electric hot water heater of suitable size into the system as shown. Then the electric unit will warm your domestic supply only under conditions of unusual demand.

This Solartec system appears to have great promise for using solar energy for multipurpose gains in many households, and for larger buildings. For those who don't have a swimming pool, a much smaller insulated hot water storage tank, where the sun-heated water is kept at a much higher temperature than pool water, will perform a similar function. John DeVries, the pioneering solar engineer of Sol-R-Tech in Hartford, Vermont, has used hot water storage and heat pumps in several installations with considerable success.

In any climate, however, the economics of such solar installations indicate that you shouldn't expect to get all your energy from the sun. In places like the American South and Southwest, if you can get 80% or more of the energy required for heating a swimming pool, heating and cooling your home, and heating your hot water, your payoff will be realized in a very few years. You'll be saving a substantial amount of valuable fuel energy as well as thousands of dollars.

9
Solar Heating Systems
Need Automatic Controls

In this chapter are described some of the automatic control systems which are available to make operation of your solar heating system efficient. Without such controls, you will waste solar energy, use more electricity to run pumps and/or blowers, and wear out these moving elements in your solar installation faster.

You can't control the temperature of water or air in a solar collector by turning a knob. There is more to it. In a conventional home, apartment, or commercial building you have two kinds of thermostats. One you set for room temperature, now recommended to be no higher than 68°F for heating and perhaps 75°F for cooling. The other thermostat is for hot water, typically kept at 140°F. Referring specifically to heating, if either your room air or hot water goes below the set point, your heating system is turned on automatically. If the temperature exceeds the setting, the heat goes off. Because the heat source in a conventional system, whether fossil fuel or electric, is much hotter than the desired temperature, there's no need to know the temperature at the burner flame. So each of the two conven-

tional thermostats needs to sense only a single temperature—that of a room or of hot water.

But in a solar installation that includes a pump or fan, it is important to sense two temperatures and compare them: the temperature of water or air coming from your solar collector panels, and the water in a storage tank or air in a rock bin. Therefore, you need a different kind of thermostat, a differential device which measures both temperatures, compares them, and, based on that comparison, sends out an electrical control signal which turns on your pump and/or fan, or shuts the system off. In brief, it is a thermostat with a selective brain.

Since the operation of an automatic control system incorporating a differential thermostat is essentially the same for both liquid and air solar collector systems, and the operation of such systems has been described in previous chapters, the remainder of this chapter will be devoted to controls for liquid systems. Remember, you can apply the same principles to a solar installation heating air as the transfer medium.

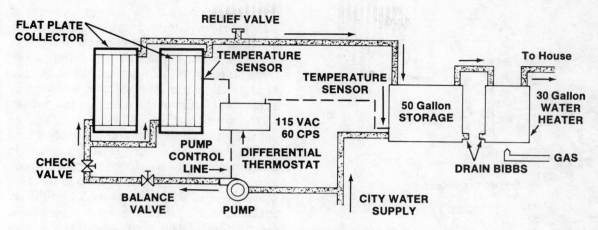

FIGURE 9-1.   Typical Application of Rho Sigma Controls and Sensors for Solar Heating

Automatic Control for a Solar Hot Water System

Figure 9-1 is a diagram of a typical solar hot water heater using automatic controls developed by Rho Sigma, Inc. of Van Nuys, California, a leading manufacturer of solar controls and instrumentation. The 50-gallon storage tank is the preheater collecting sun-heated water ahead of a conventional 30-gallon gas or electric water heater. Using efficient solar panels now on the market—including designs you can build partially or entirely by yourself—you will need about 50 square feet of collector area to supply from 60% to 90% of the hot water requirements for a family of four. As you know, the percentage you can get from the sun will depend on insolation available at your site.

On the assumption that your conventional water heater has a mixing valve on the output, which you set for the desired temperature, say 140°F, you will not need a "high set" thermostat. This is a sensor placed in the upper part of the 50-gallon preheater tank to prevent transfer of extremely hot water through your conventional heater to your home supply. It's better and more usual to have a mixing valve on the output. This is a reasonable safeguard because even on winter days, bright sunlight may heat your storage water higher than 160°F.

Although your differential controller is normally installed inside, near your pump and storage tanks, it can be mounted outside. Typical price of such a controller is about $100, with an additional charge for the matched thermistors enclosed in suitable housings and needed as temperature sensors. One of these sensors is threaded into a fitting, shown in Figure 9-2, which uses standard pipe threads and is attached to the outlet pipe from your solar collectors. The second sensor is similarly connected into the return pipe from the bottom of your 50-gallon storage tank. Wiring from the sensors is brought to the marked terminals in the control box.

In many communities it will be necessary to have such work done by a licensed electrician or plumber. When you are specifying the automatic controls you want, be sure your equipment carries Underwriters Laboratory approval to avoid any problems with your insurance company or with local building codes. At the end of this chapter is a list of several companies making high-quality solar control equipment.

Switches for automatic control units are usually designed for three positions: AUTO—OFF—ON. The ON position gives you manual control of the recirculating pump, making it easier for you to test the system when you have installed your solar panels,

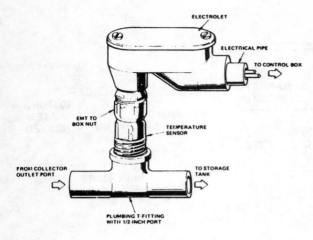

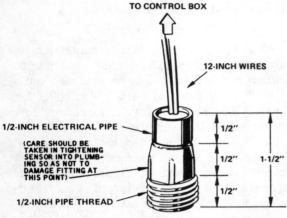

**FIGURE 9-2.   Matched Sensors for Use with
Differential Thermostat**

storage tank, pump, valves, piping, and
controls.

How a Differential Thermostat
Saves Energy

In Figure 9-3 is a temperature-versus-time
graph showing how a differential thermostat system controls your pump on a typical
day. This explains how the correct differential settings—preset for you by the control
system manufacturer—and a hysteresis
(time-lag) circuit prevent unnecessary cycling of the system. Typically the *turn-on* differential temperature for the pump is when
the collector outlet temperature is 20°

$\pm 3°F$ greater than the storage tank outlet
temperature. The comparable *turn-off* differential temperature is preset at $3° \pm 1°F$.

As shown in Figure 9-3, the pump is initially off early in the morning. When the sun
has heated your collector water so that it is
at least 17°F above the water at the bottom
of the storage tank—shown as T_{on} at
point 1—the controller automatically turns
on the recirculating pump. Cooler water in
the storage tank absorbs heat from the collectors and causes an initial drop in temperature to point 2. But so long as this differential is greater than 4°F—our preset limit
for turn-off of the pump—water will continue to be circulated through the collectors
by the pump.

Late in the day, at point 3 on the collector
curve, temperature of the outlet water from
the collectors has dropped to a level so close
to the storage temperature that the pump is
turned off. But water in the collectors is still
being heated by the sun, so there is a temporary sharp rise to point 4. However, this
is usually not high enough—more than
17°F, the minimum differential for turn-on
—to start the pump again.

Thus the differential thermostat controller has a hysteresis, or built-in lag feature, that prevents the pump from being
turned on or off unnecessarily because of
sharp rises or drops in water temperature
from the solar collectors. As a result, your
automatic system not only turns the pump
on when it should help collect solar heat,
and off when insufficient heat is available—
a job very difficult to accomplish manually,
even if you enjoy climbing on your roof to
check collector outlet temperature—but
this automatic controller also saves unnecessary wear on the pump, pump motor, and
relay contacts in the control unit.

Another interesting feature of the graph
in Figure 9-3 is that the temperature of the
water in the storage tank shows far less
variation over a 24-hour period, as you
might expect, than the water in the solar
collectors. Also, while it takes longer for a
much bigger water storage tank, with a ca-

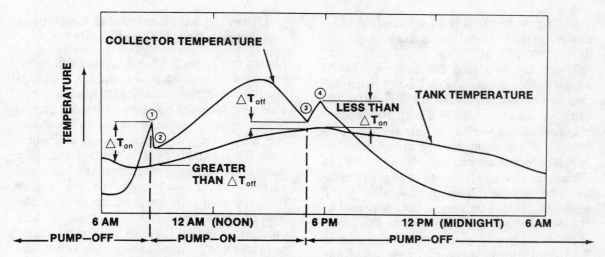

FIGURE 9-3. Typical Operating Cycle for a Solar Heating System Controlled by a Differential Thermostat

pacity of 500 gallons or more, to reach a useful temperature, the water in a larger tank will show still greater stability and serve as a "heat bank" for a couple of sunless days. The same stability is found in reservoirs of solar heat such as sizable rock bins and much smaller bins containing eutectic salts.

Automatic Controllers for Various Purposes

A refinement of this differential control system has recently been developed by Robert J. Schlesinger, president of Rho Sigma, and his associates. The system previously described activates or halts the *full flow* of a pump or fan on command of the differential thermostat system—and might be called a "Bang-Bang" approach because it's hard-on or hard-off. The new technique, called a *proportional* controller, produces a small flow as soon as there's a small temperature differential between the collector output and storage. Then the flow is automatically increased in proportion to a preset function of the temperature differential, up to the maximum capability of the pump.

Tests show that such a proportional controller does a better job of getting useful solar energy from the system at fairly low levels of insolation—on winter days and in partially cloudy weather—than the "Bang-Bang" or "Slam-Bang" (S/B) differential thermostat system. To quote the conclusions in a technical paper by Schlesinger:

At insolation levels from about 1,400 $BTU/ft^2/day$ and greater, and flow rates below 0.05 GPM/A_c, both control techniques achieve performance. Below this insolation level the S/B system will require careful consideration of flow adjustment for proper operation and to avoid cycling. The proportional control provides a technique of automatic flow adjustment over a wide range of insolation levels. It appears that this advantage makes the proportional control to be worthy of serious consideration for solar energy installations.

By way of explanation, the term GPM/A_c means gallons per minute divided by the collector area. The proportional controller is not designed for high flow rates such as are used in a solar collector system for heating a swimming pool. But in a space heating and cooling and hot water application, where the flow rate through the collector is 1 GPM

217

and the collector area is 30 square feet (A_c), the fraction in Schlesinger's description will be $1/30 = 0.033$ GPM/A_c.

There are two Rho Sigma proportional solar control units, the RS 500-1 with 3.8 amperes of continuous output current at 120 volts AC, and the RS 500-2 with 10 amperes of output. Each varies the pump speed as a function of the temperature differential between collector output and storage ($\triangle T$) to achieve increased efficiency in energy transfer. The $\triangle T$ for minimum flow is $3° \pm 1°F$ while the $\triangle T$ for maximum flow is preset at $11° \pm 1°F$. Power is delivered to the pump at full voltage and zero crossover, assuring full torque at low speed and absence of line noise. The controller is compatible with permanent-capacitor and shaded-pole motors. A pulsing indicator light indicates pump speed. Optional features are a high-temperature turn-off to limit upper storage temperature, typically to 140°F; and a low-temperature turn-on circuit which starts the pump at a collector temperature of 37°F if there is water in the system, to prevent damage to the collectors because of freezing.

There are other Rho Sigma standard differential controllers, some with the collector freeze-protection circuit, designed for solar space heating and cooling and hot water systems. As this author has previously recommended, in an area where freezing temperatures are certain to be encountered we suggest:

- Design your solar system so that it automatically drains down into storage when the pump is shut off.

- Use an antifreeze mixture as an alternative, a silicone compound or one of the other suitable solar liquids to avoid danger of freezing, and then a heat exchanger in your thermal storage tank.

- Use air collectors for space heating and cooling, and a drain-down collector system for domestic hot water. In many installations this will be the most economical combination of techniques.

Differential Thermostat Control for Sun-Heated Pools

Shown in Figure 8-12 is a typical solar system for a swimming pool using the Rho Sigma RS-260 differential thermostat control. This unit includes a thermostatic setting to prevent your swimming pool from overheating, with a very wide range of adjustments, from 56°F to 120°F. The control turns on the solar heater by closing the solenoid valve when the collectors are 5°F hotter than the pool temperature, so long as the pool temperature is below the preset thermostatic overheat level. When the pool temperature climbs over this preset value, the solenoid valve is automatically opened so that the collectors are bypassed.

This control unit operates with an input of either 220 volts AC or 120 volts AC, and has a desirable low-voltage output (12 volts DC) for safety in pool operation. Like other controllers subsequently listed, it is readily wired into pump timers so that the control unit functions only when the pump is operating. The unit is contained in a rain-tight enclosure.

Manufacturers of Differential Thermostat Controllers

As with solar collectors, we provide only a partial list of manufacturers of differential thermostat control systems for use in solar installations. The following manufacturers are active in the business in mid-1977, but there will always be additions and subtractions because of the dynamic nature of this industry.

Rho Sigma Inc., 15150 Raymer St., Van Nuys, CA 91405. Listed first as a pioneer in solar controllers, with a more complete and widely used line. This company also furnishes a photovoltaic pyranometer for measuring insolation, as well as a programmable data acquisition system including a microprocessor being used by utilities, universities, government laboratories, and research organizations making engineering studies of solar energy systems.

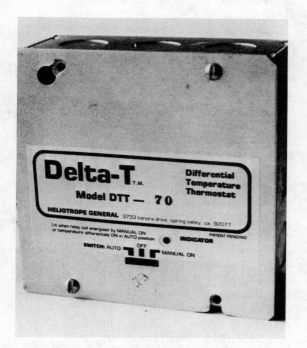

FIGURE 9-4. Differential Temperature Controllers Made by Heliotrope General for Solar Applications

Honeywell Inc., Honeywell Plaza, Minneapolis, MN 55408. Provides single-stage T87 and T882 controls, and the two-stage T872 controller with Q672 subbase. Also the T238 outdoor thermostat, used to change system operation in response to changes in outdoor conditions. Also provided are automatic control valves and actuators for liquid solar systems; and dampers, switches, damper motors, and other primary controls for solar air flow control. Newest item is the RT7406 solar temperature differential controller, with limit controls for collector over-temperature and storage temperature.

Independent Energy, Inc., P. O. Box 363, Kingston, R.I. 02881. Supplies a C-50 differential controller with 20°F turn-on, 5°F turn-off, mounted in a junction box and selling for $49.95.

Heliotrope General, 3733 Kenora Drive, Spring Valley, CA 92077. This company's diversified line of Delta-T differential temperature controllers for solar applications

includes 24 models approved by Underwriters Laboratory (UL). See Figure 9-4.

Helios Corp., 1313 Belleview Ave., Charlottesville, VA 22901. Makes several models of controllers in addition to liquid-type solar collectors.

Hawthorne Solar Energy Division, 1501 South Dixie, West Palm Beach, FL 33401. Provides 8 models of differential temperature controllers "designed for quick, simple installation without the use of professional trades." One-year replacement warranty.

British American and Eastern Co., Inc., 17 Battery Place, New York, NY 10004. Supplies the WW85 and SB 35 differential thermostat controllers that adjust to a temperature difference range of 0° to 15°F, and respond to a maximum temperature limit set for the storage tank. Used with a Type Pl flow regulator, they can provide a proportional control system.

Simons Solar Environmental Systems Inc., Mechanicsburg, PA 91055. Manufactures Model 1108F differential thermostat control as part of a solar hot water system.

Solar Control Corporation, Boulder, Colorado. Numerous models of differential controllers for air and liquid systems, as well as other components for solar air systems.

Solar Energy Systems of Georgia, 2616 Old Wesley Chapel Rd., Decatur, GA 30339. Provides the Solar Pak control unit for solar domestic hot water systems. This unit contains a pump, drain valves, proportional controller, five plumbing connections, and two sensor connections. It works with any copper collector that can be drained down. Turn-on is 2°F with increasing flow as $\triangle$T increases, and turn-off at $\triangle$T$=$0°F. Drain-down is set at 37°F.

Taco, Inc., 1160 Cranston St., Cranston, RI 02920. This company, one of the leading manufacturers of circulation pumps for solar installations, has a packaged pump, heat exchanger, and control system called the SSM Solar Systemizer, designed to make it easy to install a solar domestic hot water heater. It includes an exchanger for transferring heat from an antifreeze (ethylene glycol)

FIGURE 9-5. A Packaged Pump, Heat
Exchanger, and Control System,
Designed to Facilitate the Installation
of a Domestic Hot Water Heater.
By Taco, Inc.

solution in the solar collectors to the potable water for home use; an all-bronze circulator pump widely used with conventional domestic hot water systems; an expansion tank and float vent for air elimination, plus pressure gauge; and a differential temperature controller. See Figure 9-5.

Robertshaw Controls Company, Long Beach Blvd., Long Beach, CA 90805. This prominent maker of controls supplies the SD-10 Solar Commander with solid state thermistor sensors which can be used up to several thousand feet from the control box if required. Options include high-temperature sensors which permit the control to be used with fluids at temperatures up to 400°F—particularly interesting for systems including concentrating collectors such as Total Energy Systems described in the next chapter. Other options include adjustable turn-on differential from 8°F to 20°F; recycling upper limit at 195°F; positive off lower limit at 90°F. The pump switch action is accomplished with solid state components.

Scientific-Atlanta, Inc., 3845 Pleasantdale Rd., Atlanta, GA 30340. A variety of differential controls and heat pumps is provided.

Solar Research Division of Refrigeration Research Inc., 525 North Fifth St., Brighton, MI 48116. This company makes collectors, heat pumps, and other components, and has a complete packaged control system, including differential thermostat, for solar hot water heaters.

Solar, Inc., P. O. Box 246, Mead, NE 68041. The Solar-Aire system includes air-type collectors, differential controls, and a self-stacking tray system for storage using eutectic salts.

American Solar Heat Corporation, Danbury, CT 06810. Makes liquid solar collectors and a drain-down system including the Amsolheat differential thermostat controller. This device has a protective feature so that if a wire to the collector sensor or to the ambient (air temperature) sensor breaks, or if there is a power failure, the solar collectors automatically drain down.

Solar-Eye Products, Ft. Lauderdale, FL 33300. Differential thermostat controls T300 and T400 include, beyond the controls, a circulating pump and pipe clamp thermistors as sensors.

Solar Innovations, 412 Longfellow Blvd., Lakeland, FL 33801. Supplies a pump with 200 GPH capacity, solenoid valve, and electronic control assembly which plugs into a 120-volt outlet and needs no electrical wiring. Five-year guarantee.

Troger Enterprises, 2024A De La Vina, Santa Barbara, CA 93105. This control unit activates the pump supplying water to the collectors. The unit's action is triggered by a signal from a solar cell, mounted beside the solar panels and measuring insolation. One Troger model, selling for $149, includes a drainage sensor for automatic draining of the collectors when their water temperature is less than 40°F. Another model, without the drainage feature, is designed for pools and spas and sells for $85.

Bob Schlesinger of Rho Sigma reports that his firm has tested all the following pumps with the RS 500 series proportional controller, with good results:

Taco 007

All Grundfos models.

March 821BR and 809

Teal 1P761 and 1P760

Sundstrand LAA4302

W. W. Grainger pumps and fans.

Sun Tracking Controls

Most solar tracking systems have been designed by the makers of concentrating collectors. The majority of these systems, including those made by Albuquerque Western Solar Industries, Aerotherm, Northrup, Sunpower Systems, and others, utilize a pair of photovoltaic sun sensors—solar cells—set at an angle of about 60° apart. After sunrise, the difference in signal level from these two cells causes a motor drive system to turn until the collectors are perpendicular to the sun's rays, when an electronic bridge is balanced. Once such a solar tracker is locked in on the sun, it keeps operating the motor drive so that the collectors are picking up a maximum amount of solar energy throughout the day.

Most drives of this kind have a feature that returns the collectors, if they are parabolic troughs, to an inverted or upside-down position when no useful heat is being collected. This keeps the collectors from filling with rain, sleet, or snow—one of the notable Sunpower Systems installations is providing hot water for a large laundry high in the Rockies on an Indian reservation in northern Arizona. This company is particularly proud of its use of gallium arsenide cells, which are exceptionally sensitive to the sun's infrared radiation.

The Sun-Track 100, made by Energy Applications, Inc., P. O. Box 5694, Titusville, FL 32780, costs only $59.95 in lots of 1 to 3. The unit is designed for use with either a permanent split capacitor 120 volt 60 Hz reversible gear motor with 12 volt DC controlled solid state relays for directional switching, or a universal DC motor which is reversed by changing voltage polarity of the motor. The tracker control weighs only 3-1/2 ounces, has an accuracy in bright sunlight conditions of 15 to 20 minutes of arc.

In the morning position, 15° off the horizon, the device begins tracking when the sun reaches its field of view, and then follows the sun all day. Sundown activates a day/night sensor, which causes the concentrating collectors controlled by this unit to rotate in a reverse direction until they reach the morning position and are ready for the dawn. Energy Applications also makes other models of sun-trackers, including both single-axis and multiaxis units.

Another firm which furnishes dual-axis sun trackers is Mann-Russell Electronics, 1401 Thorne Road, Tacoma, WA 98421. This firm's Heliostat Mark IV has been furnished to experimenters as well as manufacturers.

For anyone who might want to build his own tracking system, there is a description of a heliotrope tracker in a government-sponsored patent application entitled "Turning Collectors for Solar Radiation" by Amitzur Z. Barak. You can get a copy for $3.50 from National Technical Information Service, 5285 Port Royal Road, Springfield, VA 22161. Ask for PAT-APPL-579 179/WE. This system rotates a collector around the polar axis, using the action of the sun on two heat-expansive elements and a shadow plate. The first expansive element is heated in the morning and expands to rotate the collector while the second element is shaded from the sun. In the afternoon, the second element is heated and expands to turn the collector to face the sun, while the first element is shaded by the shadow plate. You can get a license to manufacture this device from ERDA.

If you want to try a mechanical sun tracker operated by a clock, motor, and gear train, get in touch with Fred Hottenroth, ZZ Corporation, 10806 Kaylor St., Los Alamitos, CA 90720. This company builds parabolic concentrating collectors and also a simple miniature solar collector with temperature gauge to give an indication of insolation in your area whenever the sun is shining.

10

Solar Energy for Your Business: A Necessity Soon

A manufacturer in Erie, Pennsylvania, with a 55,000-square foot plant calls up a maker of solar space heating systems in California. "It's finally warmed up here," he says, "but last winter we were shut down, off and on, for nearly six weeks because of the natural gas shortage. I can't stand that and neither can my employes. What's a solar heating system going to cost me?"

In a round-up article headed "A Growing Rush to Solar Energy," it is pointed out in *U.S. News & World Report* (April 4, 1977) that "dozens of office buildings already are heated by the sun, along with fast-food restaurants, schools, remote ranger stations, prisons, dormitories, apartment buildings and laboratories."

The magazine *Solar Engineering* recently published an editorial by Sheldon Butts, president of the Solar Energy Industries Association, principal trade organization of this new business, with headquarters in Washington, D.C. Butts makes the following point:

The use of solar energy as a source of industrial process heat appears to be the "sleeper" among solar applications. Few installations have been made and to date, ERDA's research and development activity in the area has been modest.

Industrial heat applications cover a very wide range of temperatures and processes. There are process requirements for warm or hot water and for warm or hot air in temperature ranges which may even be below those normally associated with space heating and domestic hot water. At the same time, there are heat requirements involving very high temperatures, quite beyond the potential of present solar equipment. The individual applications are generally large and characteristically year-round. Fuels used are usually natural gas or oil, and present priorities for natural gas put industrial use at or near the bottom of the list.

Thus many industrial firms have been forced to make arrangements for propane or oil standby for use during periods of interrupted natural gas supply. Furthermore it now seems likely that the price of natural gas to industrial users will increase very rapidly. Another factor to consider is that industry, particularly large industry, is now under great pressure to decrease energy consumption and particularly, consumption of gas and oil.

Put all these factors together and it seems obvious that the prospects for solar energy as a source of industrial process heat are becoming very bright indeed.

In large heat volume applications, and particularly in those in which solar heat is used to preheat water, air or some other fluid, one of the most promising approaches would seem to be sizing the solar system to provide a modest proportion of total energy requirements, such that the full capacity of the solar installation could be used without provision of storage. This will maximize productivity of the solar collectors involved while, at the same time, the cost of storage will be eliminated. Quite low cost solar BTU can be produced in this manner.

In this chapter you'll find a discussion of many of the ways in which the sun's heat is being—and will be—used for industrial and commercial purposes. These are called *solar thermic* applications. In Chapter 11 is a description of solar cells which generate electricity directly when exposed to sunlight. Both present and enormously promising future applications of this technique are called *solar photovoltaic*.

An interesting point to keep in mind is that both thermic and photovoltaic techniques can be used to generate heat as well as electricity from the sun's energy. Therefore, both kinds of systems will be increasingly important and will sooner or later prove lifesavers to all kinds of business. If you think that's an overenthusiastic statement, keep in mind these facts:

- Availability of gas and oil is limited, and their prices continue to rise.

- Production of nuclear power plants has slowed down throughout the industrial-

ized world for a variety of reasons: cost, safety, ecology.

- Renewable free energy sources—sun, wind, geothermal, hydroelectric, biochemical—show up better as technology improves because once the initial capital investment has been made, operating costs are lower than with expendable resources.

Simple Industrial and Commercial Uses of Solar Energy

An earlier chapter told of the owner of a flea market who used old beer and pop cans painted black to build a solar air heater to heat his snack bar. Many other do-it-yourselfers, including farmers and ranchers, are using some of the solar heating techniques with both water and air as transfer fluids to save energy in their business activities.

For example, air heaters warmed by the sun are proving useful in many parts of the world for drying crops. Farmers in Colorado are using solar heat to dry wheat, corn, soybeans, rice, and sorghum. Since the moisture content of corn, for instance, must be reduced from 26% to 14% for safe storage, a controlled solar system, built at very low cost, provides the 10° above ambient air needed to do this job.

Agricultural experts from Maine to California and from Washington to Florida—as well as others in Alaska and Hawaii—point out that farmers who have been using natural gas, propane, or fuel oil for drying crops are able to make their capital investment in solar equipment pay for itself in a single year. From then on, they're saving money as well as energy.

Lumbermill operators in various states, as well as Australia, New Zealand, and other countries have used solar energy for drying wood. In northern New Mexico a solar lumber kiln designed by Quentin Wilson of La Medera uses air collectors and fans which direct sun-heated air by convection through stacked lumber in the kiln. To conserve energy even more, sawdust and slabs are burned to generate gas that drives a sawmill.

Near Grants in northeastern New Mexico, Sohio Petroleum Company has built a 6-acre system of outdoor shallow ponds lined with black plastic to absorb solar heat, and covered with clear plastic bubbles as glazing. Pond water about 4 inches deep is heated by the sun to 140°F. This simple solar system, similar to those used extensively in Israel and Australia, provides more than half the heat needed for processing uranium ore, according to Dr. Lynn Jacobsen, Sohio physicist.

A few miles south of Gila Bend, Arizona, on a huge ranch owned by Northwestern Mutual Life Insurance Company, Milwaukee, Wisconsin, is what was reputed to be the world's largest operating solar irrigation pump when the installation was dedicated in late April 1977. Solar energy is collected by 5,500 square feet of parabolic trough concentrating collectors mounted north-south in nine rows. Troughs are of sandwich construction, using aluminum honeycomb backing for aluminum reflectors 4 feet wide. One of these reflector segments is placed on either side of the linear absorber, blackened copper pipe, so that each trough has an aperture about 8 feet wide. The reflecting surface is metallized plastic, and the structural sandwich is 1 inch thick. Maker of these concentrating collectors is Hexcel, Inc., of Dublin, California, noted as a maker of honeycomb structures for aircraft and space vehicles.

Each of the 9 rows of collectors has its own sun-tracking control unit. At sunrise each trough is rotated from its upside-down storage position as the tracker hunts for the sun and finds it. Then all the troughs are slowly turned in an east-to-west direction as the tracker follows the sun until late afternoon. As is usual with such trackers, during storms and at night the motorized control system automatically returns all collectors to the storage position to minimize chance of damage—in Gila Bend, from dust collection.

Battelle Memorial Institute in Columbus, Ohio, which provided the solar engineering for this irrigation project under the direction of Dr. Sherwood L. Fawcett, specified that part of the absorber tubes at the focus of the parabolic collectors should have glass-covered copper tubing, with the rest unglazed copper. In any case, the copper tubes are painted with a temperature-resistant nonselective black coating.

Heat absorbed by these concentrating collectors provides water under pressure at an outlet temperature of 300°F. This superheated water boils freon, which drives a Rankine cycle turbine operating the big irrigation pump, feed pump, and circulating pumps for solar hot water. Freon gas exhausted from the turbine circulates through a heat exchanger and condenser to be converted back to a liquid, in a closed-cycle process.

According to Bill Edmondson, publisher of *Solar Energy Digest*, the turbine in this system is about the size of a football. It is made by Barber-Nichols Engineering Company of Arvada, Colorado. In the turbine is a tiny rotor spinning at up to 30,000 revolutions per minute (RPM) and directly connected to a speed reducer much larger than the small gas turbine. The drive for the main irrigation pump and all the smaller pumps is taken off this speed reducer.

Some interesting features of this irrigation system powered by the sun include the fact that the turbine speed is not held constant—the rotor speeds up or slows down depending on the amount of sunshine received by the large collector system. Thus, the turbine builds up speed during the morning, running at full capacity from about 10 A.M. to perhaps 4 P.M. and then gradually slowing down. The amount of water pumped can be regulated by turning one or more rows of solar collectors into their storage position—or back into service. The turbine develops about 50 HP at full capacity and can lift 10,000 gallons of water per minute to the installed height of 14 feet.

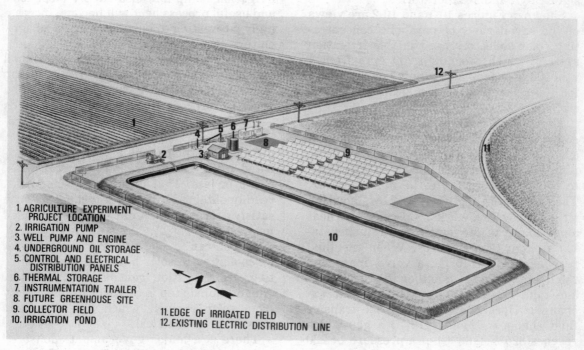

1. AGRICULTURE EXPERIMENT
   PROJECT LOCATION
2. IRRIGATION PUMP
3. WELL PUMP AND ENGINE
4. UNDERGROUND OIL STORAGE
5. CONTROL AND ELECTRICAL
   DISTRIBUTION PANELS
6. THERMAL STORAGE
7. INSTRUMENTATION TRAILER
8. FUTURE GREENHOUSE SITE
9. COLLECTOR FIELD
10. IRRIGATION POND

11. EDGE OF IRRIGATED FIELD
12. EXISTING ELECTRIC DISTRIBUTION LINE

FIGURES 10-1 & 10-2.   This Solar-Powered Irrigation Project at Willard, New Mexico, Is an Efficient Large-Scale System to Use Solar Energy to Pump Water from a Well for Irrigation Purposes

Another Major Solar Irrigation Project

Economists, ecologists, and other wise people agree that food, water, and energy are critical commodities on our planet as the world's population grows. So it's no wonder that there is increasing interest in using solar energy for irrigation in India, Pakistan, Iran, Israel, and many other countries.

On July 7, 1977, several hundred farmers, scientists, engineers, and government officials attended a national solar irrigation workshop at the Albuquerque Convention Center. On the following day the party traveled to a large solar-powered irrigation system operating in Willard, New Mexico, about 65 miles away.

This program is sponsored by ERDA, the U.S. Department of Agriculture, the state of New Mexico, and New Mexico State University—with the solar installation designed by Sandia Laboratories.

Shown in Figures 10-1 and 10-2 are views of the seven rows of parabolic concentrating solar collectors used in this irrigation system, which can pump 700 gpm from a well 100 feet deep and supply enough water for 100 acres planted in various vegetable crops.

These solar collectors, made by Acurex Aerotherm of Mountain View, California, are capable of heating liquids or gases to temperatures between 60° and 311°C (140° to 600°F), according to the manufacturer. The diagram in Figure 10-2 shows how the irrigation system works. The collectors heat an oil-like transfer fluid which remains stable at high temperatures. When the fluid reaches 420°F (216°C), a valve opens and the heated fluid flows either to a heat storage tank or directly to a boiler/heat exchanger. Here solar heat from the transfer fluid changes Freon R113 to a gas which reaches 325°F (163°C) at a pressure of 220 psi. This high-pressure gas drives a turbine which powers the well pump.

Water from the well is pumped into a plastic-lined storage pond to be used for irrigation. Since the solar power system is a closed loop, the heat transfer fluid and the freon are recycled for continuous usage.

The solar-powered turbine can deliver 25 HP to the irrigation pump. According to Sandia engineers, when the system is not operating the pump during the 100-day annual irrigation season, it can generate 10 million BTU of heat each day or 20 kW (200 kWh per day) of electrical power for other uses on the farm. An electric motor is provided as emergency backup for the solar-driven pump, but it's very unlikely that it will be needed because the solar system has a minimum of moving parts, requires very little maintenance, and should work well for many years.

The Energy-Sufficient Company

The fact that the sun's heat can drive an irrigation pump and also supply electricity and useful process heat will become increasingly interesting to business as well as agriculture in coming years. An ERDA-sponsored survey made recently by McDonnell Douglas engineers headed by James Rogan showed that about 85% of all industrial needs for process heat in a variety of fields —foods, clothing, cement, ceramics, petroleum refining, chemicals, paper, lumber, metals, electronics, and others—can be satisfied with relatively low temperatures, 500°F or less. That means that solar heat, readily obtained by today's technology, can satisfy a large amount of the industrial need for heat.

As you can understand from the chapter on cooling with solar heat, it's also feasible to get refrigeration from sun-heated water. An additional step is to generate electricity from solar energy, which has also been proved to be practical.

There is a major government-sponsored program, the Solar Total Energy Program (STEP), in which many industrial firms, research organizations, universities, and others are participating, with technical di-

FIGURE 10-3.   Omnium-G Solar Generator, Designed to Produce 7.5 kW of Electric Power

rection and considerable hardware development by Sandia Laboratories. But before describing some of the activities of this broad effort, it's interesting to note what some small, inventive companies are doing to speed such commercial applications of the sun's energy.

In this author's first book on solar activities, there is a description of how a group of four engineers, all working in their spare time, were developing a small solar power plant. Figure 10-3 is a view of the Omnium-G solar generator, built in Anaheim, California, which is designed to produce 7.5 kW of electric power. Note that there is a parabolic reflector which stands 22.5 feet high on its concrete base 10 feet in diameter. This concentrates solar energy on a small stainless steel boiler at the focus, with a solar cell directing a tracking system to keep the large "dish"—like an inverted umbrella —aimed at the sun. The tracker automatically returns the reflector to its starting position at sundown.

Steam from the sun-heated furnace or boiler powers an engine which produces 7.5 kW of electricity by driving an electrical generator on a typical summer day in Southern California. At the same time, the steam return to the boiler goes through a heat exchanger in a 600-gallon water storage tank, where 80,000 BTU per hour are stored in water at a temperature of 200°F.

There is another method of storing the sun's energy, in that the generator will, when desired, operate a compressed-air system, with the compressor using solar energy to fill one or more cylinders with compressed air. Then a single cylinder of compressed air will store 66 kWh of energy. This air can be used to drive the electrical generator, and to supply enough electricity for about 3 days with all appliances used normally in an American household.

Thus a small Total Energy System has been developed which will provide a modest amount of electrical power; a sizable reservoir of sun-heated water which can be used for space heating and cooling and domestic hot water; and compressed-air storage to provide a few days of carryover capability to generate electricity during prolonged bad weather.

It is possible to parallel Omnium-G systems to supply more power, heating, and storage capacity. This device has a useful potential in many areas, particularly in "underdeveloped" countries where there are no big electric power grids, and on isolated farms and ranches where brownouts and blackouts occur only too often because of severe weather or events beyond control of the utilities. Add a wind generator to such a solar system, and you have gone a long way toward sufficiency in energy, using modern technology and Mother Nature's bountiful resources.

Another Small Total Energy System

Also in this author's first solar book is a description of an entirely different system

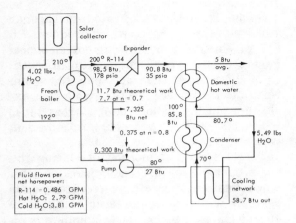

Solar collector

Expander

210°
4.02 lbs.
H₂O

200° R-114
98.5 Btu
178 psia

90.8 Btu
35 psia

5 Btu
avg.

Freon
boiler

11.7 Btu theoretical work
7.7 at n = 0.7

Domestic
hot water

192°

7.325
Btu net

100°
85.8
Btu

0.375 at n = 0.8

80.7°

Condenser

5.49 lbs
H₂O

0.300 Btu theoretical work

Pump

80°
27 Btu

70°

Cooling
network

Fluid flows per
net horsepower:
R-114 = 0.486 GPM
Hot H₂O: 2.79 GPM
Cold H₂O: 3.81 GPM

58.7 Btu out

FIGURE 10-4. Power Generating System Using Solar Collector Panels and a Freon Boiler, Developed by Sun Power Systems, Inc.

developed by Sun Power Systems, Inc., of Sarasota, Florida, whose president is Wallace L. Minto. A diagram of this system appears in Figure 10-4. In this engine, a Rankine cycle unit similar to those previously described in the larger irrigation pump systems uses Freon R-114. Minto's freon engine can produce 10 kW of electric power when the water from solar collector panels is at a temperature of only 185°F (85°C), the inventor states.

This means that a wide variety of flat plate collectors including many of those previously mentioned, as well as the efficient panels designed by Chamberlain Manufacturing Corporation, Elmhurst, Illinois, are quite adequate for use with this system under insolation conditions where the collectors will deliver 185°F. However, this is a better application for the concentrating collectors made by Acurex, Albuquerque Western Solar, Hexcel, Sunpower Systems (Tempe), Sheldahl, Northrup, ZZ Corp., and others. One new lightweight collector, recently developed by KTA Corporation of Rockville, Maryland and which has a concentration ratio of 3 to 1, would qualify. Each collector element consists of a spirally wound 3/8-inch copper tube enclosed inside a 5/8-inch glass tube similar to a fluorescent light. The bottom half of this outer tube is

silvered to reflect light back onto the black copper absorber. These elements are joined to a header at each end, and the assembly is enclosed inside a lightweight aluminum frame covered with a heat-shrunk glazing of 4 mil Tedlar.

It's important to mention, in addition to concentrating collectors previously described in this book, a new vacuum tube solar collector developed by General Electric Space Division in Philadelphia. Individual tubes are like thermos bottles with an outer transparent glass tube, surrounding a 0.1-inch vacuum space and then a black-coated inner tube containing an antifreeze mixture. Tubes, each 4 feet long, are connected on a reflective metal surface. This type of collector will provide sun-heated liquid at temperatures of 250°F. Corning and Libby-Owens-Ford are other major manufacturers developing improved tubular glass solar collectors, joining Owens-Illinois's widely used units previously described.

Power output of the Minto system is somewhat proportional to the temperature of the water heated by the solar collectors. The inventor claims that his units will produce as much as 8 kW from sun-heated water at 150°F in an improved freon engine design going into production in mid-1977. Eight pilot plants have been under test for a year, and deliveries of 110 solar power systems have been made as of July 1977. Sun Power Systems is hoping to get into mass production of 10 kW solar power plants at a rate as high as 100 a week late in 1977. Minto says that he and his associates can design and build solar power systems which will deliver as much as 2,000 kW (2 million watts or 2 megawatts of electric power). He is currently discussing with a major steel company an installation developing 1,600 kW, using waste heat from a blast furnace.

One interesting installation of a Minto unit is at Benson, Arizona, about 90 miles from Phoenix. A rancher named Neil Pennington, who has become prosperous from his own inventions, is paying Sun Power Systems of Sarasota (Minto's company) for the freon engine and electric power generator, while Sunpower Systems Corporation of Tempe, Arizona, has supplied the concentrating solar collectors. One unusual feature of the installation, according to Bill Matlock, president of the Arizona company, is that this is the first field test of his carousel collector system—where the parabolic collectors traveling around a track while simultaneously tilting can provide liquid heated to 500°F. This will mean efficient generation of probably 15 kW of electric power. The system built in Tempe will also furnish space heating and cooling, as well as domestic hot water at Pennington's ranch. Here is a wave of the future—an individual using the sun for practically all his energy requirements.

Solar Energy in Shenandoah, Georgia

President Jimmy Carter is joined in his enthusiasm for solar energy by most citizens of his home state of Georgia. One of the first factories to be equipped with a Total Energy System is being built in Shenandoah, 25 miles south of Atlanta. The solar plant, which will supply a knitware manufacturing facility with electric power, process steam, heating, and cooling, is an ERDA project and will be operated by the Georgia Power Company. Solar energy will provide the 42,000-square foot factory, which will have 300 employees, with up to 200 kW of electric power and 1,200 kW of heat energy.

Here is a striking indication of what many utility experts believe must happen, as solar electric power begins to contribute substantially to the national energy total. In recent years, the trend has been toward huge central power stations using fossil or nuclear fuels. It takes an average of 10 years and a capital investment of possibly $2 billion or more to build such a station. So utility engineers and economists are taking a close look at Solar Total Energy Systems (STES) of relatively small size—like the one for the

Shenandoah clothing plant, which will be owned and operated by a West German manufacturer.

It appears that an integrated solar plant, backed up by electric power from the local utility, can be built and operated at lower cost—once there are many such plants, with mass production of components—and put in operation much more quickly than huge central power plants. Another factor in favor of these STES is that, particularly if they are operated by an electric utility or in cooperation with the utility, these factory-size units may contribute useful power at times of heavy demand and thus further decrease the need for billions invested in big power plants. For instance, many food processing plants and canneries have a seasonal need for large amounts of electric power—perhaps 100 days during the year. An STES can supply such a food operation with sun-generated electric power, process heat, heating, and cooling during the busy season and then feed power into the electric utility grid during the off-season, making the payoff of the STES investment both quicker and more certain.

An electric power system with numerous small integrated STES installations could be most useful in helping utility companies to avoid such disastrous blackouts as the one in New York City in July 1977.

STES Tests Many Collector Designs at Sandia

In May 1977 this author was guided by Robert Gall, a well-informed information officer for Sandia Laboratories, through the STES test facility in Albuquerque. We also visited the nation's largest solar power tower and saw arrays of various kinds of solar cells with concentrators, both described in subsequent pages.

The STES facility at Sandia, shown in the diagram of Figure 10-5, includes several acres where concentrating solar collectors are heating Monsanto Therminol 66, a fluid

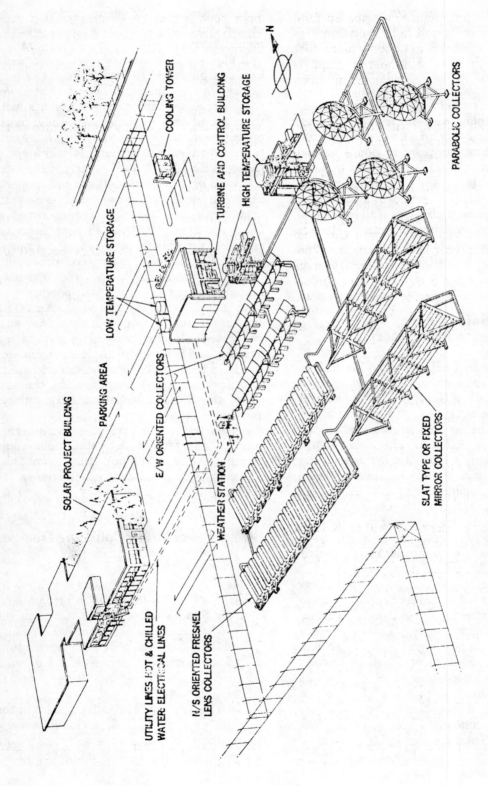

SOLAR PROJECT BUILDING

PARKING AREA

COOLING TOWER

LOW TEMPERATURE STORAGE

E/W ORIENTED COLLECTORS

TURBINE AND CONTROL BUILDING

HIGH TEMPERATURE STORAGE

N

PARABOLIC COLLECTORS

UTILITY LINES HOT & CHILLED
WATER, ELECTRICAL LINES

WEATHER STATION

N/S ORIENTED FRESNEL
LENS COLLECTORS

SLAT TYPE OR FIXED
MIRROR COLLECTORS

FIGURE 10-5. Solar Total Energy System Test Facility, Albuquerque,
New Mexico

with a high boiling point. This heated fluid is stored in an insulated tank shown in Figure 10-5 not far from a 12,000-square foot office building. The sun-heated fluid is pumped through a heat exchanger in which toluene is boiled and superheated.

Then this superheated toluene is used as a vapor to drive a 32 kW turbine generator developed by Sundstrand. Inlet temperature to this turbogenerator is 570°F (300°C) and the inlet pressure is 275 psi. You can see why concentrating solar collectors are needed to produce such high temperatures.

The condenser coolant derived from the generator operation then serves the dual purpose of supplying heat for warming the office building and providing hot water as thermal energy for a 60-ton Arkla chiller. This coolant water temperature can be adjusted. You need 190°F to operate the lithium bromide (LiBr) absorption chiller, as described in an earlier chapter. Space heating and hot water in the winter require somewhat lower temperatures.

One large array of solar collectors has been designed, fabricated, and installed by Sandia. An attempt was made to produce these units shown in Figures 10-6 and 10-7 at low cost. The reflector structure consists of 3/4-inch plywood covered with aluminized teflon as the reflective surface. Each parabolic trough is 12 feet long and 9 feet wide, and there are five such collectors in a row 60 feet long. The total field of 20 large line-focusing concentrators provides 2,160 square feet of reflective surface or aperture area in the four parallel rows of collectors. The surface heated by the sun's rays concentrated by these collectors consists of a steel pipe 1-5/8 inches in diameter at the focus of each parabolic section. The pipe is coated with a selective black chrome, and then is enclosed in an evacuated glass cylinder to trap the solar heat the pipe absorbs.

Thus Sandia engineers, in addition to using low-cost materials, have combined some of the best techniques developed by leading manufacturers of solar collectors. That is, these collector arrays provide a large parabolic surface and high concentration ratio, comparable with the best designs of manufacturers such as Acurex, Sunpower Systems, and others. Also, these collector systems utilize an evacuated tube technique similar to those developed by Owens-Illinois, Corning, and General Electric. It is no wonder that the outlet temperature of the heated Therminol in these collectors is 590°F (310°C)—the transfer fluid has absorbed a great deal of solar energy.

Another type of collector being tested at this STES facility is made by Sheldahl Company and is shown in Figure 10-8. Here the absorber pipe is mounted in an east-west direction, and the sun's heat is directed to it by sun-tracking mirrored slats.

Other concentrating collectors to be installed for test include the following:

- McDonnell Douglas Astronautics Company supplies a V-shaped trough lined with reflective material. Over the trough is a plastic Fresnel lens. The trough is about 20 feet long and 6 feet wide at the mouth, with blackened copper pipe inside the apex of the V. The long axis, and therefore the pipe, runs north-south, and the collector is moved in a single-tilt axis by a motor controlled by a simple one-axis tracker. Output fluid temperature is about 600°F.

- General Atomic Company is providing east-west reflective troughs with tracking absorber tubes.

- Raytheon, Inc., will furnish parabolic dish concentrators.

Since one of the major objectives of the ERDA-sponsored STES program at Sandia is to evaluate various designs of concentrating solar collectors, a good start has been made in this direction. However, it would be desirable to leave the door open for additional designs such as the Sunpower Systems carousel concentrating collectors made in Tempe, Arizona; collectors made by Acurex Aerotherm of Mountain View, California; and any other promising units made by smaller companies large in ingenuity.

FIGURE 10-6. Parabolic Solar Collectors at Sandia Laboratories' Solar Total
Energy System Test Facility Convert Solar Energy to Electricity and to Provide
Space Heating and Air Conditioning

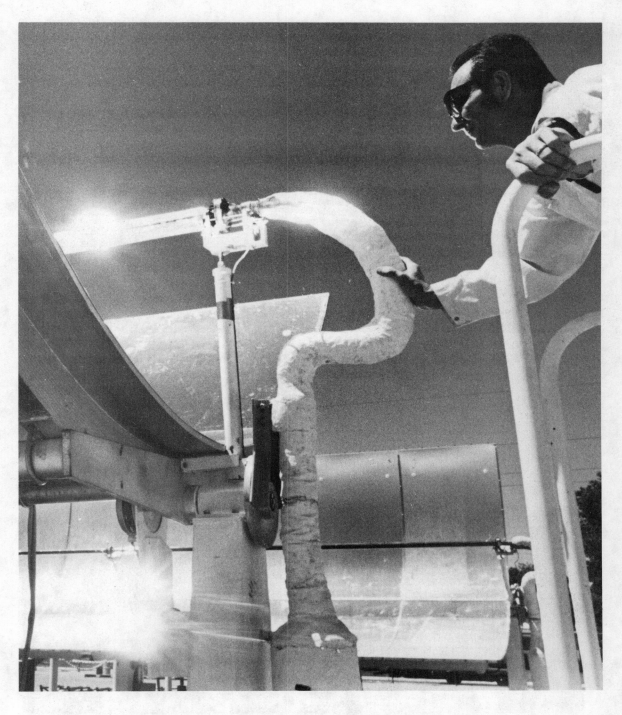

FIGURE 10-7. Sun's Rays are Focused on Receiver Tubes in Center of
Parabolic Solar Collectors at Sandia Laboratories' Test Facility

FIGURE 10-8. Concentrating Collectors Using Mirror Slats, Made by Shaldahl

FIGURE 10-9. Meteorological and Solar Instrumentation at the Sandia Total Energy Test Facility, Albuquerque

Shown in Figure 10-9 are some of the instruments used by Sandia and ERDA scientists in connection with the test facilities for concentrating solar thermal collectors and also for the numerous arrays where solar heat is concentrated on several kinds of solar cells. There is an anemometer to measure wind direction and velocity, plus instruments such as heliopyranometers which measure insolation—the intensity and wave length of the solar radiation—along with thermometers and hygrometers to measure the ambient temperature and relative humidity. Inside the small building housing the 32 kW electrical generator and the air conditioner is a bank of computers to analyze the data from these instruments and the solar energy system producing electricity and space heating or cooling as called for by automatic controls.

Total Energy System at Fort Hood, Texas

About 1,600 persons in the Army will enjoy a completely solar energy system being built to supply electricity, space heating, hot water, and summer air conditioning for a large new barracks at Fort Hood, Texas. Design of this system is being performed by the American Technological University in Killeen, Texas, and at least part of the collector system, sun-tracking mirrored slats, has been installed by Sheldahl.

Meanwhile at Marshall Center in Huntsville, Alabama, many of the scientists and engineers whose Saturn rockets sent the astronauts to the moon are now involved in solar research. They are also evaluating a wide variety of solar collectors and controls made in many states by companies large and small. There is a continued search for more efficient designs produced at low cost.

Solar Power Tower at Georgia Tech

One step beyond the total energy system concept is the creation of a large solar power plant. The first concept aimed at that goal and awarded substantial federal funding is a logical extension of the solar energy systems where concentrating collectors are used to produce temperatures around 600°F in a heat transfer fluid. This hot fluid then serves to drive a turbogenerator and produce electricity, with space heating, process heating for industrial uses, air conditioning, and hot water as supplementary benefits. The step beyond STES is to build a solar power tower.

Back in 1961, at an international energy conference in Rome, a suggestion was made by Dr. Valentin Baum, director of the Heliotechnical Institute in Moscow, that a boiler be placed on top of a tower about 300 feet high. Around this tower would run some 20 locomotives on concentric circular tracks, each engine pulling a train of flat cars on which were mounted mirrors. This was the Soviet tracking scheme to focus solar energy on the boiler on top of the tower. It was estimated the superheated water from the boiler could generate enough electricity and heat for a city of 20,000 people in Siberia.

More recently, the French scientists of the Centre National de la Recherche Scientifique (CNRS) built an effective solar furnace at Odeillo, high in the Pyrenees—the same town where Professor Felix Trombe has designed efficient passive solar heating for several houses, as described in Chapter 7. The solar furnace consists of about 5,000 square meters of mirrors, forming a fixed solar concentrating system which heats up a fluid called Gilotherm in a boiler located behind the focal point. The fluid, which has a high boiling point, reaches a temperature of 335°C (660°F). The hot liquid is piped downhill to a generating plant where, through two series of coiled heat exchangers, steam is produced to run a conventional steam turbine generating unit. This plant is producing about 100 kW of electric power, which is fed into the Electricite de France power network. The next step at Odeillo is construction of a 10-megawatt (10 MW or 10,000 kW) solar power plant designed to operate at higher temperatures, and esti-

FIGURE 10-10.   Sandia Laboratories' Solar Thermal Energy Tower, Planned to
Generate 5 Megawatts of Thermal Energy

mated to cost $30 million, with operation expected in 1979. Efficiency of the pilot plant, now producing 100 kW, is about 20% but larger plants are predicted to be more efficient.

On the Georgia Tech campus in Atlanta a solar thermal power tower, surrounded by a field of 530 mirrors and under computer control, automatically tracks the sun and aims solar energy at a boiler on top of the tower. Technology developed by the staff of Georgia Tech and Professor Giovanni Francia of the University of Genoa, Italy, has been funded by a $600,000 grant from ERDA. Superheated steam is produced in the boiler; this steam will then drive a turbogenerator to produce electric power, while the condenser coolant through heat exchangers can provide space heating and cooling for nearby buildings.

Solar Thermal Energy Tower at Sandia

When this author visited Sandia Laboratories' 200-foot tower and 78 heliostats—reflector panels aimed by computer—Sandia engineers put on a demonstration of the sun's heat for visiting newspaper, magazine, TV, and radio reporters. The heliostats were focused on a steel target high on the reinforced concrete tower. With a concentration ratio of 1,100 to 1, the heat intensity of 1,100 suns was directed at a thick steel plate 6 feet wide and 15 feet high. Within less than two minutes, this concentrated solar energy heated the steel to a temperature of more than 3,000°F and burned a large hole in the steel plate.

Coming along later with Bob Gall of Sandia, we collected some molten pieces which

FIGURE 10-11.   One of the Initial 78 Heliostats Which Focus Sun's Rays on a
Boiler Atop the Solar Thermal Energy Test Tower at Sandia Laboratories

FIGURE 10-12.   Computer and Associated Equipment for Controlling Heliostats
and Tr. / .ing System of Solar Thermal Energy Tower

FIGURE 10-13.   Single Operator Controls Huge Solar Power Station at Sandia
Laboratories

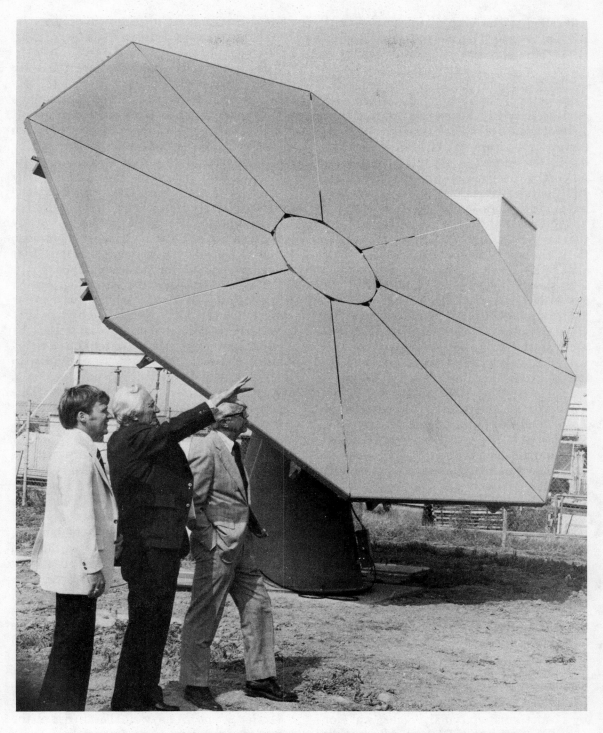

FIGURE 10-14. Sun-Tracking Heliostat Designed by McDonnell Douglas Astronautics

had fallen to the base of the tower—solar souvenirs of an historic occasion, May 20, 1977. The partially completed facility is shown in Figure 10-10.

This test facility is planned to generate 5 megawatts of thermal energy, which could at some later date be used to produce about 1.5 megawatts of electrical energy—enough power for a community of 1,500 persons living in the American style. The project is under the direction of John Otts of Sandia and George Rhodes of ERDA, highly competent engineers.

The first 78 heliostats and tracking system have been provided by Martin-Marietta Corporation of Denver. Each heliostat consists of 25 square mirrors mounted in a panel as shown in Figure 10-11, with each mirror 40 inches square. Thus each panel has 156.25 square feet of reflective surface. Two electric motors drive the heliostat in azimuth and elevation under computer control, with signals from a sun sensor at each heliostat fed to a central computer so that solar tracking is completely automatic. In the computer control room in a building about 1/4 mile from the tower are Hewlett-Packard computers and associated peripheral equipment shown in Figure 10-12. An operator sitting at the console in Figure 10-13 can control the entire operation of this massive solar power station.

Eventually there will be 320 heliostats placed around the tower to heat water in the boiler 200 feet above the ground to a temperature, under about 1,400 pounds of pressure, of about 800°F. This superheated water could then—and probably will—be used ultimately to generate 1.5 MW of electric power.

Makers of other sun-tracking heliostats with different designs are McDonnell Douglas Astronautics, with a design shown in Figure 10-14; Boeing Company of Seattle, with 15-foot diameter heliostats protected by 17-foot inflated Tedlar domes; and Honeywell Solar Products Division, Minneapolis.

Southern California Edison Solar Power Plant

After some of the test work at the solar power tower at Sandia is complete, the world's first large solar power plant will be well underway near Barstow, California, at a site northeast of the present Southern California Edison steam plant in Daggett by the Mojave River. This is a desert site blessed with insolation exceeded only by one area of the Sahara Desert. It is owned by the electric utility, which won an ERDA contest partly because of the site and partly because SoCal Edison engineers have been quietly but efficiently doing valuable solar energy research for several years.

The new commercial plant, diagrammed in Figure 10-15, is expected to have a tower about 300 feet high surrounded by a field of more than 2,300 heliostats controlled by computers. Superheated water at a temperature of about 890°F will be fed down to drive a multistage turbogenerator, at a throttle pressure of about 1,450 psia. This generator will have a capacity of 10 MW, enough electric power for a town of perhaps 10,000 persons.

Part of the solar heat energy will be stored in a large thermal storage cylinder, probably containing stones and a fluid such as Monsanto Therminol, Exxon Caloria, or a Dow Chemical compound—some oily fluid with a very high boiling point. On demand, heat from storage will be delivered through a heat exchanger to one of the secondary stages of the massive turbogenerator.

In addition to Southern California Edison, the California team involved in this first big commercial solar power plant consists of the Los Angeles Department of Water and Power and the California Energy Resources Conservation and Development Commission. Competing to build the solar power system are McDonnell Douglas, Martin-Marietta, and Honeywell. Total cost of the project is estimated at $100 million, with

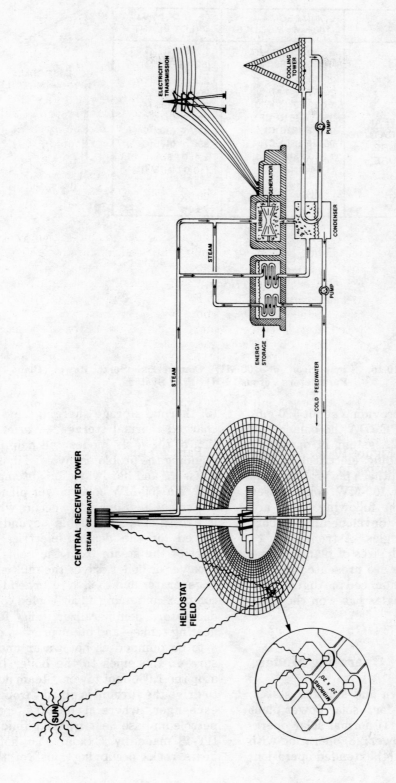

FIGURE 10-15. Design of Large Solar Power Plant to be Built by Southern California Edison Near Barstow, in the Mojave Desert

241

CHARACTERISTIC	COMMERCIAL (100-MWe MODULE)	10 MW PILOT PLANT
FIELD DIMENSIONS	5,650 X 6,220 FT (1,723 X 1,896 M)	1,728 X 1,728 FT (527 X 527 M)
NUMBER OF HELIOSTATS	29,300	2,350
HELIOSTAT SIZE	20 FT (6.1 M)	20 FT (6.1 M)
TOWER HEIGHT	1,000 FT (305 M)	312 FT (95 M)
RECEIVER TEMPERATURE (PEAK)	950°F (510°C)	890°F (475°C)
THERMAL STORAGE TEMPERATURE	600°F (316°C)	575°F (302°C)
TURBINE INLET TEMPERATURE	950°F (510°C)	890°F (475°C)
TURBINE THROTTLE PRESSURE	1,800 PSIA (12.4 MN/M^2)	1,450 PSIA (10.0 MN/M^2)
NET PLANT EFFICIENCY		
DIRECT (RECEIVER STEAM)	33%	28.9%
THERMAL STORAGE STEAM	27%	23.0%

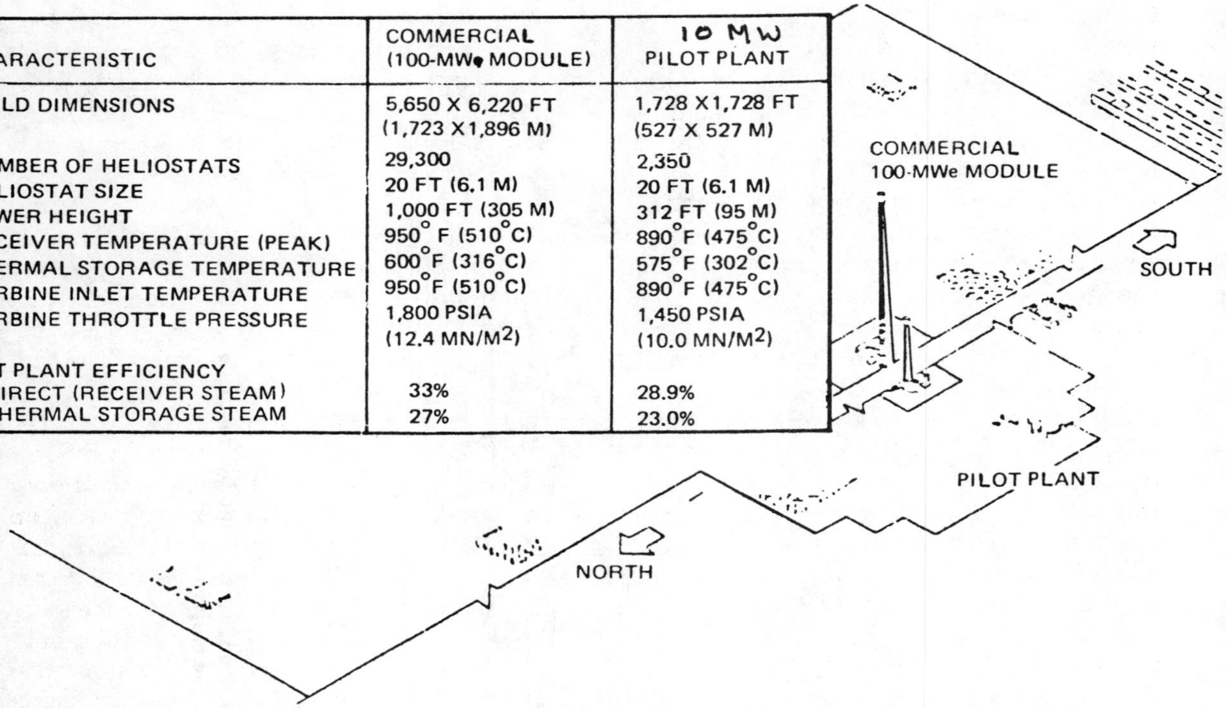

COMMERCIAL 100-MWe MODULE

SOUTH

PILOT PLANT

NORTH

FIGURE 10-16. Comparison of 100-MW Commercial Solar Power Plant Parameters Versus 10-MW Pilot System

the California team providing about $20 million of this total and ERDA the balance.

After this 10-MW system is operating successfully and feeding electrical energy regularly into the Southern power grid, it is proposed to build a 100-MW solar power tower station. On the following pages are some of the concepts developed in a report by McDonnell Douglas Astronautics to ERDA studying both sizes of plants. Some condensed estimates are presented in Figure 10-16. (It was announced in August 1977 that McDonnell Douglas has won the competition.)

Six Power Plant Operating Modes

Aside from shutdown and standby states, six operating modes for a solar power plant have been defined: (1) normal solar operation; (2) low solar power; (3) operation with intermittent clouds; (4) extended operation;

(5) thermal storage charging; and (6) fully charged thermal storage. A brief description of these six modes will help in understanding the problems involved in designing software and hardware for automated control of a 100-MW solar power plant.

Normal solar operation occurs when there is excess steam available beyond that required for the desired electrical output. Part of the steam from the central tower receiver or boiler drives the multistage turbogenerator and then is returned through a complex containing an air-cooled condenser, deaerator, demineralizer, and feedwater heating tanks—and other process plumbing —to be pumped as hot water under pressure up the pipes to the boiler (receiver) atop the 1,000-foot tower. Steam not needed to drive the turbine is piped through a heat exchanger, where it heats a commercial petroleum-base heat transfer fluid, Caloria HT-43 made by Exxon. The hot Caloria heats rocks occupying most of the giant thermal storage unit. When additional steam to drive the turbogenerator is needed, it can be obtained from the steam generator associated with the thermal storage tank. However, this is not typical of the normal solar operating mode, in which by definition there is surplus steam for heating the thermal storage unit; this surplus steam, after doing its work in the heat exchanger, is returned to the feedwater system through a flash tank and other stages, and thence back to the boiler.

Low solar power is a mode in which all the solar-heated steam produced by the central boiler is needed to produce the desired electrical output. No steam is diverted to heat the thermal storage tank. In fact, when necessary, steam from the thermal storage unit's steam generator is fed into a secondary stage of the turbogenerator. This mode serves as a natural transition between the normal solar and extended or intermittent-cloud operating modes, and thus adds flexibility to the solar power plant.

Operation with intermittent clouds is a mode in which the turbine is driven entirely by thermal storage steam. All steam produced by the solar boiler goes directly to the heat exchanger, where it heats the Caloria piped into the top of the rock bin. Cooler fluid from the bottom of the huge storage cylinder is pumped back into the heat exchanger to be heated by solar steam. An alternative to Caloria, now being tested, is Monsanto Therminol 66.

Extended plant operation occurs when the central solar receiver (the boiler) is not getting enough insolation, because of bad weather or darkness, to produce solar-heated steam. Now derated steam—at 525°F and 385 psia instead of 960°F and 1,515 psia directly from the boiler—is supplied to the turbine from the three-stage steam generator associated with the thermal storage unit.

A fifth mode of operation involves *charging the thermal storage unit*. Outlet steam temperature from the boiler is reduced because all solar-heated steam goes to the heat exchanger, heats the Caloria, and then goes to the flash tank. Flashed steam provides all the heating required for deaerating feedwater, and any excess steam is condensed and mixed with flash tank condensate as a further source of feedwater returned to the solar boiler. This mode of operation is capable of handling severe transients in solar insolation—a sudden storm preceded and followed by brilliant sunshine, for example. The SPT system could readily be programmed to continue in this mode, providing no steam to drive the turbine, until the thermal storage unit is almost fully charged.

The final set of operating conditions occurs when the *thermal storage tank is fully charged* by means of solar energy; or when there is a malfunction in the charging equipment and the appropriate sensors signal "fully charged thermal storage" meaning "Send us no more steam from the solar boiler." In the case of a 100-MW commercial SPT system, the turbogenerator is being designed to accept only a portion of the peak summer noon flow of collected solar energy in the form of steam. If the thermal storage subsystem is fully charged, then a portion of the heliostat field must be shut down so that solar heating of the tower receiver (the boiler) is just enough to drive the turbine, with no additional steam to be diverted to the thermal storage heat exchanger. While the pilot plant (10 MW) turbine is designed to accept full summer noon flow of steam, and thus there need never be a problem because of fully charged thermal storage, this sixth mode will be duplicated and studied during operational tests of the pilot plant or plants before commercial 100-MW plants go on stream.

30-MW Solar Power Plant in Canary Islands

Lest we imagine that American solar technology is leaving the rest of the world behind, consider this fact. A complex housing 60,000 inhabitants of the Canary Islands is

243

under construction on a 3,000-acre site at Lanzarote and will include a 30-MW solar power plant.

There will be 6,500 flat plate solar collectors on the homes. The 44-acre power plant will contain 600 heliostats and 20,000 flat plate collectors to produce steam for driving multistage turbogenerators.

The power plant and the collectors on the roofs of the houses will provide about 85% of the domestic hot water, 70% of the space heating, 50% of the cooling, and all the desalinization for the water supply of this large community. With all these solar blessings, the system is expected to furnish more than 25% of the total electricity needed.

Designed by a Spanish consulting firm, Panelsol Simplex, this project is privately financed (with Arab oil billions?). The complex will contain villas, apartments, hotels, and a shopping center.

The comment about Arab oil money was not intended to be facetious. Among the many solar projects under way in the OPEC countries, which have ample sunshine and are wise enough to use it while their oil riches continue to flow, is a solar heating system for a large school in Saudi Arabia. Designed by the architectural and engineering firm, Sverdrup & Parcel of St. Louis, the school complex consists of 14 buildings arranged around a plaza 230 feet x 950 feet.

A total of 2,592 flat plate solar collectors will be used for domestic hot water and for space heating in the 325,000 square feet of school buildings. Heat will be stored in large central insulated water tanks and distributed to the buildings through underground tunnels.

This system is expected to supply at least 70% of the school's space heating and hot water requirements with solar energy 35 years or more. Participating with the consulting firm is the U.S. Army Corps of Engineers; financing is by the government of Saudi Arabia. It was decided to wait before installing solar-powered cooling until some of the new techniques being investigated in various laboratories here and in other countries are further developed.

Commentary on Solar Power Tower Plants

One of the most practical and well-informed solar engineers is William B. Edmondson, publisher of *Solar Energy Digest* and developer of the efficient SolarSan flat plate collector, ingenious solar cookers and other devices. His comments about large solar power tower installations, expressed in the June 1977 issue of his magazine, come from a thoughtful expert.

Since the huge hole in the ground 150 feet deep for the foundation of the relatively small Sandia power tower is so awesome, says Edmondson, what's going to happen when foundations are required for a tower 1,000 feet tall? Such a tower is obviously enormously expensive in itself. Digging foundations in the unconsolidated desert soils adds further problems and cost.

Edmondson likes the compromise suggestion made by Otto J. M. Smith, professor of electrical engineering and computer sciences of the University of California at Berkeley. Smith proposes a 100-MW solar farm covering a total of 2.4 square kilometers, divided into 1,100 almost identical interlocking hexagons. Each hexagon, or module, would cover an area of 2,175 square meters and contain 312 mirrors of 2 square meters each. These mirrors would concentrate solar energy on a boiler, or receiver, mounted on a tower only 40 meters (about 125 feet) high. This tower would be a simple steel structure held erect with guy wires—no need for the giant subterranean anchor of concrete and steel now designed as the foundation for each free-standing power tower.

The heat collected at each of Smith's 1,100 towers would be transported by pipeline to a central power plant. There the sun-heated steam would drive conventional turbogenerators, using a reheat cycle for increased efficiency, with thermal storage similar to that now planned.

Professor Smith points out that his relatively small heliostats, towers, and other components can be produced inexpensively with mass production techniques. He estimates that one of his solar plants producing 1,000 MW could be built for $1.3 billion. This is in 1976 dollars, but this figure is actually lower in cost than a nuclear plant developing 1,000 MW, the author believes. Future operating cost would give the solar power plant a marked advantage over any other kind, with the possible exception of hydroelectric and geothermal plants.

Since public utilities, whether privately or publicly owned, would be reluctant to build such a 1,000-MW solar plant without assurance of cost figures, Smith suggests that the federal government should guarantee to cover all cost overruns and thus speed construction of such power plants. A precedent is the $200-million geothermal loan guarantee program already established by ERDA.

Edmondson has a further thought. Since each hexagonal power field would have a capacity of 500 kW of thermal energy, industries in the Sun Belt States should be interested in building one or more of these solar power modules at their plants. Such a modest-sized installation reverts to the STES concept, providing electricity, process heat, space heating and cooling, and hot water.

This author heartily endorses this idea. Trying such installations, with a combination of private and public investment, seems to be a program with tremendous future benefit for the nation's industries. Electric power utilities are taking a keen interest in solar development. Perhaps a cooperative program promoting a few STES installations with these relatively small, low-cost towers and small, inexpensive heliostats—the two biggest expense items in big proposed solar power tower stations—will save dollars and make sense. Such an installation could be useful even for big shopping centers and housing developments in suburban areas, projects now on the drawing boards of major real estate development firms. With a tie-in to the local electric grid, to supply backup power when needed for the solar installation, and to accept surplus power created by solar energy when available, such programs with mini-towers for solar power are bound to succeed economically in the near future. The basic technology is here now.

Other Proposed Big Solar Power Plants

In this author's previous book is a description of possible solar power plants on platforms in some suitable location, like the Gulf Stream a few miles off the coast of Florida. Cold water from a depth of 2,000 feet is pumped up to the platform to cool a condenser in a Rankine cycle engine, which uses a working fluid, such as propane or ammonia, with a low boiling point. This liquid is first compressed and then goes into an evaporator containing a heat exchanger. Warm surface seawater—and you need year-round temperatures of 75°F to 80°F—causes the liquid propane to turn into a vapor under pressure. This gas flows into the turbogenerator, expanding through its vanes and generating electricity.

To complete the closed-cycle process, the gas from the turbine, which has gone from the high-pressure side to the low-pressure side of the turbine, flows into a condenser. Here another heat exchanger uses the 35°F water pumped up from the cold depths to chill the gas and cause it to return to its liquid state. Next the liquid propane passes through a pressurizer and is pumped back into the evaporator, where warm seawater again vaporizes the pressurized fluid.

There are many good engineers interested in such a program. ERDA has a group sponsoring studies by such companies as

TRW Systems of Redondo Beach, California, Westinghouse Electric, and Lockheed Oceanographic Systems of San Diego, as well as Sea Solar Power in York, Pennsylvania, and academic research including Carnegie-Mellon University in Pittsburgh, and University of Massachusetts in Amherst.

A basic problem with such a sea solar power plant is its low efficiency—estimated at no better than 3%. It would take a very large investment to build such a plant. It would also take a considerable amount of power to run the pumps, compressors, and other equipment involved, which is one reason for the low net gain in power from such a plant. Thus it remains to be seen whether such offshore power plants will be built.

A far more practical approach seems to be along the lines advocated by Bill Edmondson, publisher of *Solar Energy Digest*. His idea consists of locating such a power plant on a desert site a few miles inland. One major advantage is that you can obtain much hotter water at such an inland location than at any ocean platform. Therefore, the Carnot efficiency is increased since Nicolas Carnot's equation says that

$$\text{Efficiency}_{max} = \frac{T_1 - T_2}{T_1}$$

where T_1=temperature of the hot water (in this case) in degrees Kelvin (°K) and T_2= temperature of the cold water, also in °K.

Following are this author's suggestions as to such an inland plant which could combine some of the best features of modern solar, geothermal, and desalinzation concepts.

- The solar power plant would be built as close as possible to a source of cold ocean water, at any site where there is hot water underground. The reason for placing the plant near the seacoast is to keep the temperature of the water pumped up from 1,500 feet below the ocean surface at a level no higher than 50°F (10°C). Even to maintain this moderately cool temperature, it will be necessary to insulate the pipeline bringing this cool seawater to its warm inland destination.

- There are many areas of the world where there are subterranean sources of very hot water, as has been established by geothermal surveys. It has also been found that there are much larger areas, many contiguous to oceans, where subterranean rocks are at very high temperatures. Scientists of Los Alamos Scientific Laboratory of The University of California, have drilled and blasted to form underground caverns which can be used to heat water. This water, under pressure at temperatures up to around 400°F (about 205°C), can be pumped to the surface for use in our inland Carnot power plant. The site doesn't have to be a desert: locations in Alaska, Hawaii, Iceland, Japan, and Chile are a few examples of promising areas, in addition to Southern California, the Arabian peninsula, and many others.

- The cold water pumped ashore to our Carnot-Rankine cycle power plant, after it has served its purpose of creating a condensate by chilling the working fluid from its gaseous state to a liquid, could be fed into large solar ponds. Such shallow ponds, used in Australia, Chile, and Israel to provide fresh water, are relatively inexpensive to build and maintain. The bottom of each pond is painted with a black absorbent coating. The surface of the pond is covered with a tent of transparent plastic—DuPont Tedlar would do well. Salt water is fed into the pond at a rate which replenishes its level as the sun heats the water, causing evaporation and condensation on the underside of the plastic cover. Droplets of fresh water, condensate on the plastic sheet, roll into channels at the sides of the pond. Thus there is a steady flow of fresh water, created by solar action, into insulated storage tanks. Maintenance involves cleaning brine deposits from the bottoms of the solar ponds when the salt buildup becomes excessive and the pond begins to lose its efficiency as a solar cooker generating fresh water. However, even this maintenance is profitable because the recovered salt is valuable.

- The hot water from its underground cavern can be kept reasonably hot during the duty cycle of the Carnot power plant, before being returned underground for additional heating. By using several underground heat reservoirs at our power plant site, we should be able to keep the operation going indefinitely with water heated to a suitably high temperature and kept under pressure.

- Some simple arithmetic shows the advantages of such a program. Under the best conditions, the maximum theoretical efficiency obtainable from a Carnot cycle ocean platform power plant is

$$E_{max} = \frac{305 - 275}{305}$$

$$= \frac{30}{305}, \text{ or less than 10\%.}$$

This is on the assumption that the cold ocean water is used at 35°F (1.67°C = 274.67°F) and the warm surface ocean water is used at 80°F (305.22°K).

By contrast, the maximum theoretical efficiency obtainable from an inland Carnot power plant is

$$E_{max} = \frac{423 - 283}{423}$$

$$= \frac{140}{423}, \text{ or nearly 33\%.}$$

This is on the assumption that the cold ocean water has warmed up to 50°F (10°C or 283°K) by the time it reaches our inland power plant, and that the underground hot water is available at 302°F (150°C = 423°K).

FIGURE 10-17.   NASA Concept of Space Spiders

We consider all these assumptions to be reasonable and believe that such an inland power plant could and should be built soon with a combination of private and federal funding. Or maybe an investment by the World Bank?

Among other interesting proposals is one made several years ago by a husband-and-wife team, both with doctorates in physics, who live in a solar house in Tucson. Aden and Marjorie Meinel of the University of Arizona proposed a vast farm of solar collectors in the desert, tied together to produce megawatts. They came up with a good idea, except for the use of liquid sodium as a coolant; and now the technology of concentrating collectors and reflectors will soon make such a concept practical. On a relatively small scale, such systems are already proving themselves. The Canary Islands installation will be one of the first really big systems.

Probably the most imaginative work is proceeding on the concept of building huge power stations in space. Long advocated by such solar pioneers as Dr. Peter Glaser of Arthur D. Little Company in Boston, and Dr. Krafft Ehricke, an associate of the late Wernher Von Braun and now with Rockwell

Space Division in Seal Beach, California, the plans for orbiting solar power plants are being studied with increasing vigor and ERDA support. Funded studies by Boeing, Rockwell, and others are underway. NASA-Marshall has issued a request for quotation on development of a Space Spider, to be used in conjunction with the soon-to-fly Space Shuttle. This device will carry a roll of prestamped material and will attach itself to the rim of an established core and spin out the newly formed material into a useful structure, as shown in Figure 10-17. This illustration shows how two Space Spiders might build the structure for a solar power satellite, attaching it to the external tank of a Space Shuttle.

Since the basic method of generating power from the sun in outer space depends on the use of large arrays of solar cells, a more detailed discussion of solar satellite power stations will be found in Chapter 11. Such far-out power stations, capable of generating as much as 5,000 MW of electric power on a 24-hour basis—which no terrestial solar power station can do because they can't generate at night or during bad weather—are beginning to look both technically feasible and economically desirable. This author believes we shall have our first satellite solar power beamed to Earth some time after 1990.

11
Solar Cells, Space Stations, and Electric Cars

On an experimental farm near Mead, Nebraska, an array of 120,000 solar cells is converting sunlight into electric power. While the sun is shining, these cells generate 25 kW—enough to operate a 10-HP pump used for irrigating 80 acres of corn and soybeans.

There are two parallel rows of solar cells facing south and tilted to get maximum insolation during the midsummer irrigation season. About 60,000 cells are mounted in each row on racks 8 feet high and 325 feet long. These solar cells are connected to a sizable number of storage batteries, which supply the actual electric power to operate the irrigation pump. This is a sensible arrangement if you want a power source delivering a consistent 25 kW because the output of the solar cell array will vary markedly during daylight hours, depending on the insolation level—and will be vastly reduced during stormy weather.

Another point is that each solar cell generates a small amount of direct current (DC). The total array of solar cells charges up a large bank of storage batteries, which welcome a DC input. However, electrical inverters are necessary in this Nebraska farm

System to convert the DC power into the AC power required for the pump motor and other electric loads.

Designed by the M.I.T. Lincoln Laboratory in Lexington, Massachusetts, the solar cell array went into service early in the summer of 1977. This irrigation project, in which the University of Nebraska at Lincoln is cooperating with M.I.T. under ERDA sponsorship, is the first use of electricity directly produced by the sun's radiation from solar cells in a major program for watering crops.

When the irrigation season ends, the same solar photovoltaic power will drive large fans for drying grain in storage bins. There are two bins, each with a 5-HP fan, used to store and dry about 12,000 bushels of corn harvested from this farm.

The solar engineers running this program, Dr. Leonard Magid of ERDA, and Marvin D. Pope and Ronald W. Matlin of M.I.T., pointing out the value of this experimental installation, note that more than 35 million acres are irrigated in the United States at an annual fuel cost of more than $500 million. In some locations fossil fuels are increasingly difficult to obtain in adequate quantities, and their costs keep rising. While at the mid-1977 price of the solar cells of about $15 per peak watt, an array of photovoltaic cells is not a competitive way to power irrigation pumps, the ERDA objective of a cost of 50 cents per watt by 1985 looks more and more achievable. As soon as solar cell research brings the cost down to about this level, there will be widespread application of these useful devices, which convert sunlight directly into electricity—without the need of heat transfer systems, collectors, pumps, fans, valves, piping, or ducts.

Present Uses of Solar Cells

For many years you have read about solar cell arrays, often shaped like large weird paddles attached to space vehicles, used to provide electricity for a variety of valuable orbiting satellites, moon landers, and planetary probes. So long as this was the principal application for solar cells, their production was small and their cost high. Even so, the price of the silicon solar cells used to power electrical equipment in space vehicles has come down by leaps: from $500 per watt in 1959 to $175 per watt in 1961, and to a small fraction of that amount now.

In the communications business on land and sea, solar cells have been used extensively for two decades. Power for telephone, TV and radio relay stations, and forest rangers' towers on remote mountain tops; for emergency telephones along interstate highways from New Jersey to California; for signals and gates at railway crossings; for marker buoys on the Great Lakes, inland waterways, and along coastlines—these are typical current uses for solar cell arrays charging storage batteries. Remote transmitters for alarms along pipelines, in refineries, and mines also get electricity from batteries recharged by solar cells.

In early 1977 one of the largest manufacturers of electronic calculators, Sharp Corporation of Osaka, Japan, started mar-

keting a solar-powered calculator which sells for about $86. This unit includes 16 tiny square silicon solar cells which will recharge the battery in the calculator under fluorescent light as well as sunlight. Manufacturers in the United States and other countries are supplying flashlights, cassette tape recorders, portable radios, and model airplanes with batteries charged by solar cells. There are digital watches and clocks which require only a few minutes' exposure to sunlight for these useful tiny cells to keep such timepieces operating for days.

If you sail a boat, chances are you've seen solar cell arrays built into upper decking and covered with a durable transparent plastic, capable of delivering 14 volts DC with sufficient current to recharge the boat's battery in a few sunny hours. If you're a frequent sailor, you may have such a solar battery charger installed on your own boat. Such units, considered a useful accessory by thousands of boat owners, are now available for about $150. Should you lack for amusement while sailing, there are several toys powered with solar cells, including one where a single cell in sunlight powers a small DC motor driving a miniature plastic propeller. This small demonstrator and a "solar inventor's" kit are available from Clover Solar Corporation of Glendale, California.

What Are Photovoltaic Cells?

Don't think for one moment that solar cells are merely a technical curiosity because they're being used to power toys as well as irrigation pumps. In this author's opinion solar cells will contribute more to mankind's welfare during the last 20 years of this century than any other device. That's because solar cells can be used in very large arrays to serve as big power stations, probably orbiting; and they can also serve economically in smaller clusters in the fairly near future to supply both electricity and heat for your family-size home.

The basic principles causing photovoltaic cells to produce electricity are easy to understand. Sunlight contains tiny energy particles called photons. When these photons strike the surface of materials called semiconductors, some of the photons cause electrons in the semiconductors to move around. Since the flow of electrons is by definition an electric current, the action of photons from sunlight generates electricity.

There are quite a few materials which exhibit this photovoltaic effect—using the photon energy from sunlight to produce an electric current. Some materials, usually semiconductors, are more efficient for use in solar cells, readily available, and relatively economical to produce. A semiconductor can be classified as being less good a conductor of electricity than metals such as copper, aluminum, and steel, and a better conductor than such insulators as glass, stone, and ceramics.

Figure 11-1 helps to explain how solar cells function. It is useful to consider a cell made of silicon because this element is one of the most common on our planet—you've probably seen the TV commercial of Bell Laboratories (part of American Telephone & Telegraph) showing that sand consists largely of silicon dioxide.

If you introduce a small amount of phosphorus into a layer of pure crystalline silicon, this doped crystal is called an N-type semiconductor because it has an excess of electrons, which carry negative electrical charges. If you dope a silicon crystal with boron, you create a P-type semiconductor, so named because it has an excess of holes —a *hole* being defined as the absence of an electron and therefore a positively charged spot. Between the two layers is an intermediate surface called a P-N junction, where there is considerable mobility of electrons and holes.

In a silicon solar cell, the N-type layer is extremely thin—about 0.5 micron, or half of one-millionth of a meter. Photons penetrate this layer far enough to create pairs of electrons and holes near the P-N junction. Thus

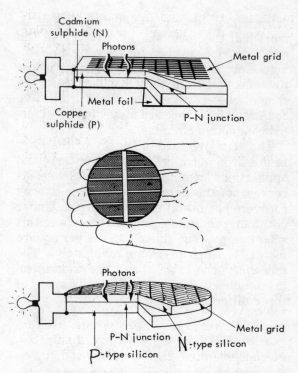

FIGURE 11-1. Operation of a Solar Cell

electrons collect in the N-layer and holes in the P-layer until there's a voltage built up in the silicon crystal which pushes any further electrons back into the thicker P-layer. This voltage is about 0.65 volt in a typical silicon solar cell.

Electric current is drawn from the cell by making a conductive circuit from the front surface to the back. The front carries a grid of wires connected to the back, which is completely plated with a thin coating of a conductive material. It's important not to cover too much of the front surface, because this covered area reduces the useful N-type layer bombarded by photons. At the same time, the solar cell designer wants to keep the electrical resistance of the circuit very low.

The efficiency of a silicon solar cell is limited by several physical factors. Most notable is the requirement that solar radiation, to be useful in energizing electrons in the cell, must have a wave length shorter than

1.1 microns—which immediately makes almost half the solar energy arriving on the earth's surface useless for creating a photovoltaic current. Other radiant energy is lost by reflection from the front surface, even though the solar cell has an antireflective coating. Also, there are losses in the external conductive circuit.

Thus the practical efficiency of the very best silicon solar cells made for terrestial applications amounts to about 18%. This represents the percentage of solar energy recovered as useful electric current. Under optimum conditions, you might expect this solar energy to be about 1.15 kW per square meter (10 square feet approximately). The following brief table shows the theoretical maximum efficiency of solar cells made of three different materials:

Silicon 22%
Gallium arsenide 27%
Cadmium tellurium 24.35%

Even ideal photovoltaic cells have an efficiency of less than 25%. But this isn't so bad as you might think if you consider that your automobile converts energy with an efficiency of less than 20%, and an electric power plant is not much better when you add the losses required to get electricity to your home.

Processes for Making Solar Cells

For many years the cost of silicon solar cells has been high. There are several reasons for this. The material itself must be very pure before the tiny amounts of phosphorus and boron are added. One process, called the Czochralski method after its inventor, involves rotating a "seed" crystal and dipping it into a crucible of molten silicon, then slowly pulling out a resultant cylinder about 4 inches in diameter and several feet long. Boron is usually added to the melt to dope this big crystal uniformly, making a P-type semiconductor. The cylinder is then sliced into thin wafers—so that much of the material is lost as silicon sawdust. Next, one

surface of each wafer is doped with phosphorus at high temperature, passing many wafers through a furnace and creating the N-layer over the P-layer. Then electrical contacts are attached, an antireflective coating applied on the upper surface, and the cell assembly is encapsulated in a plastic skin.

A promising alternative method for making silicon solar cells, described in this author's first book, is called the edge-defined film-fed growth (EFG) process and has been under development for about 11 years by a company now called Mobil Tyco Solar Energy Corporation, located in Waltham, Massachusetts. A graphite die is lowered into molten silicon. The hot liquid rises through the center of the die by capillary action and forms a layer of liquid on top of the die. Then a seed crystal of silicon is dipped into the liquid at the top of the die. A film of liquid silicon coming through the die feeds the growing crystal, forming a ribbon with a cross section corresponding to the top of the die.

This ribbon grown by EFG produces a film 1.5 millimeters thick and is grown at a rate of about 25 millimeters (1 inch) per minute. Then this film is cut into rectangular wafers 2.5 centimeters x 10 centimeters (1 inch x 4 inches) having a conversion efficiency as good as 12%.

One of the most attractive features of this process is that it is possible to grow many ribbons simultaneously in parallel, using a sizable number of dies and drawing from one or more large tanks of molten silicon. According to Dr. Abraham I. Mlavsky, executive vice president of Mobil Tyco, it should be possible to produce 20 silicon ribbons at once, with each ribbon about 2 inches wide and some economical length such as 100 feet. Then if the price of raw silicon, through the efforts of producers like Dow Chemical, is reduced to $10 per pound, a manufacturing cost of $15 per pound for silicon ribbons suitable for making solar cells appears realistic. Or silicon ribbons could be priced at $125 per kW. This would represent a giant stride toward the goal of finished silicon cells at $500 per kW, or 50 cents per watt. Remember that you still have to cut the ribbon into rectangles, add electrical conductors and an antireflective coating, and then encapsulate the assembly.

Low-Cost Silicon Solar Array Project

Although silicon is not the only material from which solar cells are made, its availability and potential for low cost are so promising that ERDA is supplying substantial federal funds for the Low-Cost Silicon Solar Array (LSSA) project. Under the direction of the Jet Propulsion Laboratory of the California Institute of Technology in Pasadena, some 40 organizations are working on various aspects of the drive to produce silicon solar cells for 50 cents a watt by 1985. This program at JPL is headed by Robert Forney, formerly in charge of the inertial guidance system for the Mariner space vehicles and long expert in the use of solar cells beyond the Earth's atmosphere. The LSSA program consists of 4 phases.

PHASE 1.

First part of the LSSA project is *to improve the processes for obtaining the silicon material itself*, and for *testing solar cells with various impurities*. There are three major subdivisions of this task, with subcontractors and their specific assignments as follows:

A. Semiconductor grade processes:
Battelle Memorial Institute, Columbus, Ohio—producing silicon from silicon chloride or silicon iodide.
Motorola, Inc., Phoenix, Arizona—producing silicon from silicon fluoride.
Union Carbide Corporation, Sisterville, West Virginia—producing silicon from silicon hydride.

B. Solar cell grade definition:
Monsanto, St. Louis, Missouri, and Westinghouse Electric, Pittsburgh, Pennsylvania—examining solar cell performance versus impurities.

C. Solar cell grade processes:
Dow Corning, Hemlock, Michigan—producing silicon from metgrade silicon and other processes. (The silicon used for transistors, integrated circuits, and other electronic products is far more pure than metgrade and therefore more expensive.)
Stanford Research Inc., Menlo Park, California—providing silicon from silicon fluoride.
Texas Instruments Inc., Dallas, Texas—producing silicon from metgrade silicon or silicon dioxide.
Aero-Chem Inc., Princeton, New Jersey—developing nonequilibrium plasma jet processes.
Lamar University, Beaumont, Texas—studying the commercial practicality of processes for producing silicon material for solar cells.
Westinghouse Electric, Pittsburgh, Pennsylvania—reducing silicon chloride using an arc heater.

PHASE 2.

The second principal task in the LSSA project is *development of large silicon sheets*. Organizations and their respective tasks involved in this phase, divided into four parts, are the following:

A. Ribbon Growth:
Mobile Tyco, Waltham, Massachusetts, and IBM, Hopewell Junction, New York—working on edge-defined film-fed growth (EFG).
Motorola, Phoenix, Arizona—exploring laser zone ribbon growth.
RCA, Princeton, New Jersey—looking at an inverted Stepanov process.
University of South Carolina, Columbia—studying a web-dendrite technique.

B. Sheet Growth:

General Electric, Schenectady, New York—developing a method of using chemical vapor deposition on a liquid or floating substrate.

Rockwell International, Anaheim, California—trying chemical vapor deposition on low-cost substrates.

Honeywell, Bloomington, Minnesota—working with dip-coating on low-cost substrates.

C. Ingot Growth and Cutting:

Crystal Systems, Inc., Salem, Maine—casting silicon ingots with a heat exchanger process, and then using multiple-wire sawing to produce slices of suitable size for solar cells.

D. Ingot cutting:

Varian, Lexington, Massachusetts—using breadknife sawing.

University of Pennsylvania, Philadelphia—hot-forming silicon ingots prior to cutting.

PHASE 3.

A third major task of the LSSA subcontractors is *encapsulation of the solar cells*, performed by the following:

Battelle, Columbus, Ohio—studying manufacturer and user experience with various encapsulants, as well as defining the environment in which encapsulants must perform and setting up test methods.

Rockwell International, Anaheim, California—developing both accelerated and abbreviated tests for encapsulants.

Simulation Physics, Burlington, Massachusetts—developing bonded integral glass covers for solar cells.

DeBell and Richardson, Enfield, Connecticut—are studying the polymeric properties and aging characteristics of encapsulants.

PHASE 4.

The fourth major research task in the LSSA project involves *automated fabrication of solar cell arrays*, with the following included:

Motorola, RCA, and Texas Instruments—all working on improved manufacturing processes. TI is also trying to achieve better Czochralski growth and to improve methods for making wafers.

Simulation Physics—examining an electron beam fabrication technique.

Mitre Corporation, McLean, Virginia, and Solarex Corporation, Rockville, Maryland—evaluating tests for solar cell arrays.

In addition to supervising all these research and development tasks, it's the job of the LSSA task force at JPL to buy fairly substantial quantities of encapsulated arrays of solar cells now commercially available from the five principal American manufacturers:

M7 International, Arlington-Heights, Ill.

Sensor Technology, Chatsworth, California

Solar Power Corporation, Wakefield, Massachusetts

Solarex Corporation, Rockville, Maryland

Spectrolab Inc., Sylmar, California

As of mid-1977 about 176 kW of electric power are being produced at the JPL test facility in Pasadena, using arrays of solar cells made by these five companies. So as to compare the performance of these manufacturers' products fairly, JPL engineers had to set up detailed specifications for the size and output of these arrays.

Big Companies and Small

If you glance over the preceding list, you'll notice the familiar names of giants in the electronics business—GE, IBM, Honeywell, Motorola, RCA, Rockwell, Texas Instruments, Varian and Westinghouse—as well as chemical colossi, Dow Corning, Monsanto, and Union Carbide. About $50 million has been invested by Mobil Oil in the development of the EFG process with Mobil Tyco Solar Energy Corporation in Waltham, Massachusetts. Exxon has a multimillion-dollar stake in Solar Power Corporation, also in Massachusetts. Spectrolab in Southern California is a subsidiary of Hughes Aircraft Company, a major manufacturer of military electronics and optics.

Beyond these big corporations taking an active part in the development of silicon solar cells, there are several small companies with an excellent record of producing useful devices. M7 International, Sensor Technology, and Solarex are three firms which have been assured of supplying 40% of the total kilowatts in solar arrays to be purchased for evaluation by JPL. There is a definite effort, backed by Congress as well as the Carter administration, to make sure that inventive small business will have a fair chance in the race to develop and manufacture solar cells.

But the very fact that such oil and chemical giants as Exxon and Mobil have already invested heavily in pioneer companies producing silicon solar cells, while Shell Oil Company has invested several million dollars in SES, Inc., in Newark, Delaware, a producer of cadmium sulphide/copper sulphide solar cells, is proof that the potential for these devices is more than a dawning promise. It's apt to be a sunburst as millions turn to electric cars powered by storage batteries charged repeatedly with current from solar cells.

Although the cadmium sulphide/copper sulphide cells (CdS/CuS) produced so far are not quite so efficient as silicon solar cells —operating usually at about 8% efficiency —processes for making the former hold promise for low-cost mass production. Early in 1977 basic solar modules 8 inches x 8 inches in size with an output of 12 volts were announced by SES Inc. to furnish low to medium power for remote transmitter and alarm units, cathodic protection for

natural gas wells, navigational aids and other applications. This Shell subsidiary supplied solar panels of CdS/CuS cells long used to provide part of the electric power for a solar house in Newark, Delaware, designed by Drs. Karl Boer and Maria Telkes of the University of Delaware Institute for Energy Conversion. Now SES is offering solar cell modules which may be connected to supply power outputs from 1 watt to as much as 500 watts.

More Power from Solar Cells with Concentrators

Another ERDA-financed program as impressive as LSSA is a project to produce substantially greater amounts of electric power from solar cells by concentrating the sunlight delivered to these cells. Under the technical direction of Sandia Laboratories in Albuquerque, and with considerable research being performed by Sandia engineers led by Dr. Donald G. Schueler, this avenue of development looks increasingly good. It makes sense, since solar cells are still expensive, to use optical techniques and concentrate sunlight on arrays of cells and thus obtain more electricity from the same area of photovoltaic cells.

In Figure 11-2 a single Fresnel lens is used to concentrate the sun's rays on a single solar cell. Figure 11-3 pictures an array of 135 plastic Fresnel lenses mounted in front of the same number of silicon solar cells, with the array delivering 1 kW (1,000 watts) of electric power to storage batteries.

Each lens is a foot square and concentrates the sunlight 50 times. Sandia engineers calculate that this high-intensity illumination causes each solar cell to produce a maximum output of about 7.4 watts—or just about 50 times the output of the same cell under the best conditions of direct sunlight. A tracking mount controlled by a sun-locked sensor keeps the array of lenses and cells pointed at the sun.

Usually it takes about 100 square feet in surface area of solar cells to produce a peak

FIGURE 11-2.   A Fresnel Lens is Used to Concentrate the Sun's Rays on a
Solar Cell as Part of Sandia Laboratories' Research on Solar Cells Operating at
High Illumination Levels

FIGURE 11-3. Using 135 Plastic Fresnel Lenses Mounted Directly in Front of 135 Silicon Solar Cells, the Photovoltaic Concentrator at Sandia Laboratories Produces One Kilowatt of Electricity

output, at solar noon, of 1 kW. By contrast, the Sandia concentrator uses only 2.9 square feet of solar cells illuminated by the sun shining through 135 square feet of Fresnel lenses.

The economics of this concentrator appear impressive. At 1977 prices of $15 per watt, using an array of conventional solar cells—without concentrated sunlight—it would cost about $15,000 to deliver 1 kW of electric power. Estimated cost of the much smaller number of solar cells with Fresnel lenses is $3,500, or less than 1/4 as much.

Another interesting point is that this so-lar array is cooled by water circulated in copper tubing behind the cells. It has long been known that silicon solar cells are more efficient if you keep them at a temperature of 100°F or less. But when you concentrate sunlight by shining it at a cell through a Fresnel lens that acts as a magnifying glass, you're bound to heat the solar cell.

So Sandia engineers carry this undesired solar heat away by transferring the energy to water, which reaches a temperature at high noon of about 200°F (90°C). When you have a panel of solar cells on your roof, such sun-heated water can be piped into your

**FIGURE 11-4.   Engineer Placing Square Solar Cell of Improved Performance
on Sandia Laboratories' Sun-Tracking Test Fixture**

home for space heating and domestic hot water, or even for operating an absorption chiller or a Rankine cycle cooler.

A further significant statistic is that the efficient solar cells used in this array, and developed by Sandia research scientists, convert 14% of the solar energy they receive into electric power. These cells collect another 50% at high noon as heat, so that a total of 64% of the insolation can be used.

Exciting Prospect for Your Home and Business

With so much brainpower concentrated on producing improved arrays of solar cells at ever lower cost, you can see how efficient your home can be in just a few years. You will be able to mount a concentrator array or two on your roof or on a tracking mount near your house. Then your solar cells will deliver most of the electricity you need, stored either in batteries or perhaps in some improved device such as a fuel cell for use

throughout the 24 hours. Meanwhile the heated water, warmed by the underside of the solar cell array, will be stored and used for space heating and cooling as well as domestic hot water.

This looks to this author like the most attractive prospect for future Total Energy Systems, which can be sized for anything from a small house or apartment to a large factory or shopping center.

Silicon solar cells used in early Sandia arrays are 2 inches in diameter, with metal conducting lines on the face of each cell like spokes of a wagon wheel. The cell design has been improved by lowering the resistivity of the cell substrate by more than 70%, thus helping to maintain the voltage output at high temperatures caused by the Fresnel lenses. The back of each cell has also been treated by Sandia researchers to produce better ohmic contact for high electrical currents.

Because square solar cells can be packed more closely together, it is likely that they will be used in future arrays. Figure 11-4

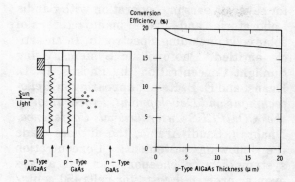

FIGURE 11-5. Construction of New Varian Solar Cell (Left) and Graph Showing its Efficiency in Converting Sunlight to Electricity (Right)

shows a Sandia engineer placing cells of this shape and still further improved performance on the sun-tracking test fixture. This work was being done when the author visited the facility in late May 1977.

In the same test area, other designs of solar cells and concentrators are also being evaluated by the Sandia team as part of the total ERDA program. For example, gallium arsenide (GaAs) cells developed by RCA and Varian are being tested with concentrators designed by those firms. Actual structure of such cells consists of an upper layer of P-type aluminum gallium arsenide exposed to concentrated sunlight; then a layer of P-type gallium arsenide and a P-N junction followed by a thicker layer of N-type gallium arsenide.

As described in some detail in this author's previous solar book, a Varian solar cell with a diameter of only 1/3 inch but with a parabolic concentrator that steps up the solar energy by a factor of 1,000 can produce a maximum power output of 10 watts. This is because this cell's material permits efficient operation at temperatures up to 360°F (200°C) and even higher—without cooling by water pipes or a fan blowing cooling air past the underside of the hot solar cells. Figure 11-5 shows construction of this type of cell and a graph of its efficiency, with Figure 11-6 an actual photograph (magnified) of the cell and concentra-

FIGURE 11-6. Magnified View of Aluminum Gallium Arsenide and Gallium Arsenide Solar Cell in Concentrator Mount by Varian Associates. Cell's Active Surface is Actually 1/3 inch in Diameter

tor. In Figure 11-7 we see an array of these Varian cells with parabolic concentrators enclosed in a plastic bubble at the Sandia test grounds, while Figure 11-8 shows RCA cells under Fresnel lenses.

One drawback to extensive use of gallium arsenide solar cells is the relative scarcity of the raw material—gallium is by no means as common as silicon—and hence predictions by solar experts that the relatively costly GaAs will not prove as economically viable a material as silicon. This is in spite of the fact that you can operate the GaAs solar cells at much higher temperatures, achieve greater efficiency and higher electrical output.

Scientists at the IBM Thomas J. Watson Research Center in Yorktown Heights, New York, report that their new GaAs solar cells, with a construction similar to the Varian design, are achieving a conversion efficiency of about 22%. According to Jerry M. Woodall and Harry J. Hovel of IBM, the improved efficiency is largely caused by a single-step process called etch-back epitaxial

FIGURE 11-7. Array of Varian Solar Cells, Which Can Operate Efficiently at High Temperatures, Contained in Plastic Bubble

growth which produces a better internal structure. The result is that fewer electrons and holes recombine, so that more electrons are collected at the P-N junction—which means increased current flow and greater efficiency. Because these GaAs solar cells are about 20% more efficient than the best silicon cells, it is stated, and because the material will stand the high temperatures of concentrators producing energy levels as high as 1,000 suns, the IBM research team is convinced that GaAs cells will prove competitive in the race to produce electricity from photovoltaics at 50 cents a watt.

A team at Arizona State University headed by Charles E. Backus, professor of mechanical engineering, has been working

for several years in cooperation with Sandia Laboratories and several manufacturers of solar cells, including Spectrolab. In an article entitled "Photovoltaic Systems Using Sunlight Concentration" by Backus, D. L. Evans, and E. L. Ralph, appearing in *Heliotechnique and Development, Proceedings of the COMPLES International Conference*, Dhahran, Saudi Arabia, the authors made the following statement: "Concentration systems can be cheaper than flat arrays even at projected costs for cells (50 cents/ peak watt). Conventionally processed silicon cells can operate at light intensities over 100 Suns at efficiencies comparable to current product space cells. Passive cooling techniques can be adequate for relatively high aperture-to-cell area ratios (up to 50)."

In this paper and others, Backus discusses a variety of concentrators ranging from the Winston trough, with no tracking and a concentration factor of 10; to the line focus and Fresnel lenses, with tracking and factors to 100; and ultimately the paraboloids, with tracking and intensification of the insolation up to 1,000 times or more. He and his associates have also done considerable work with cooling techniques, passive and active, to keep the undersides of solar cells at favorable temperatures. Much of this effort is performed cooperatively with Sandia. Incidentally, although a resident of Arizona, a state blessed with close to the maximum insolation in the United States, Backus believes that the northern areas of this country—and perhaps others—will derive the greatest benefits from more extensive use of solar energy. Certainly efficient use of the sun's radiation will help people living in the whole tier of northern states to live more comfortably without being smothered by escalated utility bills.

Progress by Small Companies

Significant progress is also being made by many of the smaller companies working with solar cells. Solarex Corporation in Rockville, Maryland, is now making a

FIGURE 11-8.   RCA Solar Cells Under Fresnel Lenses

square silicon solar cell 5 centimeters x 5 centimeters (2 inches x 2 inches) with a peak efficiency of 15%. The square design permits closer packing of cells than with previous round units in a sun-illuminated space. Further, according to Peter Veradi, executive vice president, Solarex has found it possible to use relatively impure semicrystalline silicon instead of the more expensive single-crystal silicon. Test results indicate stability of this more economical material at much higher temperatures than were previously considered feasible. Here's another candidate for increased power output with concentrator solar cell arrays. Even without concentrators focusing sunlight on these square silicon solar cells, Solarex states that up to 120 watts can be obtained from 1 square meter (about 10 square feet). This means that with about 200 square feet of roof surface covered with solar cells, you can generate enough electricity for your home—and by carrying away excess heat from the underside of the solar cells get part of your space heating and hot water needs.

According to Photon Power of El Paso, Texas, this firm's research team, headed by John F. Jordan, has developed a chemical spray process to lay down film a few microns thick on a glass substrate, producing solar cells which convert 5% of the insolation to electricity. Though this efficiency is low, Jordan believes it can be increased to about 8%. The major advantage of the process is that the cost of cells at a production level of 1 million square feet a year is stated at about $425 per kilowatt. This is below ERDA's magic goal of 50 cents a watt by 1985—and actually the production rate of 1 million square feet annually is not very high. We hope Photon Power's process proves technically and economically viable.

Meanwhile Simulation Physics, Inc., of Burlington, Massachusetts, is using ion implantation for doping and then annealing single-crystal silicon solar cells with electron-beam pulses. The process takes only 2 minutes from wafer to finished cell, uses little energy, and produces cells with 12% efficiency.

Also in Massachusetts, John Yater, an independent inventor, is working with large numbers of microminiature resistors in an effort to create a different kind of solar cell. Yater is trying to concentrate about 1 million resistors on 1 square centimeter (about 1/6 square inch) in an effort to generate electricity from solar heat, and has been awarded a $40,000 research contract from ERDA. The award was based on a recommendation from the National Bureau of Standards, which is evaluating energy-related inventions and has received more than 4,000 ideas as of mid-1977.

Another inventor, George H. Hamilton, believes he has designed a solar cell with an efficiency of 30%. His firm, Solar Energy Company of Gloucester Point, Virginia, produces a new type of design consisting of several layers of overlapping miniature solar cells connected in parallel and superimposed over a conventional solar cell. Hamilton says this technique is based on Nature's designs in certain leafy plants which collect solar energy for photosynthesis. Although the theoretical maximum efficiency of various solar cell materials is no greater than 25%, as pointed out previously, it's possible that Hamilton's technology achieves a concentration effect and therefore increases the output of his hybrid cell.

In Albuquerque a retired University of New Mexico professor has developed a germanium and quartz solar cell about 6 inches in diameter and 1/16 inch thick. After 15 years of research, Dr. Samuel J. Keith says this new solar cell offers the prospect of achieving a cost of about $1 per watt in mass production.

Satellite Solar Power Stations

For at least 20 years, many space enthusiasts have been advocating that we build giant orbiting solar power stations. Scientists like Dr. Peter E. Glaser, vice president of Arthur D. Little Company in Cambridge, Massachusetts, and Dr. Krafft Ehricke, advanced projects adviser with the Space Division of Rockwell International in Seal Beach, California, have pointed out both technical and economic advantages to be gained by generating as much as 5,000 MW using massive arrays of solar cells mounted on a vehicle in geosynchronous orbit.

Shown in Figure 11-9 is an artist's concept from a Rockwell study of such a huge power station in space. Note that the length of the array on which the solar cells are mounted is 27 kilometers, or nearly 17 miles. Electric power collected from millions of solar cells, comprising an estimated 65% of the weight and 60% of the cost of the satellite power station, would be beamed back to Earth after a conversion of the electrical energy from direct current (DC) to microwave frequencies.

It will be possible, with such a power station in geosynchronous or geostationary orbit, to direct the power beam very accurately to a relatively small receiving station, probably at some desert site. Scientists at Boeing in Seattle, and Rockwell estimate that a receiving station only about 5 miles in diameter will be adequate to collect the solar power transmitted from the satellite power station about 22,000 miles overhead.

At the terrestial receiving station, the microwave energy will probably be converted back to DC power. It turns out that transmission of huge amounts of electric power on Earth is achieved most efficiently as direct current.

There are some interesting points made by the advocates of satellite solar power stations, including the following:

- *Solar power collected by a satellite station would be available on a 24-hour basis,* whereas a solar array on Earth gets sunlight only part of the time. Thus, a satellite solar power station can perform the "baseline" function of a conventional electric utility, providing electricity on demand at all times.

- *Removed from our atmosphere, solar cells on such a satellite would perform*

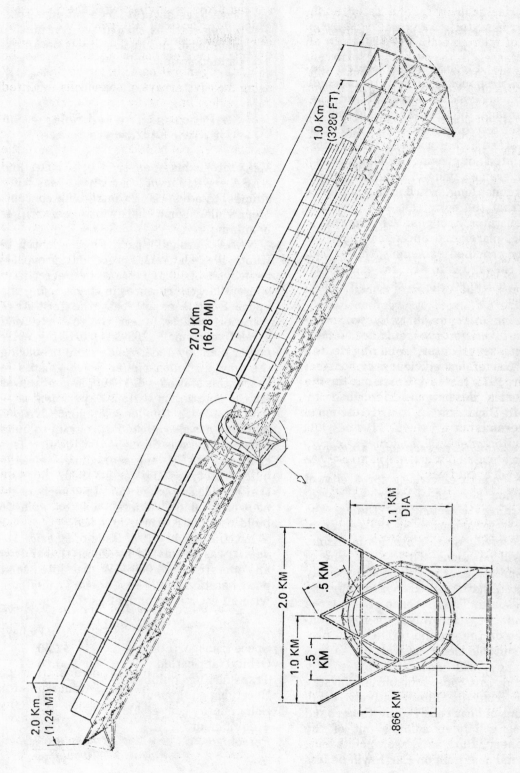

2.0 Km
(1.24 MI)

27.0 Km
(16.78 MI)

1.0 Km
(3280 FT)

2.0 KM

.5 KM

1.0 KM

.5 KM

1.1 KM DIA

.866 KM

FIGURE 11-9.   Artist's Concept of a Rockwell International Study of an Earth-Orbiting Solar Power Station. Power from this 17-mile Long Array Would Be Beamed Back to Small Receiving Station

263

more efficiently—receiving more and better insolation and thus delivering more electricity.

- *There is a considerable contest between proponents of gallium arsenide and those advocating silicon solar cells.* Advantages of the GaAs cells include greater conversion efficiency and ability to stand higher concentration ratios, as pointed out previously. This means a considerable saving in weight of arrays many miles long. You'll notice in Figure 11-9 that the solar cells are placed in concentrator troughs. On the other hand, Solarex and Spectrolab have recently provided extremely thin silicon solar cell arrays to JPL for evaluation, these designed specifically for space applications.

- *Beaming huge amounts of power to Earth by microwave would not be inefficient*, says Glaser, referring to the 82% conversion efficiency demonstrated in 1975 tests at Goldstone in the California desert and described by R. M. Dickinson in a JPL technical memorandum.

- *There should be essentially no danger to man, bird, or beast with even 5,000 MW*—enough electricity for a city of 5 million persons—beamed to Earth. According to scientific studies, the highest temperature at the center of the receiving station 5 miles in diameter will be about 450°F. The cone of transmitted energy will be so precisely directed that it will always occupy the same space. The presence of this large amount of microwave energy (converted on the ground to D-C) will provide suitable electrical warning so that airplanes will not attempt to fly through this cone, and birds will stay away from it. The relatively small amount of heat received by the ground station will keep animals out of the periphery. But, as Glaser points out, the total heat gain on Earth will be less if we have several large satellite solar power stations than if we continue to burn fossil and nuclear fuels on an expanded scale.

Progress Toward Solar Power Stations in Space

Many programs sponsored by ERDA and NASA are underway, largely as feasibility studies, to advance this intriguing concept. Meanwhile, some hardware research is beginning.

NASA-Marshall Space Flight Center in Huntsville, Alabama, is receiving proposals for ways to package, transport, erect, and operate large structures in space, using the Space Shuttle as at least the first-stage transport vehicle. In fact, the goal is to build a relatively small (100 kW) orbiting solar power plant by 1984. Aside from preparing the way for much bigger power plants in space, this station would supplement power for the shuttle for various experiments.

In line with this development, NASA-Marshall has also started a program to build Space Spiders as described in the previous chapter. NASA engineers have already built prototypes and tested them to prove that the idea is sound, and that such astronaut-controlled "spiders" will be able to build useful structures in space.

In the February 1977 issue of *Physics Today* it was estimated by Peter Glaser that an operational 5,000-MW satellite solar power station would cost about $7.6 billion, with an estimated budget as follows:

	Billions of Dollars
Space transportation	$3.30
Orbital fabrication	0.60
Transmitting equipment	0.50
Receiving equipment	1.30
Solar energy conversion equipment	1.80
Personnel	0.08
	$7.58

Expected life of this station would be at least 30 years, with total revenues of $35 billion and operating expenses of $4.2 billion. On this basis, the operation would be profitable at 27 mills per kilowatt-hour (kWh).

Glaser believes that it's going to mean an investment of perhaps $20 billion for the power station technology, and another $24 billion for the transportation system. He thinks these initial investments will be repaid when we have 60 satellite solar power stations operating—it is hoped by 2014—when it is assumed that it will cost an average of 35 mills per kWh to generate electricity by the various earthbound methods.

Such a program might well be encouraged. There are certainly far worse ways in which to invest in future electric power needed by the growing population of this planet. About 1/4 of our annual national military budget would pay for many years of this promising program.

Electric and Hybrid Cars Coming Slowly

In this author's previous book, there were descriptions of a few electric cars. Several thousand 2-passenger CitiCars, made by Sebring-Vanguard in Sebring, Florida, using lead acid batteries, a built-in battery charger, and a 3.5-HP electric motor made by GE, were sold and licensed. The company had financial problems and suspended operations, but efforts are underway in mid-1977 to revive the enterprise. International Nickel Company, major producer of nickel, metal alloys, and storage batteries (ESB), owns a considerable amount of stock in this small electric-car producer.

A few hundred Elcars, a slightly lighter and faster import from Italy, have been distributed in the United States from Elkhart, Indiana. Range of this electric car is about 50 miles between battery charges, and its top speed is about 38 miles per hour. In driving an Elcar with improved power modified by

Erwin A. Ulbrich, owner of Creative Automotive Research of Whittier, California, we found the vehicle to be highly maneuverable. It turns on the proverbial dime. Ulbrich, who is a senior computer engineer at the McDonnell Douglas Aircraft plant in Long Beach, quite often commutes nearly 50 miles a day in his Elcar.

"Operating economy is excellent," he reports. "It costs me less than 1 cent per mile to operate this electric car. So long as I stay in the right lane, overtaking traffic doesn't bother me."

His two biggest problems so far have been getting insurance at a reasonable rate, and trying to promote the idea of electric cars with his peers. "Until Americans get over their concept that a man's worth is measured by the length of his car, there won't be much of a market for electric cars," Ulbrich predicts.

Unfortunately it appears that he's correct. There have been several attempts by small corporations to build electric cars, but with no success. AM General Corporation, a subsidary of American Motors, has supplied 350 electric jeeps to the U.S. Postal Service. Otis Elevator of Cleveland, Ohio, and Battronic Corporation of Boyertown, Pennsylvania, have also built limited quantities of commercial electric vehicles.

At a solar energy exhibit at Convention Hall in Los Angeles, in October 1976 the author saw a Corvette chassis transformed into an electric car by Kaylor Energy Products of Menlo Park, California. This vehicle included a 30-HP DC continuous duty shunt motor and a transistorized 400-ampere controller, with a battery set consisting of a 72-volt 220-ampere assembly of lead acid cells. According to the designers, this machine operates smoothly at speeds from 0 to 70 miles per hour. Their brochure stated that "one dollar of electricity will last up to 400 miles."

Going one step further, some owners of electric cars actually have mounted panels of solar cells above their car roofs for recharging their batteries. The May 2, 1977 issue of *Design News* carries a photograph and description of a "Honsep"—an acronym for Honda Solar Electric Propulsion—developed by Wallace C. Moore. This car is powered with a 36-volt electric motor driven by 9 battery modules which produce about 100 watts of power. Mounted on the roof of Moore's modified compact is an array of 132 solar cells in three panels separated from the car top by an air space. These silicon cells, made by Sensor Technology of Chatsworth, California, take about 6 hours on an average sunny day to recharge the car's batteries. Then the Honsep, which is a hybrid having both an electric motor and a small gasoline-driven generator, is capable of traveling for about 6 hours at 39 miles an hour.

Most exciting new electric car is the Fiat 128 modified by Sears, Roebuck & Co. and Globe-Union Inc., maker of Diehard batteries. With 20 batteries adding 450 pounds, the Fiat XDH-1 goes 60 mph; 60 to 80 miles between charges; operating cost, about 1 cent per mile. If enough customers line up, Sears may sell you one in a couple of years for upwards of $4,000. WOW!

Two Australian engineers, Selwyn Wood and Dennis Bradshaw, have designed a solar electric commuter car powered by 4 individual printed armature servo motors fitted into the hubs of the 4 wheels. Solar cell arrays, suitably encapsulated, above the roof of the car are used to recharge 16 conventional lead acid batteries. There is a small gasoline-driven generator which supplies about 60% of the motive power during a trip. This car will do up to 60 miles per hour (100 kilometers an hour) with a range of about 200 miles. After 5 hours of parking in bright sunshine, the solar cells will furnish enough energy to operate this car for 1 hour at average commuting speeds.

Erwin Ulbrich of Creative Automotive Research has not only modified Elcars. He has also built two hybrid vehicles, one on a 1971 Hornet chassis, the second on a 1972 Dodge. He used a 2-cycle Onan gasoline-driven generator as well as an electric motor for his drive train; each car charges its batteries when driven slowly or idling. The Hornet hybrid was purchased by Southern California Edison for test use by meter readers and security personnel. The author has driven this vehicle, which performs smoothly at speeds up to about 45 miles per hour and gives about 40 miles per gallon. Built into a smaller and lighter chassis, such a hybrid drive train could be very economical and give quite adequate performance over commuting distances.

According to estimates by Ulbrich, there have been several thousand kits sold to modify various VW models so that they perform as electric cars. A leading maker of kits is Corbin Gentry in Massachusetts.

Battery Research Progressing

A far more important factor in the development of the next generation of electric cars is improvement in storage batteries. Everyone agrees that lead acid batteries are heavier and less efficient than they should be, but based on both performance and price this type still represents the only satisfactory units for today's electric cars.

But there is hope for the future. In a recent speech, Elliott M. Estes, president of General Motors, said this giant is providing research space in its Delco-Remy battery manufacturing plant in Muncie, Indiana, to test the manufacturing process for the company's new zinc/nickel oxide battery. Batteries produced in this plant will be used in prototype electric vehicles being developed by GM.

Ford and Chrysler are also sponsoring extensive battery research as well as building electric versions of their subcompacts to operate secretly on test tracks.

Rockwell's Atomics International Division in Chatsworth, California, recently tested a 1-kWh lithium iron sulfide battery, one of the high-density types which will prove useful for load-leveling in electric utility operations as well as for driving electric cars. This battery has solid electrodes: the negative electrode is made of a lithium-silicon alloy, the positive electrode of iron sulphide. The electrolyte is molten lithium chloride and potassium chloride. During discharge, lithium is oxidized at the negative electrode. Lithium ions migrate to the positive electrode, where they replace iron atoms, which are reduced to metallic iron. When the battery is charged, these reactions are reversed.

This new Rockwell battery operates at temperatures above 400°C (750°F) and has 3 pairs of electrodes. Its present energy density is 36 watt-hours per pound, but engineers believe this can be raised to about 75 watt-hours per pound. This compares very favorably with lead acid batteries delivering 15 watt-hours per pound.

Other promising storage battery developments include research with refrigerated zinc chloride batteries and a molten sodium sulphur battery. ESB Corporation of Philadelphia, a subsidiary of INCO, is engaged in a broad spectrum of battery research. One phase involves using porous carbon plates as the positive electrodes, aluminum plates as the negative electrodes, and sodium chloroaluminate as the electrolyte. Aluminum ions come off the negative plates, with chloride ions moving to and from the carbon plates.

Although there have been no dramatic recent developments, it is inevitable that there will be a marked improvement in the power output of storage batteries per pound. This will go a long way toward making practical the electric commuter car which can help us get rid of smog, save fossil fuels for other purposes, and drastically reduce the cost of driving.

At the risk of appearing disillusioned, this author believes that the great American buying public will keep on climbing into oversize automobiles—the gas guzzlers—until it really hurts where it counts, in His wallet and Her handbag. When gasoline sells for more than $1 per gallon, and the price of solar cells has come down considerably, it's also likely that body designers will have styled small electric cars more attractively than the boxy little vehicles available

so far. Then we'll really have a good chance of getting rid of most urban smog.

Future Potentials for Solar Cells

Beyond all the subjects discussed in this chapter are all kinds of additional applications for solar cells. It was suggested in the April 1977 issue of *Smithsonian* that dirigibles might be partially covered with arrays of solar cells which would provide part of their motive power.

A small company named Sun Tap Inc., in Arlington, Illinois, offers a solar cell panel which delivers 10.25 volts and charges 4 AA nickel-cadmium batteries supplied with a 4-way plug to operate equipment with 6-volt power jacks, all for less than $40.

Two Midwestern scientists, Bernard L. Sater of Olmstead Falls, Ohio, and Chandra Goradia of Cleveland State University, have calculated that a combined photovoltaic and thermal High Intensity Energy System (HISES) requires only 36 meters square of solar concentrator/solar cells/solar-heated fluid transfer to provide almost all the electricity, heating, cooling, and hot water for an average American family in an area with good year-round insolation like Atlanta, Jacksonville, Birmingham, New Orleans, Albuquerque, Dallas, Phoenix, or LA.

The interesting point made by Sater and Goradia, in a paper presented at the 11th Intersociety Energy Conversion Engineering Conference and reported in *Solar Energy Digest* for May 1977, is that once a substantial number of home owners are willing to buy such a solar system, the price will be very reasonable indeed. If half a million of these HISES are installed annually, each unit is estimated to cost less than $4,500. It will save the homeowner about $600 a year in utility bills, which are going up. Thus the payoff will be in 7 years or less.

Equipping 500,000 American homes with these solar energy systems would save the nation more than 30 million barrels of oil a year. Such saving will become increasingly important in reducing our balance-of-trade deficit and in helping to fight inflation.

12
Windmills as Power Plants

In many rural sites, using both wind and solar energy makes good sense. During storms, when there's no sunshine, there's apt to be wind velocity sufficient to generate many kilowatts of electricity.

Ever since power companies began having brownouts and blackouts, and fuel prices began soaring, popular interest in windmills has freshened from almost a dead calm to a strong breeze. When a popular women's magazine such as *McCall's* runs an article on "Windmill Power," you know the breeze of interest is going to become stronger.

One of the facts Mary McLaughlin brought out in the *McCall's* story is that there are about 175,000 windmills in this country, half of them operating or operable, according to a survey by New Mexico State University. Practically all are used for pumping water from wells on farms and ranches.

Relatively few of these windmills are used for generating electricity for two reasons:

- Until recently electric power has been very cheap and quite reliable.

- As you'll see later in this chapter, even if you own an operating windmill, it will cost you several thousand dollars to build your own small power plant, including wind generator, battery storage in racks, inverter, and standby engine generator.

Facts for the DIY Handy Person

Space in this book, devoted largely to solar energy, is too limited to provide complete plans for building your own windmill. However, there are some useful references in Appendix ?? to both sources of information and hardware. For instance, you can buy a set of plans for a small wind power plant with 12-foot three-bladed propeller from Hans Meyer of Windworks in Mukwonago, Wisconsin, for $15 and get expert information for your project.

However, we're including a number of facts you'll find useful in planning a windmill generator and advice on various hardware items that are part of the system. At the end of the chapter you'll learn about some large-scale power projects underway to add windpower AC to utility power lines.

Tower Height Important

The amount of electrical energy you can generate with a windmill is directly proportional to two major factors:

- The wind velocity *cubed*
- The propeller diameter or sailwing area *squared*

Because wind speed is so important, experts in windmill design state that a tower height of 60 feet appears to be optimum for a home-size power plant. With a tower this high you'll get about 35% more power output than if your propeller is on a 30-foot tower.

You should choose a tower site very carefully. It should be on a high, exposed point with 300 yards of open ground around it. The generator should be at least 20 feet higher than any nearby obstacles.

If there are trees or buildings near your site, try to place your tower so that it's on the windward side of these obstructions. Any object higher than the propeller-generator assembly on top of your tower will diminish the air flow. This zone of disturbed air will extend about 300 yards upstream and 100 yards downstream from your tower.

Since a windmill power station represents a sizable investment, equip yourself with a simple hand held anemometer for measuring wind speed at various possible sites. It's best to do this over a prolonged period, preferably five or six weeks, so that you'll know where the *average* wind velocity is greatest.

If the site you've selected is on hilly ground, you may want to have the building housing your inverter, rack of storage batteries, and standby generator in a separate location so that the structure doesn't obstruct air flow.

As to the tower itself, you have several alternatives. One of the best is to find an unused windmill whose tower can be disassembled and removed to your site, if the owner is willing to sell it. In most rural areas where there are sizable numbers of windmills, you can find a dealer who sells used windmill towers. Another good source is a manufacturer of radio, TV, and microwave towers. The upper section of one of these steel units is usually available in 20-foot modules which can be bolted together. The finished tower is then anchored with guy wires. This kind of tower is somewhat more expensive than many used towers, but it is easy to climb, paint, and maintain. These are all important considerations because you must be able to climb your tower to maintain the gear train between the propeller and generator, as well as the generator and propeller themselves.

Probably the least expensive type of tower is a long power company pole in excellent condition, weatherproofed and properly guyed. But then, unless you have climbing irons and are an expert lineman, you must install rungs up the side so that you can climb it.

Selecting a Propeller

There are some new sailwing designs which appear to have good potential. One, shown in Figure 12-1, is the creation of Thomas Sweeney, a research aeronautic engineer at Princeton University. This unit has sails of dacron that fill out in a breeze, is light in weight and capable of generating 5 kW of electric power—enough for a small, *conservative* family—in a moderate wind. Grumman Corporation may build a wind generator in quantity using this design if the market looks big enough.

Except for areas where there is heavy ice, this design will probably work well. However, in many parts of the country a conventional three-bladed propeller with a streamlined housing and aerodynamic feath-

FIGURE 12-1.   New Sailwing Design of Dacron. Unit Can Generate 5 kW of Electricity in a Moderate Wind

ering to avoid overspeeds in high winds is found to be the best choice. One of the best is the Windworks' 12-foot model.

A larger design well worth investigating is the 15-foot bicycle-wheel turbogenerator designed and built by Tom Chalk of American Wind Turbine in St. Cloud, Florida. This has blades in the form of an efficient aerodynamic Y wing. Blades are attached to the hub plate by wires extending out to a rim which serves as part of the electrical generator. Within the rim are field poles of an AC generator. They revolve rapidly enough about the armature so that there's no need for a gear train between the windmill and the generator—the generator is part of the "propeller." This saves both the energy lost in the gears and the cost of maintaining a gear train.

Chalk's design has 45 vanes and seems capable of developing up to 25 kW in a 25-mile-an-hour wind on a 60-foot tower. As a result, considerable research is being done

with this bicycle-wheel design by a team headed by Dr. William Hughes of Oklahoma State University. It's been tested in a wind tunnel, and there's talk of building a version 150 feet in diameter to generate megawatts of power.

Components of Your Windmill Power Plant

Your complete electrical system will include a generator, a voltage regulator, and a battery bank.

GENERATOR

A three-phase brushless AC generator or alternator should be connected to your windmill's propeller through a suitable gear train. Because the total cost of a windmill power plant represents a sizable investment —several thousand dollars—it makes good sense to install the best electrical generator you can buy at reasonable cost. The type which will give you maximum service is built on the same basic principles as the large power generators in utility plants. It is an *AC brushless generator*.

This generator has a stationary armature with a rotating field. Mounted on the shaft is an exciter using silicon diodes. There are many good manufacturers of such generators, or you may be able to buy a used one in good condition. Be sure that your generator's diodes include protection against voltage transients.

VOLTAGE REGULATION IMPORTANT

Voltage regulation is very important to prevent surges of overvoltage and undervoltage in the AC power converted into DC by a rectifier charging your bank of batteries. Most alternators are wound three-phase to reduce size and cost. Particularly from a variable frequency source like a propeller, you must have voltage regulation of the AC or you will damage your batteries and shorten their life. Ripple in the DC from the wind generator, without regulation, will heat the batteries and cause gassing, the generation of hydrogen and oxygen.

Most good converters include a voltage regulator, which is usually a full-wave rectifier using silicon diodes. Be sure any unit you buy has this feature. Also, the output of the regulator must be adjustable for proper battery charging with DC.

WHAT YOU NEED
IN A BATTERY BANK

Batteries are available in three general classifications. There are inexpensive car batteries for lowest cost; medium-quality units—the best automotive batteries; and high-quality batteries like those used in marine and communications applications.

Most commercial batteries are a combination of cells, with each cell rated at 2.0 volts. Thus a 12-volt car battery has six cells. In order to have a 120-volt system, which is what you'll need to operate your AC appliances, you must have a battery bank with from 57 to 60 cells. This means 20 of the 6-volt batteries; 10 automotive or marine batteries; and 5 if you buy 24-volt batteries.

This discussion has been dealing with lead acid batteries. In Chapter 11 there was a brief description of other types of batteries, including nickel cadmium—the NiCads well known in the aeronautical and aerospace industries because of their relatively small size and light weight. General Electric has announced a series of appliances with NiCads which can be charged in 15 minutes. Gould has recently indicated a breakthrough in this type for automotive use. If you can get nickel cadmium batteries at a price you can afford, by all means use them. Remember that your batteries in series must deliver 120 volts for full utility of your wind power system.

MORE ADVICE ABOUT BATTERIES

Most home windmill installations generating power require batteries to provide 24 hours of service during conditions when there is no wind, or when the wind generator must be serviced.

This brings up the important point that your windmill should have a *brake* so that you can stop it when you need to.

For 24 hours of standby and an availability of 1,000 watts of power, you must specify battery cells with a rating of at least 260 ampere-hours. This figure is cited for two reasons:

- With 1,000 watts you can continue to operate essential appliances, including a refrigerator-freezer—although a 14-cubic foot frostless unit will draw about 600 watts.

- The 260 ampere-hours give you a safety factor in that your batteries should never be fully discharged in order to conserve their life. Never draw them down below 20% of full charge. Also, you'll find that drawing relatively small amounts of energy over a long period of time is better for your batteries than sudden discharges of a lot of power. For instance, at an 8-hour discharge rate, a typical marine battery is rated at 320 ampere-hours, while at a 72-hour discharge rate it's good for about 430 ampere-hours—about 30% greater.

Try not to discharge your batteries at a rate that's more than 15% of their ampere-hour rating. Control the charging rate carefully. For final charging, use a trickle charge that is about 2.17 volts per cell for lead acid batteries and 1.4 volts for NiCads.

Once a month give your batteries an equalization charge for 12 hours at 2.33 volts per cell for lead acid and 1.5 volts per cell for NiCads. This is to make sure all cells are brought up to full readiness. It means that the output of your voltage regulator must be adjustable, as stated before.

If this seems like a lot of advice about batteries, it's because your rack of storage batteries is one of the most expensive items in your system and also one of the most important for reliable home power. As to cost, the 1,000-watt standby set of batteries will range in price from about $800 for cheap types (meant for cars), to $1,500 for medium grade (high-quality automobile), batteries and $3,000 for the best quality. This is for 120 volts and 260 ampere-hours per cell, as previously mentioned. In batteries, as in solar collector panels, you get what you pay for.

FUSE BOX OR CIRCUIT BREAKER

Any DIY person with a small amount of electrical experience will understand the need for this kind of protection between the electric supply and the demand. It's illegal —and dangerous—to omit such protective devices, which are available from any hardware, electrical, or department store.

If your battery bank is capable of 1,000-watt storage, then it would be sensible to use fuses or breakers no larger than 15 amperes rating.

INVERTERS FOR AC APPLIANCES

There are rotary inverters of the electro-mechanical type, consisting of a motor operating on DC from your batteries and a generator supplying 120 volts AC. However, these units have relatively low efficiency, typically 60%, and thus waste battery power. Also they have brushes, which wear out and must be replaced. If you can put up with these disadvantages and can maintain your inverter yourself, this is the lowest cost unit you can buy. Very likely you can find a good used inverter at a bargain price.

If, however, you want a system with greatest efficiency and least maintenance, you'll select a solid-state inverter that has no moving parts and uses transistors and/or silicon controlled rectifiers (SCRs) to convert DC to AC. Again, there is a choice between good and best. There are good solid-state inverters with square-wave output which will supply AC that's adequate for many purposes but will result in some heating of electric motors and distortion of your stereo system's output.

The best and most expensive solid-state inverters have a filtered output so that the AC is a relatively pure sine wave. Also, any inverter you buy should have protection against reverse current and voltage transients or surges, plus good frequency stability and high efficiency under both full-load and no-load conditions. A good inverter of this type that will handle up to 3,000 watts, which you're apt to need for any small array of household appliances all going on at once, will cost over $2,000. And if you want 3,000 watts of storage battery capacity with an 80% drawdown factor for 24 hours, your battery cells should be rated at about 800 ampere-hours.

Inverters are made by many manufacturers. Some of the best-known solid-state types are supplied by Globe-Union and Systron-Donner, but there are many other good makes.

General Comments

As you've learned, it's neither easy nor inexpensive to build a wind generator system. You must have a suitable dry storage area to house the electrical equipment such as the battery rack, fuse box, and inverter. Preferably this area should be reasonably cool in summer and not extremely cold in winter. Batteries, like human beings, do best in a moderate climate.

Also, it's well worthwhile to plan carefully which of your household electrical needs can be met by using DC power from your batteries and which must have AC. There is an excellent list and many useful suggestions in the book *Wind Power* by Charles D. Syverson and John G. Symons, Jr., a good manual for the planning of wind generators.

Use Solar Energy Too

One major suggestion is to use *solar energy* for your home heating, hot water—and cool-

FIGURE 12—2.   Campground Using Combined Solar and Wind Energy in Arizona. Sunpower Systems

ing, if your home requires it. These tasks are performed far better and less expensively by a solar energy system than by electricity developed by wind for these purposes. Figure 12-2 shows a combined solar and windmill installation.

One other point: be sure to include an auxiliary engine generator in the same building with your wind power unit's electrical equipment. It's not economical to have a battery bank capable of more than 24 hours of wattage for your home, farm, or ranch's electrical necessities. Beyond that period it's far more efficient to rely on a gasoline or diesel generator. Furthermore, there may be breakdowns in your windmill system, and there certainly will be times when you will want to shut the system down

for periodic maintenance. Also, depending on your location, you may have several windless days in a row.

To reiterate a significant point, using solar and wind energy to complement each other makes very good sense in many rural locations. In this way a DIY handy person can make his or her household independent of up to 100% of other energy sources. That not only gives a fine feeling, but there's a better than 50-50 chance that you'll save money and be far better off in the long run. A survey among 2,700 midwestern farmers during the period 1967-70 showed that 81% had experienced power outages averaging 10 hours each, with more than four outages per farm.

Big Windmill Experiments

There are many lively things happening in windmill design. NASA-Lewis Research Center at Sandusky, Ohio, has built a huge machine with blades 125 feet in diameter and weighing 50 tons. This machine, with its aerodynamic and computer-checked design, produces 100 kW from winds off Lake Erie. There is a self-contained generator within the ballasted housing aft of the windmill's propeller blades, and power is delivered to the base of the tower in the conventional manner through slip rings.

The blades and hub assembly for this 100-kW machine, called MOD-OA, were constructed by Lockheed-California in Burbank. This huge wind generator has been operated successfully to deliver synchronous 60-Hz AC in phase with the local utility network near Cleveland by NASA engineers. It has also operated in phase with a small diesel generator, and is being used as a test for new and advanced components.

A much larger 1.5 MW wind turbine, called MOD-1, is being developed by General Electric under the direction of NASA-Lewis. Plans for it include a rotor 200 feet in diameter designed to perform best at an average 18 miles per hour wind velocity. Subcontractor for the blade and hub is Hamilton Standard, long a maker of aircraft propellers and a division of United Technology in Connecticut.

Government studies indicate that wind generators in this size range will provide the lowest cost electricity produced by the wind—at a price between 2 cents and 6 cents per kWh. According to Dr. Louis V. Divone, head of ERDA's wind energy office, it's going to take marked improvements in equipment design, and more widespread adoption by utilities of wind power as an added source of electricity, to bring the cost down.

The town of Clayton, New Mexico, has been selected as the site for the first MOD-AO machine to be used on a regular commercial basis to supply electricity. This is a 200-kW wind turbine, similar to that being tested by NASA near Cleveland, and will be installed in late 1977. Another site will be selected from some 17 candidate communities for the second commercial MOD-AO installation. This larger MOD-1 will begin delivering its 1.5 MW to the chosen town in 1978.

An amusing sidelight is that 65 electric utilities have offered sites for these giant wind turbines. But not a single one has shown any interest in buying such a big wind generator. Companies like Lockheed, GE, and Kaman Aircraft are capable of building these huge units, but won't get into production until they can get orders. The utilities want guaranteed reliability and low cost. The NASA program is trying to stimulate interest on both sides and break this logjam.

A new Vertical Axis Wind Turbine (VAWT), which is 55 feet in diameter, stands on a base 15 feet high, and is as tall as a 6-story building, is shown in Figure 12-3. This novel wind generator shaped like a giant eggbeater owes its original design to a Frenchman, G. Darrieux, but the VAWT pictured here was created and patented by three Sandia Laboratories engineers, B. F. Blackwell, L. V. Feltz, and R. C. Maydew.

One of the improvements resulting from construction of a prototype 15 feet in diameter is a segmented blade having a curved member in the middle and straight members at each end. As a result the turbine blades behave like a giant skip rope or "troposkien." The VAWT doesn't need a blade-feathering device to protect it from high winds and to ensure synchronous output. Such device is unnecessary because the VAWT is electrically synchronized, operates at constant speed, and will accept wind from any direction with the blades driving into the wind due to aerodynamic lift. Generating equipment for this VAWT is placed at ground level, reducing tower costs.

The sizable wind turbine shown in Figure 12-3 delivers 30 kW in a 22 mile an hour wind and 60 kW in a 28 mile an hour wind. As indicated, a major advantage is that the VAWT delivers synchronized 60 Hz AC

FIGURE 12-3. Vertical Axis Wind Turbine (VAWT), Shaped Like a Giant
Eggbeater, Is as Tall as a 6-Story Building

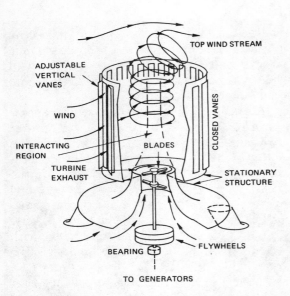

FIGURE 12-4. Vortex Tower for Omni-directional Winds. By Grumman Aerospace

FIGURE 12-5. Diffuser-Augmented Wind Turbine. By Grumman Aerospace

power suitable for feeding directly into a power grid. A wind turbine twice as large, 111 feet in diameter and capable of delivering 120 kW, will be operating in 1978. These wind generators appear most promising as ways to supplement electric utilities' power, especially in windy areas, at relatively low cost.

Illustrated in Figure 12-4 is a vortex tower wind turbine sponsored, like the VAWT and other large wind generators, by ERDA. This unit was designed by Dr. Jim Yen of Grumman Aerospace. A turbine placed inside the vortex, an area of low pressure resembling the "eye" of a hurricane, doesn't suffer from stresses like those in most other wind machines. Engineers ultimately expect to get 10 MW of electric power from a large version of this vortex tower.

Still another interesting Grumman design is the diffuser-augmented wind turbine shown in Figure 12-5. A divergent duct surrounds the rotor and creates a low-pressure area behind the wind machine. Thus, more air is drawn through the rotor, making it possible to double power output.

A device more than 40 years old invented by Julius D. Madaras has recently been revived and is being evaluated as still another way to use wind energy to generate electricity. In an ERDA-funded program headed by Dale E. Whitford at the University of Dayton Research Institute in Ohio, cylindrical rotors 90 feet high are mounted on railroad cars running on a circular track. When the wind blows against the rotors, the train moves and electricity is produced by generators attached to the wheels of the cars. This concept, first proposed by Madaras during the Great Depression of the early thirties, is said to have been abandoned for lack of money—not for lack of merit. Utilities funded the original experiment partway. Now it appears possible to generate as much as 100 MW with such a program.

Smaller Wind Generators

Numerous manufacturers are working on much smaller wind generators, which appear to be most attractive for remote locations such as farms, ranches, and mountain and beach homes where the average wind velocity year-round is perhaps 15 miles an hour or more. When you install a wind generator and a Total Energy Solar System, you're making the most of free and renewable energy from sun and wind—with an investment that seems certain to have a bigger payoff year after year as the prices of fossil fuels continue to climb.

A program to test various types of smaller wind generators has been established by ERDA at Rocky Flats, Colorado, with technical direction supplied by Rockwell International. "Wind machines now cost between 4 and 5 times as much to produce kilowatts as the least expensive conventional energy sources," says Donald A. Wiederecht of Rockwell, "but with increased interest in them and greater production, the cost is bound to come down."

On Cuttyhunk Island, Massachusetts, a 200-kW wind turbine has been installed by WTG Energy Systems of Angola, New York. This wind generator, called the MP 1-200, is an up-wind 3-bladed unit capable of producing 200 kW of electric power in a 28-mile an hour wind. Blade rotation begins at a wind velocity of 8 miles an hour. The rotor has a diameter of 89 feet and a sweep area of 5,026 square feet. It is mounted on a pinned-truss tower 80 feet high made of Cor-Ten steel. Total height of the machine to the top blade tip is 120 feet. A steel cabin 36 feet long houses gearbox, generator, and controls.

Quoted in *Solar Engineering* in May 1977, Alan Wellikoff of WTG said: "If the performance of the system is satisfactory, Cuttyhunk Power & Light Company will cover the cost of this installation." He added that this may be one of the largest commercial wind turbines in operation now. Production units made by WTG will range in size from 25 kW to 500 kW. Principal market is expected to be small applications at condominiums, industrial parks, and island locations.

Electric power for a city-owned 6,000-square foot garage in Winsted, Connecticut,

will soon be furnished by a wind generator. Francis Kane, director of the town's public works department, says the garage will house 12 public vehicles and will require no commercial power.

Along the Alaska pipeline, wind generators are being used to supply electric power for the communications system, while the state of Alaska is furnishing wind generators to three villages on a test basis. In the same area and in many other states, wind generators are being used to operate sawmills as well as to power irrigation pumps.

In England a windpower plant with blades based on helicopter technology is being developed by Wind Energy Supply Co., Ltd. This firm is planning to produce heat instead of electricity from the wind. Several sizes of wind units, starting with a rotor diameter of 3.65 meters (about 12 feet), will be produced using hydraulic power generated at the masthead and transmitting this power to the ground. Then this power may be converted into thermal energy for space heating systems, or it can be used to drive a heat pump with a hydraulic motor. A wide range of domestic and industrial uses is predicted by this company, which is a joint venture of Servotec, Ltd., of Redhill, Surrey, and Control Technology, Ltd., of Peacehaven, Sussex.

Recently the ruler of Dhofar, the southern province of Oman in southeastern Arabia, has employed the Princeton Energy Consulting Group, a New Jersey firm, to design solar and wind energy equipment— using oil profits to conserve energy in his country. Because clouds obscure the sun for long periods during the monsoon season, the first phase of this project involves using wind generators to drive water pumps, produce electricity, heat water, and air condition buildings in a nation about the size of Utah.

Electronic Advances

Several engineers, including Dr. William Hughes of Oklahoma State University, who's testing Tom Chalk's bicycle-wheel design and has built a bigger version, as well as John Roesel of Precise Power, have achieved designs for constant-frequency generators. This can result in some very important advances for two reasons:

- It will permit successful big wind generators in the megawatt class to feed precise 60-Hz power into utility lines despite wide variations in wind speed.

- Eventually, a less complex AC generator for home use, connected directly to your windmill, will make it possible to feed useful 120-volt AC to your home without some of the present expensive electrical equipment like the inverter.

It should be mentioned that NASA, in addition to its research in big windpower, also has a program at its Langley Research Center in Virginia aimed at developing a useful home wind machine and tower that can be made to sell for about $1,000—not counting the electrical system.

New Low-Cost Wind Generator

Kedco, Inc., of Inglewood, California, offers the Kedco 1200 wind-powered electric generator at a price of $1,695 f.o.b. factory. This relatively new design shown in Figure 12-6 has the following specifications:

- It delivers 1200 watts at a wind speed of 21 miles an hour. This power is supplied as 85 amperes at 14.4 volts, a good level for charging your batteries directly.

- It will charge your batteries at a minimum wind speed of 7 miles per hour.

- There are three 12-foot diameter blades made of aluminum and with a good aerodynamic design.

- A mechanical governor is provided, with automatic blade-feathering to control centrifugal overspeeds.

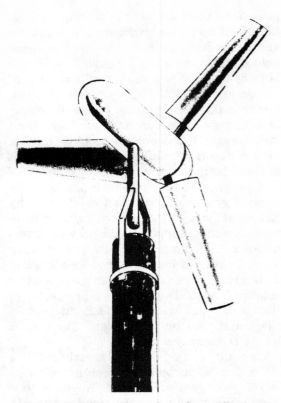

FIGURE 12-6. New Low-Cost Wind Generator

- Standard equipment furnished in the $1,695 kit includes the blades, governor, carriage, cowling, 85-ampere alternator, regulator, drive chain, lolly shaft, and tower adapter.

The wind generator blades mount downwind of the tower. Optional material available from Kedco includes a lolly commutator, tower, and inverter. Kedco supplies a warranty of one year, including parts and labor, for the wind generator, except that the alternator is covered by its manufacturer's specified warranty. There are detailed assembly and operating instructions furnished in the Kedco 1200 manual.

Wind Power, Box 233, Mankato, Minnesota 56001, publishes a good book on planning your wind generator, and also provides a practical consulting service for your specific needs.

Glossary of Technical Terms

ABS: (Acrylonitrile butadiene styrene) Black plastic material used to make pipes suitable for carrying sun-heated water in solar space heating and cooling, hot water, and swimming pool installations.

Absorber: Black material which absorbs heat from sunlight.

Absorption chiller: Refrigeration system used in solar cooling of buildings where sun-heated water, usually above 190°F, provides the operating energy. See complete description in Chapter 6.

Accumulator: Small tank installed in the return pipe from the circulation pump in a liquid-type solar heating system. Allows for expansion and contraction of water with temperature changes, provides a convenient place for air to be purged from the system, and makes sure the pump will always be primed for starting.

Ambient: Surrounding atmosphere. Thus, *ambient temperature* means temperature of the atmosphere at a particular location.

Anemometer: Instrument used to measure wind velocity.

Anodized: Coated with protective film on metal (usually aluminum) deposited by chemical or electrolytic methods to prevent corrosion.

Aquastat: Valve automatically controlled by temperature of the fluid, usually water, flowing through it.

Automatic damper: Device which cuts off the flow of hot or cold air to or from a room when the thermostat indicates that the room is sufficiently warm or cool.

Azimuth: Angle of horizontal deviation, measured clockwise; or a bearing from a standard direction, as from north or south.

Batt: Sheet of insulating material such as fiberglass.

BTU: (British Thermal Unit) Quantity of heat required to raise the temperature of one pound of water one degree Fahrenheit at 39.2°F.

Bushings: Removable cylindrical linings for an opening, such as the end of a pipe. These linings limit the size of the opening, resist abrasion, and act as a watertight guide. Thus, when two different sizes of pipe are mated, one or more bushings might be used.

Carryover or **Carrythrough:** Term used in designing solar installations, a measure of the number of days without sunshine during which the heat storage system can provide adequate space heating and domestic hot water.

CdS: (Cadmium sulphide) Material used in one type of solar cell.

CFM: (Cubic feet per minute) Measure of air flow in air-type solar heating systems.

Check valve: One-way valve usually used in liquid-type solar heating systems to prevent heated water from going through a pipe in an undesirable direction.

Coach screw: Resembles a carriage bolt; a wood screw with a round head and square shank above the screw threads.

Collector: Sandwich-like structure used in solar systems; includes a black-surface absorber to absorb solar heat. Detailed descriptions and drawings of many types of collectors used with liquid and air systems are included in this book.

Concentrator: Optical system used to concentrate sun's rays on a focal point or plane so as to increase solar heating in that focal area.

Condensate: Liquid produced from a gas, usually by cooling action in a condenser.

Conduction: Transfer of heat by contact with hot body.

Connecting socket (for pipe): Holder of metal or plastic, threaded to mate with one or more pieces of pipe. Section of pipe may have a male thread at one end; this is attached to a connecting socket having a female thread of the same pitch.

Convection: Transfer of heat energy by circulation of a liquid or gas.

Convector: Finned heated tubular unit, (e.g., steam or water radiator) used in space heating systems.

COP: (Coefficient of performance) Describes performance of a heat pump. When a pump can provide 3 BTU of heat energy for every 1 BTU of electrical energy required to drive its compressor, the pump's COP is said to be 3. See Chapter 4 for description of heat pump operation.

Degree day: A measure of the average annual temperature of a site; number of degrees below 65°F maintained as the average temperature of a specific site during one 24-hour period. E.g., if the average temperature on January 25 at your home is 40°F, this is a 25-degree day.

Dessicant: A water-absorbing material such as calcium chloride. Dessicant-type spacers may be used to keep condensation from forming in a solar collector.

Differential thrmostat: Automatic electric control system. Electronic control signal is produced by a preset differential between temperatures measured by sensors (thermometers) at 2 separated points. In a typical solar heating system, liquid- or air-type, temperatures compared are measured at the outlet point of the solar collectors and at the outlet of the thermal storage system. See Chapter 9 for details.

Diode: In electronics, a device conducting electricity in only one direction. See Chapter 7 for a description of a "Thermic Diode," passive system for solar heating and cooling.

Downpoint: Temperature at which useful heat can no longer be taken from storage. In an air-type solar heating system, useful heat can be taken from rock storage bin or eutectic bin at temperatures as low as 75°F. In liquid-type solar heating systems, except those including a heat pump, downpoint is at least 90°F.

Duct: Plastic or metal pipe, carefully insulated, used in this context for carrying air in an air-type solar heating system.

Dynamic head: Pressure differential between two points in fluid system based on vertical distance between these points, measured while the system is dynamic and the fluid is flowing.

Edge retaining system: Channel holding in place the various layers of a solar collector.

Electron: Negatively charged particle constituting a part or parts of each atom but existing outside the atomic nucleus.

Electroplating: Process of putting a metallic coating or plating on a base material, usually metal or plastic, by electrodeposition.

Emissivity: Relative power of a surface to emit heat by radiation, or the ratio of radiant heat energy emitted by a surface to that emitted by a black body (considered to have almost perfect heat absorption and therefore very low emissivity) when the given surface and the black body are at the same temperature.

Eutectic material: Chemical having the property of changing from a solid to a liquid at a relatively low temperature while maintaining a constant temperature. Eutectic liquid then stores the heat energy which caused the transformation until liquid returns to solid form and gives up heat. Eutectic salts, stored in plastic tubes or trays, are used as thermal reservoirs to store and then release solar heat.

Fan-coil system: Space heating unit containing a coil, usually of copper, filled with water at a typical temperature of 140°F, and also containing a fan which blows air over the hot-water coil on command of a thermostat. See Chapter 4 for details.

Flashing: 1. Sheet metal used in waterproofing roof valleys or ridges. 2. (in absorption chiller cycle): Abrupt change from liquid to gas when liquid strikes a hot surface. Water is flashed into steam.

Float air vent: Valve placed at the outlet of an array of liquid-type solar collectors, and containing a float so that pressure of the sun-heated liquid automatically purges air from the system. Air escapes from this valve, usually when the collectors are first filled with liquid.

Fresnel lens: Large lens, now usually made of plastic, scored so as to produce many small lenses which concentrate sunlight at a focal point or along a focal plane.

GaAs: (Gallium arsenide) Material used in an efficient kind of solar cell. See Chapter 11.

Gasket: Piece of solid material, usually metal, rubber, plastic, or asbestos, placed between two pieces of pipe to make the joint fluid-tight.

Gate valve: Used to regulate the flow of the main supply of water.

Geosynchronous orbit: Orbit of a satellite so designed that the satellite is always above the same area of Planet Earth. Also referred to as a "geostationary orbit."

Glazing: Transparent covering (e.g., glass or plastic) for a solar collector, window, or skylight.

GPM, GPH: Gallons per minute, and gallons per hour, respectively.

Grouting: Filling, finishing, or mending of cracks with a thin mortar or caulking compound to make the surface water-resistant.

Header or header pipe: Section of pipe which carries the main liquid flows at the top and bottom of a solar collector, and into which are fitted smaller pipes extending the length of the collector. Bottom header carries cool water to the collector, top header carries sun-heated water away from it. Header is usually at least 1-1/2 inches in diameter and may be 2-inch pipe.

Heat exchanger: Device for efficient transfer of heat energy from one liquid to another, from air to liquid, or from liquid to air. Many examples of heat exchangers used in solar systems are described and diagrammed in this book.

Heat pump: System using a compressible refrigerant which makes it possible to transfer heat from a source (e.g. heated water, air, earth) to another area, such as the rooms of a building. Process is reversible. See diagrams and description in Chapters 4 and 8.

Heat sink: Structure designed to absorb excess heat. Example: water pipes placed under an array of solar cells heated by sunlight pouring through Fresnel lenses. The water keeps the silicon solar cells cool enough to operate efficiently. See the description in Chapter 11.

Heliopyranometer: Instrument for measuring sun's heat energy at any suitable site.

Heliostat: Mirror or array of mirrors, usually controlled by computer, placed as one of many heliostats which focus solar energy on a receiver or boiler on a tower, heating liquid in this boiler to very high temperature under pressure. See illustrations and descriptions in Chapter 10.

Hole: Minute area in a semiconductor, with a positive charge equal in absolute value to negative charge on an electron.

Hose coupler: Metal or plastic device for joining two pieces of hose or rigid pipes by means of screw threads in the coupler which mate with threaded connections on the hoses or pipes.

Hydronic: Solar heating system in which the heat transfer fluid is liquid, usually water, or a combination of an antifreeze mixture in the collectors and water in the storage and heating system.

Hygrometer: Instrument for measuring relative humidity of the atmosphere.

Hysteresis: Time lag exhibited by a body in reacting to changes in the forces affecting it.

Hz: (Hertz) Unit of frequency used in electronic measurement equal to one cycle or one wave length of electromagnetic energy per second.

Incident: Referring to solar radiation, those rays falling on or striking a surface.

Infrared: That part of the invisible spectrum of light energy below the red end of the visible spectrum. The infrared region consists of wave lengths from 0.8 micron to 1,000 microns and contains most of the heat energy from the sun.

Inhibitor: Chemical included in the liquid used in solar collectors to prevent corrosion of fluid-carrying pipes.

Insolation: Solar radiation received over a given area, and usually expressed in langleys (defined below).

Inverter: Electrical power supply which converts DC into AC power.

Joist: One of several small parallel beams made of wood, steel, or reinforced concrete and used to support ceilings, roofs, and floors.

Joule: Work done by a force of 1 newton over a distance of 1 meter. 1 joule=1 watt-second.

K: (Kelvin) Temperature scale equals 273 + degrees Celsius (centigrade).

kW: (Kilowatt) 1,000 watts. One watt represents the power in a circuit where a current of one ampere flows across a potential difference of one volt.

Langley: Measure of insolation. One langley equals one calorie per square centimeter. See conversion tables following Glossary for useful equivalents.

LiBr: (Lithium Bromide) Compound mixed with water and used in absorption chillers supplied with heat energy from solar collectors.

Manifold: See "header."

Micron: One-millionth of a meter.

Mil: One-thousandth of an inch.

MW: (Megawatts) One million watts; 1,000 kilowatts correspond to 1 megawatt (MW). MWe means 1 megawatt of electrical energy, and is an abbreviation used in large solar thermic generating systems to distinguish between megawatts of thermal energy, produced by the sun's heat concentrated on a boiler, and the lesser amount in megawatts of electrical energy—reduced because of losses in the turbogenerator, distribution network, and other parts of the system.

Ozone: Form of oxygen having three atoms instead of two; found in the atmosphere in relatively small quantities, but forming a useful layer in the upper atmosphere called the ozonosphere, which filters out part of the solar ultraviolet radiation.

Photon: Elementary particle of electromagnetic radiation which has zero mass and charge at rest and a spin of 1.

Photovoltaic: Characteristic of materials which generate electrical energy when they are exposed to radiant energy such as sunshine.

Pinch valve: Manual or solenoid-operated valve used typically in a solar heating system for a swimming pool to pinch off or stop the direct flow pumped through the filter and back to the pool. When this pinch valve is closed, water flows through the solar collectors and then back to the pool.

Plenum: Duct which, when heated, causes movement of air.

Psia: (Pounds per square inch absolute) Units for measuring pressure, whether hydraulic (liquids) or pneumatic (gases), made without including the effect of atmospheric pressure, which is 15 psi at sea level.

Pyranometer: Instrument for measuring the heat radiated from a body.

Radiation: Process by which energy is emitted from one body, transmitted across an intervening space, and absorbed by another body.

Rankine cycle: Complete expansion cycle of a gas brought into a structure like a turbine engine, where the gas is compressed and then expands rapidly to give off energy.

Reflective loss: Energy which strikes a surface and is not absorbed but is reflected from it.

Retrofitting: Process of installing a solar heating system in an existing building, usually to take over a major part of the heating load from a conventionally fueled system.

Runner: Strip of wood mounted on a roof or wall to which one end of a solar collector, or a rack holding a solar collector, is securely attached.

Selective black paint: Paint formulated to be more absorbent of the long infrared wave lengths of sunlight than commercial black paint, and therefore more efficient in absorbing solar heat. Many experienced solar engineers doubt the value of selective black paints or coatings.

Semiconductor: Materials like silicon which are neither as conductive of electricity and heat as metals, nor as insulative as glass or ceramic. Most useful photovoltaic materials used in solar cells are semiconductors.

Sensor: Probe used in the context of this book to measure temperature, although there are sensors for measuring all kinds of physical phenomena.

Si: (Silicon) Element that is one of the most common on Earth since sand is largely silicon dioxide.

Solarate: Coined word meaning "to equip a house with a solar heating system, or at least a solar hot water heater."

Solenoid: Electromechanical device so designed that when electric current is applied to a coil of wire wound around a cylinder, the electromotive force causes a bar or plunger inside the cylinder to move.

SPT: (Solar Power Tower) Big solar electric plant. See Chapter 10.

Static head: Pressure differential between two points in a fluid system in terms of vertical distance between these two points, measured while the system is static.

STES: (Solar Total Energy System) System providing electricity as well as space heating and cooling and hot water from the sun. See Chapter 10.

Sump: In liquid-type gravity solar heating system, a sump is a small tank into which fluid from the collectors may be drained. The sump may perform the functions of an accumulator (see definition).

Tempering valve: Mixing valve set by the user and placed at the outlet of the domestic hot water system (input to home) so that some cold water is mixed with the hot water, heated either by the sun or conventional fuel. This keeps scalding water out of your faucets.

Therm: 100,000 BTU.

Thermistor: Resistor (electronic component) which changes in resistance value with changes in temperature. A negative-coefficient thermistor decreases in resistance as the temperature rises.

Thermosiphoning: Upward movement of heated fluid through a pipe. This phenomenon is very useful in making a solar water heater if you don't want to use a pump. See Chapters 2 and 3.

Thermostat: Control which delivers an electrical signal when the temperature reaches a preset level; this signal usually turns on a pump, fan or both in solar heating systems.

Ton of cooling: 12,000 BTU per hour. Term is derived from the amount of heat energy required to convert a ton of water into ice at 32°F during a 24-hour period.

Torr: Unit of pressure equal to the pressure required to support a column of mercury 1mm high at 0°C and standard gravity.

Turbulator: Coined word describing small obstacles placed on the surface of the absorber in an air-type collector to increase air turbulence and thus get more heat from the solar collector. See Chapter 5.

Turnbuckle: Hardware device consisting of a link with screw threads at each end. This link is turned to bring the two objects connected by the turnbuckle closer together.

Two-outlet heater: Water heater having one outlet going to the pipes for a domestic hot water system, and the other through a separate pipe to an insulated storage tank.

U.L.: (Underwriters Laboratory) Organization which certifies the safety as to possible fire hazard of a wide variety of electrical and electronic equipment.

Ultraviolet: Upper invisible region of light, with short wave lengths extending from 0.4 microns (4,000 Angstroms).

Vacuum-evaporated film: Film formed on a sheet or plate by electrical evaporation of a metal or alloy in an evacuated chamber.

Vapor barrier: Covering of aluminum foil or plastic sheet on one side of a batt of fiberglass used for insulation. This covering prevents water vapor from permeating the insulation and thus reducing its efficiency.

Zenith: In this text, referring to the position of the sun at noon, its maximum elevation.

Useful Conversions

ENERGY

1 BTU = 251.99 calories = 0.00029287 kWh
1 calorie = 0.003968 BTU
1 kilowatt-hour (kWh) = 3414.43 BTU

ENERGY DENSITY

1 langley = 1 calorie/square centimeter = 3.68669 BTU/square foot
1 BTU/square foot = 0.271246 calorie/ square centimeter

POWER AND POWER DENSITY

1 watt = 1 joule/second
1 BTU/hour = 0.292875 watt
1 watt/square centimeter = 3,172 BTU/ square foot/hour

FLOW RATE

1 cubic foot/minute (CFM) = 471.947 cubic centimeters/second (Air)
1 liter/minute = 0.0353 cubic feet/minute = 0.2642 gallon/minute (Liquid)

VOLUME AND WEIGHT

1 gallon = 231 cubic inches = 3.7854 liters
1 pound = 0.45359 kilogram
1 ton = 907 kilograms

LENGTH AND VELOCITY

1 foot = 0.3048 meter
1 yard = 0.9144 meter
1 mile = 1.6093 kilometers
1 foot/minute = 0.508 centimeter/second

TEMPERATURE

$°C = 5/9 (°F - 32)$

AREA

1 square foot = 0.0929 square meter
1 square meter = 10.7639 square feet = 1.196 square yards

Bibliography

American Institute of Architects Research Corporation. *Innovation in Solar Thermal House Design.* Prepared by Donald Watson (Guilford, Conn.). Washington, D.C., 1975

_____. *Solar Energy: An Introduction.* Washington, D.C., 1975

_____. *Solar Energy and Housing.* Prepared by Giffels Associates, Inc. (Detroit). Washington, D.C., 1975.

_____. *Solar Energy Housing Design.* Prepared by Total Environmental Action (Harrisville, N.H.). Washington, D.C., 1975.

_____. *Solar Heated Houses for New England.* Prepared by Massdesign (Cambridge, Mass.). Washington, D.C., 1975.

_____. *Solar Heating and Cooling Demonstration Act Information Packet.* Washington, D.C., 1975.

_____. *Solar-Oriented Architecture.* Washington, D.C., 1975.

_____. *The Design of Solar Heated and Cooled Dwellings.* Washington, D.C., 1975.

Anderson, Bruce and Michael Riordan *Solar Home Book*, Harrisville, N.H.: Cheshire Books, 1976.

Arctander, Erik H. Solar-MEC: one box heats and cools your house. *Popular Science*, January 1975.

Association of Heating, Refrigeration and Air Conditioning Engineers (ASHRAE), *Energy Conservation in New Building Design.* New York, N.Y., 1975.

Backus, Charles E. Current developments in solar energy. Paper presented at American Petroleum Institute meeting, Chicago, May 1977.

Backus, Charles E., D. L. Evans, and E. L. Ralph. Photovoltaic systems using sunlight concentration. *Heliotechnique Development*, Development Analysis Associates, Inc., Cambridge, MA, 1976.

Baer, Steve. *Sunspots*, Albuquerque, N.M.: Albuquerque, 1975.

Barber, Everett M. and Donald Watson, AIA. *Design Criteria for Solar-Heated Buildings.* Guilford, CT: Sunworks, Inc., 1975.

Beason, Robert G. *Mechanix Illustrated*, December 1976.

Bockris, John O. M. *Energy: The Solar-Hydrogen Alternative*, New York: John Wiley & Sons, 1975.

Braun, G. W., E. S. Davis, R. L. French, and A. S. Hirschberg. *Assessment of Solar Heating and Cooling for an Electric Utility Company.* Southern California Edison Company, Los Angeles, and Jet Propulsion Laboratory, Pasadena, CA, 1975.

Daniels, Farrington, *Direct Use of the Sun's Energy.* Westminster, MD: Ballantine Books.

Daniels, George. *Solar Homes and Sun Heating.* New York: Harper & Row, 1976.

de Winter, Francis. *How To Design and Build a Solar Swimming Pool Heater.* New York: Copper Development Association, 1975.

285

_____. *Solar Energy and the Flat Plate Collector.* New York: Copper Development Association, 1974.

Edenburn, Michael W. Performance analysis of a cylindrical parabolic focusing collector and comparison with experimental results. Albuquerque, NM: Sandia Laboratories, 1975.

Edmondson, William B. *SolarSan Water Heaters and Their Application.* San Diego, CA, 1974.

Foster, W. M. *Homeowner's Guide to Solar Heating and Cooling.* Blue Ridge Summit, PA: Tab Books, 1976.

Golobic, Robert A. and Walter S. White. Analysis and application of the pivotable solar heat exchanger window wall. International Solar Energy Society meeting, Orlando, FL, June 1977.

Halacy, Daniel S. *The Coming Age of Solar Energy.* New York: Harper & Row, 1973.

Hickok, Floyd. *Handbook of Solar and Wind Energy.* Boston: Cahners Books International, 1975.

Hottel, H. C. and B. B. Woertz. *The Performance of Flat-Plate Solar-Heat Collectors.* Solar Energy Research Project, publication No. 3. Cambridge, MA: Massachusetts Institute of Technology, 1940.

International Association of Plumbing and Mechanical Officials (IAPMO). *Uniform Solar Energy Code.* Los Angeles, CA, 1976.

Jet Propulsion Laboratory, California Institute of Technology, Pasadena. *Building Application of Solar Energy,* Volumes 1-4, sponsored by Southern California Edison Company, Los Angeles, 1975-76.

_____. *Low-Cost Silicon Solar Array Project Reports,* 1976-77.

James, L. W. and R. L. Moon. *GaAs Concentrator Solar Cells.* Palo Alto, CA: Varian Associates, 1975.

Kocivar, Ben. World's biggest windmill turns on for large-scale wind power. *Popular Science,* March 1976.

Lindsley, E. F. Windpower. *Popular Science,* July 1974.

Los Alamos Scientific Laboratory, University of California, Los Alamos, NM. *Pacific Regional Solar Heating Handbook,* 1976.

Lucas, Ted. *How To Build a Solar Heater.* Pasadena, CA: Ward Ritchie Press, 1975.

Mantell, Charles L. *Batteries and Energy Systems.* New York: McGraw-Hill, 1970.

McDonnell Douglas Astronautics Company, Huntington Beach, CA. *Central Receiver Solar Thermal Power System,* quarterly technical progress reports to ERDA. 1976-77.

_____. *Industrial Applications of Solar Energy,* reports to ERDA. 1976-77.

Mlavsky, Alexander I. *The Silicon Ribbon Solar Cell—A Way to Harness Solar Energy.* Waltham, MA: Mobil Tyco Solar Energy Corp., 1974.

National Technical Information Service, Springfield, VA. 1977.

N76-27671/POA. An Inexpensive Economical Solar Heating System for Homes. NASA — Langley Research Center.

ERDA 76-6/POA. National Program for Solar Heating & Cooling of Buildings. Energy Research & Development Administration.

TID-3351-R1P2/POA. Solar Energy: A Bibliography. Energy Research & Development Administration.

DSE-2322-1/POA. An Economic Analysis of Solar Water & Space Heating. Energy Research & Development Administration.

CONF-760633/POA. Solar Energy in Cold Climates. University of Detroit.

ERDA/NSF/07378/75/1/POA. Evaluation of the Potential Environmental Effects of Wind Energy System Development. Battelle Columbus Laboratories.

COO-2603-1/POA. Application Study of Wind Power Technology to the City of

Hart, Michigan. Michigan State University.

COO-2577-10/POA. Design, Construction, and Testing of a Residential Solar Heating and Cooling System. Colorado State University.

LA-5967/POA. Solar Heating Handbook for Los Alamos. Los Alamos Scientific Laboratory.

UCID-17086/POA. Flat-Plate Solar Collector Handbook—A Survey of Principles, Technical Data and Evaluation Results. Lawrence Livermore Laboratory.

PB-252 685/POA. Residential Hot Water Solar Energy Storage Subsystem. Stanford Research Institute.

CONF 75-1022/POA. Impact of Energy Production on Human Health. Energy Research & Development Administration.

NTIS/PS-76/0727/POA. Solar Space Heating and Air Conditioning. (A Bibliography with Abstracts) NTIS.

NTIS/PS-76/0393/POA. Solar Energy Collectors and Concentrators. (A Bibliography with Abstracts) NTIS.

ERDA-117. Solar Energy Subsystems Employing Isothermal Heat Storage Materials.

Palmer, Howard B. and Simion C, Kuo. Solar farms utilizing low-pressure closed-cycle gas turbines. Paper prepared for United Aircraft Research Laboratories, East Hartford, CT, 1974.

Piper Hydro, Inc. Conserve in Comfort. Anaheim, CA, 1975.

Ralph, E. L. and Ishaq M. Shahryar. Meeting electric power needs with photovoltaic power systems. Presented at International Conference of COMPLES, University of Petroleum and Minerals, Dhahran, Saudi Arabia, 1975.

Rau, Hans. Solar Energy. Edited and revised by D. J. Duffin. New York: MacMillan, 1964.

Salisbury, David F. It's all done with mirrors—and mills. Christian Science Monitor, Boston, April 22, 1977.

Sandia Laboratories, Albuquerque, NM:
Central Receiver Solar Thermal Power System, 1977.
Design Analysis of Asymmetric Solar Receivers, 1974.
Distribution of Direct and Total Solar Radiation Availabilities for the USA, 1976.
Selection of Parabolic Solar Collector Field Arrays, 1975.
Solar Collector Module Test Facility, 1977.
Solar Community Systems Analysis Projects, 1975.
Solar Total Energy Symposium Proceedings, 1977.

Schlesinger, Robert J. Solar Controls Applications Manual. North Hollywood, CA: Rho Sigma, 1977.

Schultz, Mort. Turned on by the sun, Popular Mechanics, February 1977.

Senn, James C. Solar Heating: Theory, Equipment and Systems Design. Northridge, CA: Sennergetics, 1977.

Shurcliff, William A. Solar Heated Buildings: A Brief Survey. Cambridge, MA: William A. Shurcliff, pub., 1977 (13th Edition).

Sonntag, Richard E. and Gordon J. Van Wylen. Introduction to Thermodynamics. New York: John Wiley & Sons, 1975.

Southern California Edison Company. Integration of Solar Thermal Power Plants into Electric Utility Systems. Rosemead, CA: 1976.

Southern California Gas Company, Los Angeles, CA. Minimum Energy Dwelling, 1976.

_____. Project Sage: Solar Assisted Gas Energy Project, 1976.

Sunworks, Inc. Design Criteria for Solar-Heated Buildings. Guilford, CT: 1974.

Telkes, Dr. Maria. Solar energy storage. ASHRAE Journal, 1974.

Thomason, Harry E. and Harry Lee Thomason, Jr., Solar House Plans: Solar House Heating and Air-Conditioning Systems, Solar Greenhouse and Swimming Pool. Barrington, NJ: Edmund Scientific Co., 1975.

Watson, Donald. *Designing and Building a Solar Home*. Charlotte, VT: Garden Way Publishing, 1977.

Weber, Eric R. On-site solar systems: a utility point of view. Phoenix, AZ: Arizona Public Service, 1975.

Recommended Periodicals featuring Solar Energy Information:

Solar Energy Digest, P. O. Box 17776, San Diego, CA 92117.

Solar Engineering, 8435 N. Stemmons Freeway, Suite 880, Dallas, TX 75247.

Solar Energy Intelligence Report, P. O. Box 1067, Silver Spring, MD 20910.

Solar Industry Index, Solar Energy Industries Association, 1001 Connecticut Ave., NW, Suite 632, Washington, DC 20036.

Solar Outlook, Observer Publishing Co., Canal Square, Washington, DC 20007

The Mother Earth News, 105 Stoney Mountain Road, Hendersonville, NC 28739.

Also *Mechanix Illustrated, Popular Mechanics, Popular Science.*

Appendix I:
Manufacturers of Solar Collectors and Wind Generators

Manufacturers of Liquid-Type Solar Collectors

Airtex Corporation
Sidney, OH
Albuquerque Western Solar Industries, Inc.
Rankin Rd. NE   Albuquerque, NM   87107
ALCOA
Pittsburgh, PA
Alten Associates, Inc.
Santa Clara, CA
American Building Center
3626 E. Cerritos   Los Alamitos, CA   90720
American Heliothermal Corporation
Denver, CO
American Solar Heat Corporation
Danbury, CT
American Solar King Corporation
Waco, TX
Ametek, Inc
Paoli, PA
Applied Sol Tech, Inc
P. O. Box 9111, Cabrillo Station
   Long Beach, CA   90810
Atlantic Solar Products
Reston, VA
A-Z Solar Products
200 E. 26th St.   Minneapolis, MN   55404
Berry Solar Products
Reston, VA
Berry Solar Products
Edison, NJ
Burke Industries, Inc.
2250 S. 10th St.   San Jose, CA   95112
Butler Ventamatic Corporation
Mineral Wells, TX

Calmac Manufacturing Corporation
Englewood, NJ
Chamberlain Manufacturing Co.
845 Larch Ave.   Elmhurst, IL   60540
Cole Solar Systems, Inc.
440A East St. Elmo Rd.
   Austin, TX   78745
Columbia Chase Solar Energy Division
55 High St.   Holbrook, MA   02343
CSI Solar Systems Division
12400 49th St. North   St. Petersburg,
   FL   33732
Daystar Corporation
90 Cambridge St.   Burlington, MA   01803
Edmund Scientific
101 E. Glouster Pike
   Barrington, NJ   08007
E & K Service Co.
16824 74th Ave. NE   Bothell, WA   98011
Energy Systems, Inc.
4570 Alvarado Canyon Rd.
   San Diego, CA   92111
Energex Corporation
5115 Industrial Rd.   Las Vegas, NE   89118
Energy Converters, Inc.
2501 N. Orchard Knob Ave.   Chattanooga
   TE   37406
Enertech Corp.
Golden, CO
Fafco, Inc.
Menlo Park, CA   94025
Flagala Corp.
Panama City, FL

Future Systems, Inc.
Lakewood, CO
General Electric Solar Division
P. O. Box 8555 Philadelphia PA   19101
General Energy Devices
Clearwater, FL   33516
Grumman Energy Systems
4175 Veterans Memorial Hwy
  Ronkonkoma NY   11799
Gulf Thermal Corp.
Sarasota, FL
Halstead & Mitchell
Highway 72 West   Scottsboro, AL   35768
Harrison Radiator Division
General Motors A&E Bldg. Lockport,
  NY   14094
Heilemann Electric
127 Mountainview Road
  Warren, NJ   07060
Helios Corporation
1313 Belleview Ave.
  Charlottesville, VA   22901
Heliotherm, Inc.
Lenni, PA
Hitachi America, Ltd.
437 Madison Ave.   New York, NY   10022
Honeywell, Inc.
Honeywell Plaza   Minneapolis, MN   55408
Ilse Engineering, Inc.
Duluth, MN
InterTechnology Solar Corporation
100 Main St.   Warrenton VA 22186
Kalwall Corporation
Solar Components Division   1111 Candia
  Rd   Manchester, NH   03103
Kastek Corporation
P. O. Box 8881   Portland, OR   97208
Lennox Industries, Inc.
P. O. Box 250   Marshalltown, IA 50158
Libby-Owens-Ford Technical Center
Toledo, OH
National Sun Systems, Inc.
St. Petersburg, FL
Natural Energy Systems
1001 Connecticut Ave. NW   Washington,
  D.C.   20036
Northrup, Inc.
Hutchins, TX

Olin Brass,
Shamrock St.   East Alton, IL   62024
Original Power Equipment Company
Garland, TX
Owen Enterprises, Inc.
436 North Fries Ave.
  Wilmington, CA   90744
Owens-Illinois, Inc.
P. O. Box 1035   Toledo, OH
Pipe Hydro, Inc.
2895 E. La Palma   Anaheim, CA   92806
Pleiad Industries, Inc.
West Branch, IA
PPG Industries, Inc.
One Gateway Center
  Pittsburgh, PA   15222
Raypak, Inc.
31111 Agoura Rd.
  Westlake Village, CA   91361
Refrigeration Research, Inc.
525 N. Fifth St.   Brighton, MI   48116
Revere Copper and Brass, Inc.
P. O. Box 151   Rome, NY   13440
Reynolds Metals Company
6601 West Broad St.
  Richmond, VA   23261
Scientific-Atlanta, Inc.
3845 Pleasantdale Rd.   Atlanta, GA   30340
Semco Solar Products
1054 N.E. 43rd St.
  Ft. Lauderdale, FL 33334
Simons Solar Environmental Systems, Inc.
Mechanicsburg, PA
Solar Applications, Inc.
San Diego, CA
Solar Comfort Systems
Bethesda, MD
Solar Corporation of America
Warrenton, VA
Solar Development, Inc.
4180 Westroads Dr.
  West Palm Beach, FL   33407
Solar Dynamics, Inc.
Dania, FL
Solar Energy Company
Merrimack, NH
Solar Energy, Inc.
12155 Magnolia Ave., 6-E
  Riverside, CA   92503

Solar Energy Products, Inc.
Gainesville, FL 32601
Solar Energy Systems
Carson, CA
Solar Energy Systems of Georgia
2616 Old Wesley Chapel Rd
Decatur, GA 30339
Solar Energytics, Inc.
Jasper, IN
Solar Equipment Sales Co.
Scarsdale, NY
Solar-Eye Products
Ft. Lauderdale, FL
Solar Farms
Stockton, KS
Solar Industries, Inc.
Monmouth Airport Industrial Park
Farmingdale, NJ 07727
Solar Living, Inc.
P. O. Box 15345 Austin, TX 78761
Solar Research Systems
Costa Mesa, CA 92626
Solar Shelter
Reading, PA
Solar Shingle
Straza Enterprises 1071 Industrial Place
El Cajon, CA 92020
Solar Sun, Inc.
235 N. 12th St. Cincinnati, OH 45210
Solar Systems Sales
Novato, CA
Solar II Enterprises
Los Gatos, CA
SolaPlay, Inc.
Whitewater, WI
Solarator, Inc.
Madison Heights, MI
Solaray Corporation
Honolulu, HI
Solarcoa, Inc.
2115 E. Spring St.
Long Beach, CA 90806
Solarmaster
722-D. W. Betteravia Rd.
Santa Maria, CA 93454
Solartec Corporation
8250 Vickers San Diego, CA 92111
Sol-R-Tech, Inc.
The Trade Center Hartford, VT 05047

Solus, Inc.
Houston, TX
Sol-Therm Corp.
7 West 14th St. New York, NY 10011
Southeastern Solar Systems, Inc.
1705J Bakers Ferry Rd.
Atlanta, GA 30336
Southwest Ener-Tech
3030 Valley View Blvd.
Las Vegas, NE 89102
State Industries Inc.
Ashland City TE 37015 and
Henderson, NE 89015
Sun Century Systems
Florence, AL
Sun Power Systems Ltd.
Sunnyvale, CA
Sun Source Inc.
9570 W. Pico Blvd.
Los Angeles, CA 90035
Sun Systems, Inc.
Eureka, IL
Sun Sponge
1288 Fayette St. El Cajon, CA 92020
Sunburst Solar Heating, Inc.
Menlo Park, CA 94025
Sundu Company
3319 Keys Lane Anaheim, CA 92804
Sunearth Inc.
Montgomeryville, PA
Sunsav Inc.
Lawrence, MA
Suntap Inc.
42 E. Dudley Town Road
Bloomfield, CT 06002
Sunwater Company Inc.
1654 Pioneer Way El Cajon, CA 92020
Sunworks Division of Enthone Inc.
P. O. Box 1004 New Haven, CT 06508
Tri-State Solar King Inc.
Adams, OK
Tranter, Inc.
735 E. Hazel St. Lansing, MI
United States Solar Systems Inc.
Los Angeles, CA
Wallace Company
Gainesville, GA
Ying Manufacturing Corp.
1957 W. 144th St. Gardena, CA 90249

Zomeworks
1212 Edith N.E.   Albuquerque, NM   87125
ZZ Corporation
10806 Kaylor St.   Los Alamitos, CA   90720

Manufacturers of Air-Type Solar Collectors

American Building Center
3626 E. Cerritos   Los Alamitos, CA   90720
American Heliothermal Corporation
Denver, CO
Champion Home Builders Co.
5573 E. North   Dryden, MI   48428
Future Systems, Inc.
Lakewood, CO
Kalwall Corporation
Solar Components Division   P. O. Box 237
   Manchester, NH   03105
NRG
Napoleon, OH
Solar Energy Inc.
12155 Magnolia Ave., 6-E
   Riverside, CA   92503
Solar Inc.
P. O. Box 246   Mead, NE   68041
Solar Store
Parker, SD
Solaron Corporation
4850 Olive St.   Commerce City, CO   80022
Sun Unlimited Research Corporation
P. O. Box 941   Sheboygan, WI   53081
Sunworks Division of Enthone Inc.
P. O. Box 1004   New Haven, CT   06508
Ying Manufacturing Corp.
1957 W. 144th St.   Gardena, CA   90249

Makers of Wind Generators

U.S. Companies:
American Wind Turbine
P. O. Box 446   St. Cloud, FL   32769
Dyna Technology Inc.
P. O. Box 3263   Sioux City, IA   51102
Grumman Aerospace Corporation
Bethpage, NY   11714

KEDCO Inc.
9016 Aviation Blvd.
   Inglewood, CA   90301
Rede
P. O. Box 212   Providence, RI   02901
Solar Wind Company
P. O. Box 7   East Holden, ME   04429
WTG Energy Systems Inc.
P. O. Box 87, 1 LaSalle St.
   Angola, NY

Foreign Firms:
Aerowatt,
S.A., 37 Reu Chanzy 75   Paris 11°, France
Domenico Sperandio & Ager
Via Cimarosa 13-21
   58022 Folonica (GR), Italy
Dunlite Electrical Co.
Division of Pye Industries   21 Frome St.
   Adelaide 5000, Australia
Electro Gmbh
St. Gallerstrasse 27
   Winterthur, Switzerland
Industrial Inst. Ltd.
Stanley Rd.   Bromley BR 2 9JF
   Kent, England
Lubing Maschinenfabrik
Ludwig Bening   P. O. Box 171
   D-2847 Barstorf   Vattyskland, Germany
F. L. Schmidt Co.
69 Skt Klemensuzj
   Hjallese, Denmark   5260
Wind Energy Supply Co., Ltd.
c/o Servotec Ltd.   Redhill
   Surrey, England

Wind Energy Distributors

Budgen & Associates
72 Broadview Ave.   Pointe Claire 710
   Quebec, Canada
Energy Alternatives
Box 223   Leverett, MA   01054
Enertech Corp.
P. O. Box 420   Norwich, VT   05055
Environmental Energies, Inc.
Copenisch, MI   48219
Garden Way Laboratories
P. O. Box 66   Charlotte, VT   05445

Independent Power Developers
Box 618   Noxon, MT   59853
Low Impact Technology
73 Molesworth St.
   Wadebridge, Cornwall, England
Penwalt Automatic Power
213 Hutcheson St.   Houston, TX   77003
Read Gas and Electric Co.
Box A   Guerneville, CA   65446
Sencenbaugh Wind Electric
Box 11174   Palo Alto, CA   94306
Solar Energy Co.
810 18th St. N.W.
   Washington, D.C.   20006
Windlite
Box 43   Anchorage, Alaska   99510

Useful Sources of Information

American Wind Energy Association
54468 CR 31   Bristol, IN   46507
Natural Power, Inc.
New Boston, NH   03070
Hans Meyer
Windwords   Box 329, Route 3
   Mukwonago, WI   53149
James B. DeKorne
c/o The Mother Earth News   P. O. Box 70
   Hendersonville, NC   28739

Appendix II:
Number of Sol-R-Tech Panels Required for Domestic Hot Water per Person

City	Approximate Latitude	Summer Panel Requirement (per person)	Winter Panel Requirement (per person)
Albuquerque, New Mexico	(35°)	0.5	1.4
Annette Island, Alaska	(55°)	1.2	4.0
Apalachicola, Florida	(30°)	0.7	1.2
Astroia, Oregon	(46°)	0.9	2.8
Atlanta, Georgia	(33°)	0.7	1.8
Barrow, Alaska	(71°)	1.3	175.4
Bethel, Alaska	(60°)	1.2	11.2
Bismarck, North Dakota	(47°)	0.7	2.9
Blue Hill, Massachusetts	(42°)	0.9	2.9
Boise, Idaho	(43°)	0.6	2.9
Boston, Massachusetts	(42°)	0.8	2.9
Brownsville, Texas	(26°)	0.6	1.2
Caribou, Maine	(47°)	0.9	4.0
Charleston, South Carolina	(33°)	0.7	1.5
Cleveland, Ohio	(41°)	0.8	3.2
Columbia, Missouri	39°)	0.7	2.3
Columbus, Ohio	(42°)	0.7	3.1
Davis, California	(38°)	0.6	2.1
Dodge City, Kansas	(38°)	0.6	1.6
East Lansing, Michigan	(42°)	0.8	3.7
East Wareham, Massachusetts	(42°)	0.9	2.4
Edmonton, Alberta	(53°)	0.9	4.6
El Paso, Texas	(32°)	0.5	1.3
Ely, Nevada	(39°)	0.6	1.8
Fairbanks, Alaska	(65°)	0.9	83.3
Fort Worth, Texas	(33°)	0.6	1.4
Fresno, California	(37°)	0.6	1.9
Gainesville, Florida	(29°)	0.7	1.2
Glasgow, Montana	(48°)	0.6	3.4

City	Approximate Latitude	Summer Panel Requirement (per person)	Winter Panel Requirement (per person)
Grand Junction, Colorado	(39°)	0.6	1.8
Grand Lake, Colorado	(40°)	0.8	2.6
Great Falls, Montana	(47°)	0.7	2.8
Greensboro, North Carolina	(36°)	0.7	1.9
Griffin, Georgia	(33°)	0.7	1.7
Hatteras, North Carolina	(35°)	0.6	1.5
Indianapolis, Indiana	(40°)	0.7	2.9
Inyokern, California	(35°)	0.5	1.1
Ithaca, New York	(42°)	0.8	3.6
Lake Charles, Louisiana	(30°)	0.7	1.4
Lander, Wyoming	(30°)	0.7	2.2
Las Vegas, Nevada	(36°)	0.5	1.2
Lemont, Illinois	(41°)	0.8	2.6
Lexington, Kentucky	(38°)	0.7	2.0
Lincoln, Nebraska	(41°)	0.8	2.1
Little Rock, Arkansas	(34°)	0.7	1.8
Los Angeles, California	(34°)	0.7	1.2
Madison, Wisconsin	(43°)	0.8	2.8
Matanuska, Alaska	(61°)	1.1	14.2
Medford, Oregon	(42°)	0.6	3.1
Miami, Florida	(26°)	0.7	0.9
Midland, Texas	(32°)	0.6	1.6
Nashville, Tennessee	(36°)	0.7	2.1
Newport, Rhode Island	(41°)	0.8	2.4
New York, New York	(41°)	0.8	2.5
Oak Ridge, Tennessee	(36°)	0.7	2.1
Oklahoma City, Oklahoma	(35°)	0.6	1.4
Ottawa, Ontario	(45°)	0.8	3.6
Phoenix, Arizona	(33°)	0.5	1.2
Portland, Maine	(43°)	0.8	2.3
Rapid City, South Dakota	(44°)	0.7	2.2
Riverside, California	(34°)	0.6	1.2
St. Cloud, Minnesota	(45°)	0.7	3.4
Salt Lake City, Utah	(41°)	no data	2.3
San Antonio, Texas	(29°)	0.6	1.3
Santa Maria, California	(35°)	0.7	1.4
Sault Ste, Marie, Michigan	(46°)	0.8	3.8
Sayville, New York	(40°)	0.8	2.4
Schenectady, New York	(43°)	0.9	3.7
Seattle, Washington	(47°)	0.9	3.7
Seabrook, New Jersey	(39°)	0.8	2.4
Spokane, Washington	(47°)	0.6	4.0
State College, Pennsylvania	(41°)	0.8	3.1
Stillwater, Oklhoma	(36°)	0.7	1.6

City	Approximate Latitude	Summer Panel Requirement (per person)	Winter Panel Requirement (per person)
Tampa, Florida	(28°)	0.7	1.0
Toronto, Ontario	(43°)	0.8	3.6
Tucson, Arizona	(32°)	0.6	1.1
Upton, New York	(41°)	0.8	2.2
Washington, D.C.	(39°)	0.7	2.1
Winnipeg, Manitoba	(50°)	0.8	5.0

Conversion of Pitch to Degrees

Angle in Degrees	Pitch in Inches Per Foot
10°	2.1
15°	3.2
20°	4.4
25°	5.6
30°	6.9
35°	8.4
40°	10.1
45°	12.0

Correction Factors for Panel Requirements

Roof Pitch	Multiply by	
	Summer	Winter
Latitude minus 20°	0.97	1.20
Latitude minus 10°	1.00	1.00
Latitude	1.08	0.90
Latitude plus 10°	1.20	0.85
Latitude plus 20°	1.39	0.82

Appendix III:
Facts About the Sun

Most of these statistics for the sun represent the best approximations based on available scientific data and calculations.

Solar power delivered to the earth daily . . . . 85 trillion kilowatts
  Note: The sun delivers enough energy in 15 minutes each day to supply the world's total energy needs for a year.

Solar energy per square foot
  in the United States . . . . 75 to 104 BTU per hour in summer
                                          21 to 46 BTU per hour in winter

Distiance of sun from earth . . . . 92,913,000 miles

Difference in distance of sun from earth
  between January and June . . . . 3,069,000 miles

Diameter of sun . . . . 864,000 miles
  Note: The sun is almost 110 times greater in diameter than the earth.

Volume of sun compared to earth 1,300,000:1

Mass of sun compared to earth 332,488:1

Surface gravity of sun compared to earth 28:1
  Note: 1 "solar g" equals 28 g on earth

Age of sun from radioactive dating . . . . 5 billion years

Orbital velocity of earth around sun . . . . 18.5 miles per second

Surface temperature of sun . . . . 10,800° C)

Interior temperature of sun . . . . 27,000,000° F
                                                                        (15,000,000° C)

Wavelength of sunlight . . . . 0.3 to 3.0 microns
                                          (1 micron = 1 millionth of a meter)
  Note: This includes invisible ultra-violet solar radiation, the shortest wavelengths in the solar spectrum, and equally invisible infrared long waves.

Appendix IV:
Insolation Maps —
January Through December

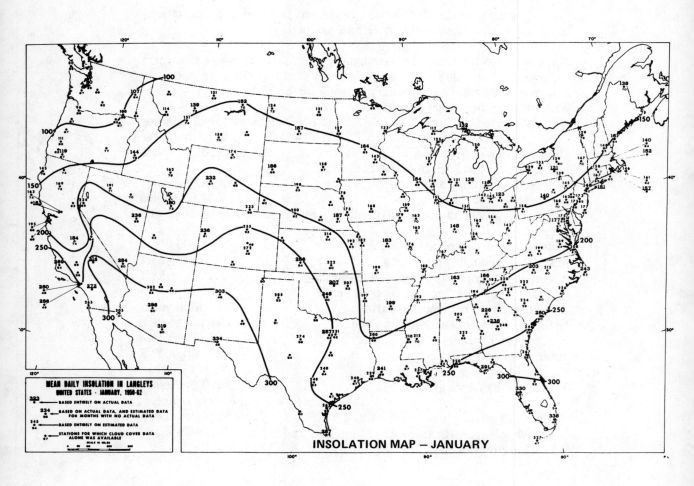

INSOLATION MAP — JANUARY

MEAN DAILY INSOLATION IN LANGLEYS
UNITED STATES · JANUARY, 1950-62

323 —— BASED ENTIRELY ON ACTUAL DATA

234 —— BASED ON ACTUAL DATA, AND ESTIMATED DATA
        FOR MONTHS WITH NO ACTUAL DATA

245 —— BASED ENTIRELY ON ESTIMATED DATA

←— STATIONS FOR WHICH CLOUD COVER DATA
    ALONE WAS AVAILABLE

SCALE IN MILES

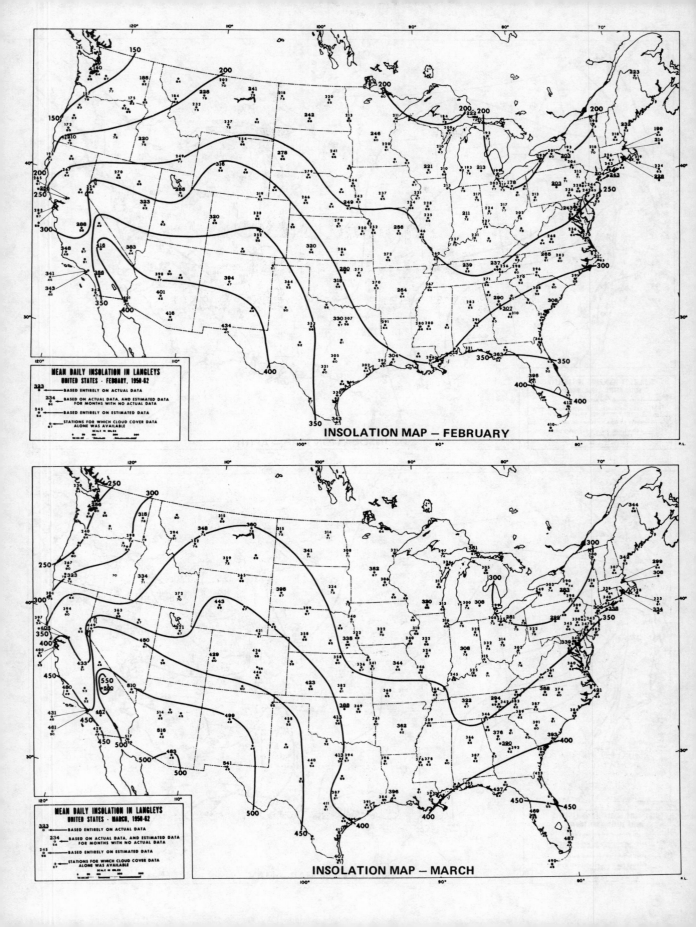

INSOLATION MAP — FEBRUARY

MEAN DAILY INSOLATION IN LANGLEYS
UNITED STATES · FEBRUARY, 1950-62

BASED ENTIRELY ON ACTUAL DATA

BASED ON ACTUAL DATA, AND ESTIMATED DATA
FOR MONTHS WITH NO ACTUAL DATA

BASED ENTIRELY ON ESTIMATED DATA

STATIONS FOR WHICH CLOUD COVER DATA
ALONE WAS AVAILABLE

SCALE IN MILES

INSOLATION MAP — MARCH

MEAN DAILY INSOLATION IN LANGLEYS
UNITED STATES · MARCH, 1950-62

BASED ENTIRELY ON ACTUAL DATA

BASED ON ACTUAL DATA, AND ESTIMATED DATA
FOR MONTHS WITH NO ACTUAL DATA

BASED ENTIRELY ON ESTIMATED DATA

STATIONS FOR WHICH CLOUD COVER DATA
ALONE WAS AVAILABLE

SCALE IN MILES

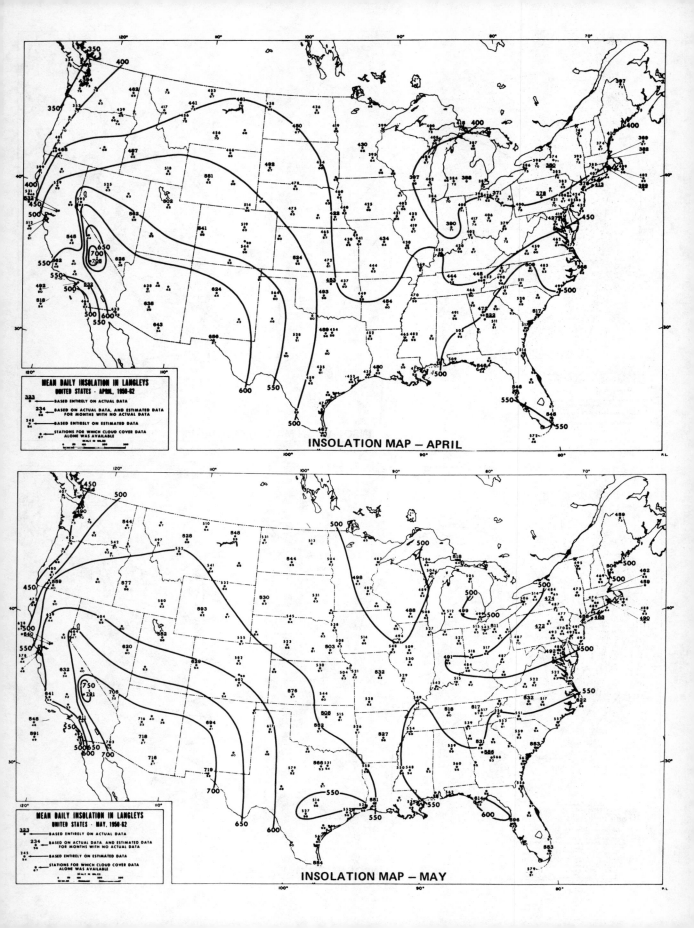

INSOLATION MAP — APRIL

MEAN DAILY INSOLATION IN LANGLEYS
UNITED STATES · APRIL, 1950-62

323 ——— BASED ENTIRELY ON ACTUAL DATA

234 ——— BASED ON ACTUAL DATA, AND ESTIMATED DATA
FOR MONTHS WITH NO ACTUAL DATA

345 ——— BASED ENTIRELY ON ESTIMATED DATA

⚲ STATIONS FOR WHICH CLOUD COVER DATA
ALONE WAS AVAILABLE

INSOLATION MAP — MAY

MEAN DAILY INSOLATION IN LANGLEYS
UNITED STATES · MAY, 1950-62

323 ——— BASED ENTIRELY ON ACTUAL DATA

234 ——— BASED ON ACTUAL DATA, AND ESTIMATED DATA
FOR MONTHS WITH NO ACTUAL DATA

345 ——— BASED ENTIRELY ON ESTIMATED DATA

⚲ STATIONS FOR WHICH CLOUD COVER DATA
ALONE WAS AVAILABLE

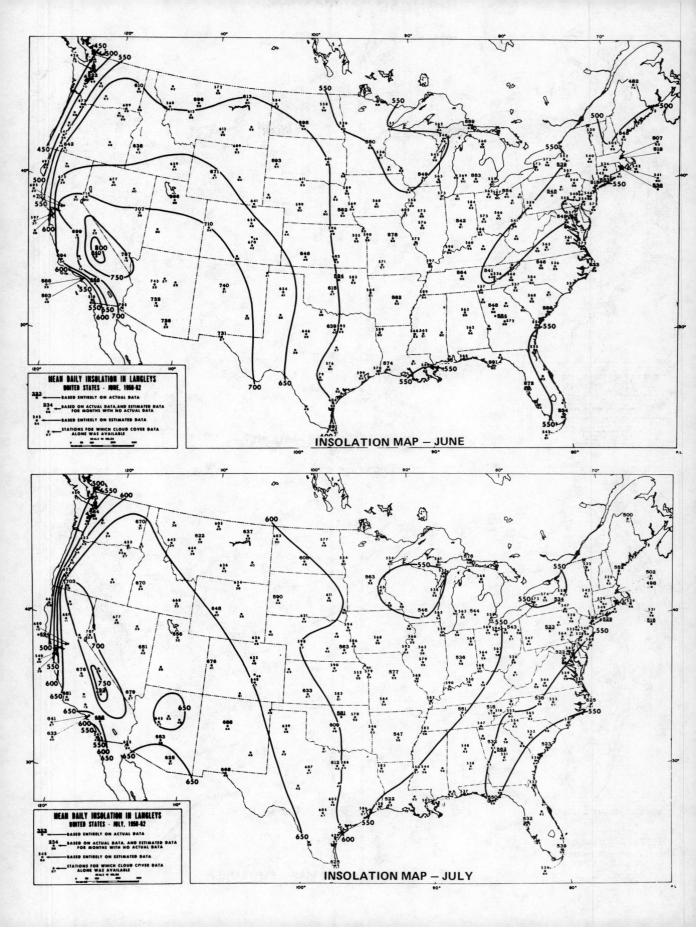

INSOLATION MAP — JUNE

MEAN DAILY INSOLATION IN LANGLEYS
UNITED STATES - JUNE, 1950-62

INSOLATION MAP — JULY

MEAN DAILY INSOLATION IN LANGLEYS
UNITED STATES - JULY, 1950-62

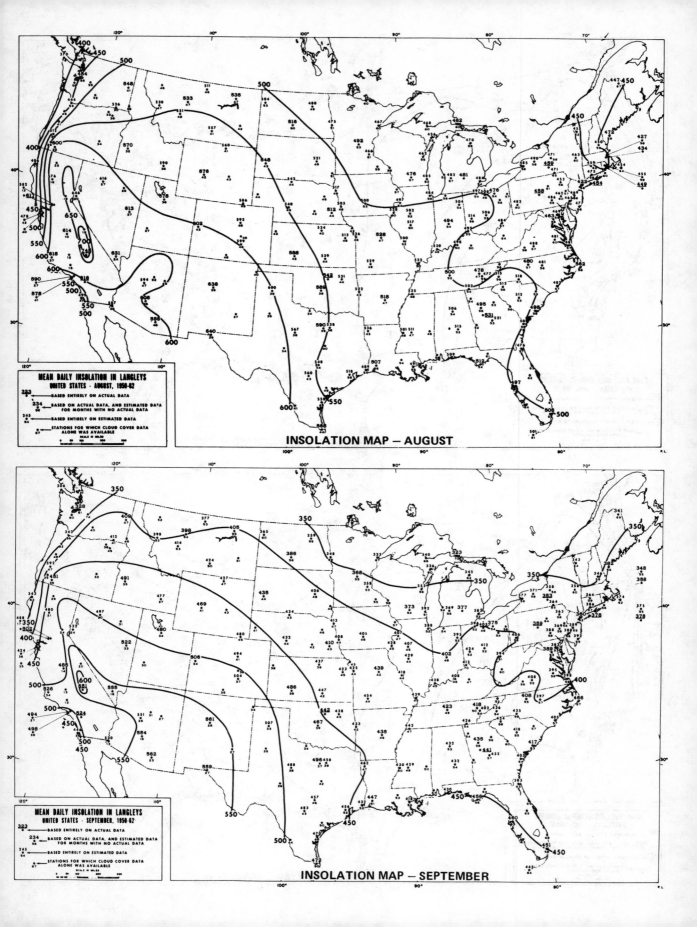

INSOLATION MAP — AUGUST

MEAN DAILY INSOLATION IN LANGLEYS
UNITED STATES · AUGUST, 1950-62

323 —— BASED ENTIRELY ON ACTUAL DATA

234 —— BASED ON ACTUAL DATA, AND ESTIMATED DATA
     FOR MONTHS WITH NO ACTUAL DATA

245 —— BASED ENTIRELY ON ESTIMATED DATA

—— STATIONS FOR WHICH CLOUD COVER DATA
    ALONE WAS AVAILABLE

SCALE IN MILES

INSOLATION MAP — SEPTEMBER

MEAN DAILY INSOLATION IN LANGLEYS
UNITED STATES · SEPTEMBER, 1950-62

323 —— BASED ENTIRELY ON ACTUAL DATA

234 —— BASED ON ACTUAL DATA, AND ESTIMATED DATA
     FOR MONTHS WITH NO ACTUAL DATA

245 —— BASED ENTIRELY ON ESTIMATED DATA

—— STATIONS FOR WHICH CLOUD COVER DATA
    ALONE WAS AVAILABLE

SCALE IN MILES

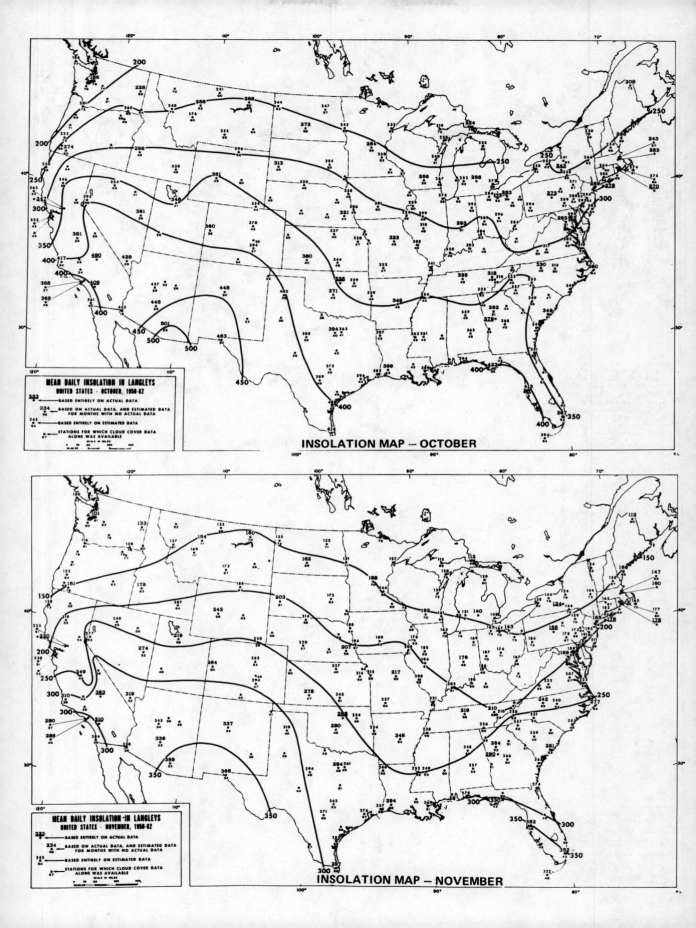

INSOLATION MAP — OCTOBER

MEAN DAILY INSOLATION IN LANGLEYS
UNITED STATES · OCTOBER, 1950-62

BASED ENTIRELY ON ACTUAL DATA

BASED ON ACTUAL DATA, AND ESTIMATED DATA
FOR MONTHS WITH NO ACTUAL DATA

BASED ENTIRELY ON ESTIMATED DATA

STATIONS FOR WHICH CLOUD COVER DATA
ALONE WAS AVAILABLE

INSOLATION MAP — NOVEMBER

MEAN DAILY INSOLATION IN LANGLEYS
UNITED STATES · NOVEMBER, 1950-62

BASED ENTIRELY ON ACTUAL DATA

BASED ON ACTUAL DATA, AND ESTIMATED DATA
FOR MONTHS WITH NO ACTUAL DATA

BASED ENTIRELY ON ESTIMATED DATA

STATIONS FOR WHICH CLOUD COVER DATA
ALONE WAS AVAILABLE

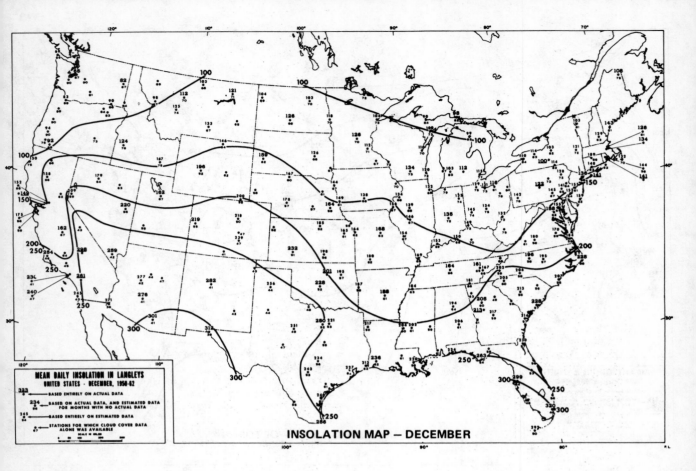

INSOLATION MAP — DECEMBER

Index

*Page numbers for illustrations
are printed in italics*